THE HAML

EDIE
MEDICINAL
PLANTS

OF BRITAIN AND NORTHERN EUROPE

EDMUND LAUNERT

ILLUSTRATED BY ROGER GORRINGE AND ANN DAVIES

HAMLYN

Preface

In line with other field guides of this series the present volume aims to enable the reader, be he pharmacist, physician, student or layman, to identify edible and medicinal native wild plants by visual means. The accurate recognition of many species depends, of course, on the application of scientific keys which cannot be provided within the framework of this book, especially since it deals with a relatively small number of species. Fortunately most of these are easily identifiable with the help of the colour illustrations accompanied by a brief description and indication of habitat and distribution. In cases where a plant could be mistaken for a similar looking species, a note pointing out the differences has been provided.

In contrast to other field guides a book on the utilization of plants must provide information on the proper and possible use of each species. This information is contained at the end of each description and, moreover, the appendix includes a number of recipes both of medicinal and culinary interest. Since it was not my brief to produce a cookery book, I have only given a selection of feasible and, it is hoped, interesting culinary experiments.

Edmund Launert

Acknowledgements

The author wishes to thank many of his friends and colleagues for all the help and encouragement he has received. Special thanks are due to Dr. G. Benl of Munich, Dr. D. Zeh of Messrs. Salus-Haus, Bruckmühl (F.R.G.) and the managements of Messrs. Schoenenberg of Margstadt (F.R.G.) and Messrs. Kleindiät of Augsburg for supplying information about their products. Valuable advice was given by Mr. P. James and Mr. J. R. Laundon both of the British Museum (Natural History). Some of the recipes in the section on culinary plants were kindly suggested by Mrs. G. Whitehead and Mrs. E. Sattler. He is grateful to his wife for checking and correcting the manuscript and to his son Victor for compiling various lists. Miss Nancy Graham and Miss Loveday Hosking are thanked for rendering a virtually illegible handwriting into a perfect typescript. Last but not least he wishes to acknowledge the painstaking care that the artists, Mr. Roger Gorringe and Mrs. Ann Davies, have taken in producing the illustrations; working with them was a joy.

This edition previously published as the
*Country Life Guide to Edible and Medicinal Plants
of Britain and Northern Europe.*

Published by The Hamlyn Publishing Group Ltd.,
a Division of the Octopus Publishing Group,
Michelin House, 81 Fulham Road,
London SW3 6RB

ISBN 0 600 56395 2

Produced by Mandarin Offset
Printed and bound in Hong Kong

Contents

Edible wild plants

A large number of books on the subject of wild plants for culinary purposes has appeared on the market over the last decade. Perhaps a main cause for interest in our edible flora is nostalgia for the good life we imagine our forefathers to have had in a world which did not know the use of chemical fertilizers and pesticides as well as the huge canning and frozen food industry. Modern means of transport have enabled our greengrocers to tempt us with an incredible array of exotic fruits and vegetables from all parts of the world and the abundance and variety of such produce makes it unnecessary for us to scratch around the hedgerows, as perhaps some of us did during the Second World War, for additional fresh material for our diet. Nor is there any need for those who worry about modern horticultural practice to do so: they may use their gardens or allotments to grow chemical-free foods with the flavour that their grandfathers remember.

There is certainly no need whatsoever for us to return to the hunting and foraging activities of our remote ancestors. If we were still dependent on this mode of feeding ourselves, each of us would have to be supported by at least thirty square kilometres of land and the continents of this world, struggling as they are to sustain the present population, would only have resources for a fraction of our number. Thousands of years of advancement through civilization are written off by such simplistic 'back-to-nature' attitudes. By taking wild plants into cultivation and, in some cases, by developing their desirable characteristics, man has freed himself from a nomadic existence and laid the foundation for his civilization, which has made possible a life enhanced by periods of leisure, the development of science and technology and the refinements of the arts.

Our ancestors have taken the best nature had to offer and handed down to us their valuable experience but it would, of course, be wrong to think that the possibilities have been exhausted. There are many genetic resources which still remain undeveloped even, as recent research has shown, in the temperate regions. It is also true to say that it can be interesting and amusing to enrich our diet by making occasional use of wild plants, for example, the gathering of blackberries for jam-making at the appropriate season is familiar to most of us. Who has not at some time picked hazel nuts or the alien sweet chestnut? Some of us may have gathered mushrooms, a veritable sport in Central and Eastern Europe. The amateur wine-makers go in quest of elderberries and an acquaintance of mine even taps birch trees for this purpose on a nearby common.

The list of plants of which we can make use may be extended but it must be remembered that unlike plants expressly cultivated the wild ones often grow over a wide area in a scattered fashion, and they or their fruits may be small and difficult to gather. The search may be exciting and provide much needed exercise and family fun but for most people it is too tedious or time consuming. The hours needed for harvesting and preparing the food are proof enough that the beautiful things around us are certainly not food for free.

Those undeterred by this realization should heed these words of caution: it took Mankind a few thousand years to establish by trial and error which plants are edible and which are not. If the majority of plants found in the wild have not been eaten, there is a reason for it. They are not necessarily poisonous or even harmful but their taste may be unpalatable, their structure objectionable, as is the case with thistles or fibrous plants, or their high content of silicic acid (in grasses) makes them indigestible. Others may not show such characteristics but may prove detrimental to health if eaten in large quantities or over a period of time, e.g. bracken and plants thriving in nitrogen-rich soils, such as *Atriplex*, *Chenopodium* or even *Urtica*.

If this and the following points are borne in mind, however, the enthusiast may derive much pleasure from his quest for edible wild plants.

Collecting edible wild plants

1 **Do** make absolutely sure that you have identified the plant correctly and that no other species is mixed up with it. It is nice to know that as far as seaweeds are concerned no poisonous species grow around our shores.

2 **Never** collect in areas which have been sprayed with insecticides or pesticides or which have been freshly manured. Be particularly careful in the case of areas bordering on arable fields. Avoid polluted waters or beaches when collecting aquatic plants and clean thoroughly before cooking in any case.

3 **Do not** assume that because one part of a plant is edible all its parts may be consumed; for example, whereas our potato is a valuable food, the plant as such is poisonous; also, to cite another case, an acquaintance who frequently collected elderberries took it into his head to cook the leaves as a vegetable: a night of vomiting and diarrhoea ensued!

4 **Do** collect only what you need and **do not** uproot plants unnecessarily. If you only need part of a plant (leaves, buds or flowers) leave the rest of the plant intact.

5 **Do** familiarize yourself with the laws governing the protection of wild plants.

6 **Do not** trespass on other people's property (which may lie within the boundaries of a National Park).

Generally speaking when cooking wild plants one can follow recipes applicable to cultivated species, but the recipes given in the appendix are a selection of more unusual methods of preparation which will perhaps be of interest to the more adventurous cooks. *Bon appétit!*

Medicinal plants

One of the aims of this book is to provide an illustrated guide for the identification of medicinal plants used in Britain and Northern Europe. It is written for the layman as well as the medical practitioner and pharmacist. The teaching of botany is no longer an integral part of medical training at most European universities, yet there is a revived interest on the part of the medical profession and the pharmaceutical industry, and this situation makes the publication of such a guide very timely.

Although a section on its healing properties and its application is given for each plant, the purpose of this book is not the propagation of an uncritical back-to-nature philosophy, nor does it advocate what is generally known as alternative medicine. The resurgence of interest in the healing properties of plants and in the medical treatment of yesteryear is partly the result of a long-held mistrust, be it justified or not, of modern medical practice and the much publicized tragedies arising from the hasty application of new man-made drugs — witness the thalidomide case. It must not be forgotten in the search for 'natural' remedies, however, that many plants contain some of the deadliest poisons in existence and that others can have a harmful effect, certainly not less than synthetic drugs, if improperly applied. Indeed, some of our decorative houseplants are not innocuous, especially to small children. In fact, a great percentage of drugs prescribed by doctors today are still plant based and in many instances scientists have not succeeded in synthesizing certain active plant principles, e.g. codeine. In other instances the synthetic product is financially prohibitive. It is for this reason that the pharmaceutical industry cultivates or imports a vast amount of plant material. According to a recent report (Wagner and Wolf 1977) referring to the year 1973, the Americans paid the astounding sum of three billion dollars for prescribed drugs which were based on higher plants. The figures showing the percentage of prescriptions based on plant and animal products for the United States in 1959 (49.2%) and 1973 (41.2%) show the continued importance of natural sources.

The search for healing properties in the vast reservoir of higher and lower plants is still in its infancy. That the search is not in vain is clearly demonstrated by the revolutionary discovery and modern application of antibiotics (mainly penicillin and streptomycin), curare, cortisone and others in the prevention and cure of serious illness.

One of the superstitions of ancient herbal medicine that did much to bring the art into disrepute was the so-called Doctrine of Signatures, prevalent in the sixteenth and seventeenth centuries and which dominated the medical thinking of the period. It was supposed that God had indicated the virtues of a plant by giving it a shape similar to a body organ or the outward symptoms of a disease; the tubers of certain native orchids resemble human testicles (the Greek name of this plant, *Orchis*, means, in fact, testicle) and these tubers were therefore believed to stimulate sexual activities; it was also believed that a preparation of a pair of young tubers would bring about a male child, but of old tubers a female.

The liver-shaped leaf of *Hepatica* was thought to be a cure for liver ailments, and the blotched leaf of *Pulmonaria* a cure for diseases of the lung. Herbs with a yellow sap were considered effective in the treatment of jaundice.

Even the most pretentious herbalist or naturopath will freely admit that there is no herbal remedy for certain conditions, such as cancer in its various forms, pulmonary tuberculosis, venereal diseases, smallpox, meningitis, and jaundice, to mention but a few. It would be ludicrous to deny the great successes of modern medical research and the pharmaceutical industry in the combating of some of the diseases which have plagued mankind for centuries. It would, however, be equally ludicrous to dismiss some of the centuries-old treatments of folk medicine in the case of benign disorders. A cup of peppermint tea at bedtime is in most cases a better remedy for insomnia than barbiturates and certainly less sinister. But even in more serious diseases herbal preparations may actively support the treatment prescribed by the physician.

The pharmacological effects of many herbal preparations are still not fully explored but modern medicine has at last learned not to discard folk remedies as a collection of old wives' tales. There are numerous instances where science has discovered the underlying sound reason for a treatment's beneficial effect. Only one striking example can be cited here. Osteomyelitis and some types of suppurating wounds which did not readily respond to medical treatment were, in the past, healed much more rapidly by the application of the maggots of the sheep blowfly (*Lucilia sericata*) to the wounds. The wounds were thus soon cleared and granulation stimulated. Research showed that the active principle contained in the maggots was allantoine (a purin derivative). Although attempts were made to find an alternative to this rather revolting treatment by using chemical preparations it was in the end the plant world which provided an acceptable solution: *Symphytum officinale* (comfrey), and this is now the source for the various preparations relating to this and similar disorders.

For the layman there must be added a word of warning. Never use herbs in the case of serious illness unless the medical practitioner has been consulted and never use a herbal remedy when already undergoing conventional treatment: the use of two drugs could have a harmful or at the very least negating effects. This caution does not of course apply to herbal teas sold for everyday use or similar well-known innocuous mixtures.

The teas (see page 271) just mentioned are familiar to us from the shelves of our local health food shop and indeed the supermarket. They have the advantage over the usual beverages (ordinary tea, coffee or chocolate) in that they contain no caffeine or tannin. They are an excellent substitute for all three and are especially recommended for people suffering from heart, nervous or digestive conditions. They are not addictive and can be given to children. Moreover, once a taste for herbal teas has been acquired and the monotonous imbibing of ordinary tea and coffee ceases, one will begin to appreciate their individual tastes and become aware of the relaxing benefit of their use. A little wise self help might shorten the queues in the waiting rooms of our doctors who, whether through their own impatience or because they are at the mercy of an impossible system, often unfortunately have no time for all our little problems, both physical and psychological.

Collecting medicinal plants

The rules for collecting are the same as for the gathering of edible plants (see page 5). But it must again be stressed that one should only use herbs which can be clearly and properly identified. The beginner is well advised to collect only in company with an experienced friend or have the name of any plant which he cannot name with the help of this guide, confirmed by an expert.

The active ingredients of medicinal plants vary in both quality and quantity in the course of the year. The best time for collecting a particular plant is indicated above each description.

Since one often collects only part of a plant (e.g. flowers, buds, fruits) there is no need to uproot and destroy entire plants unnecessarily. Never collect on a wet day or early in the morning when most plants are covered with dew; the best time is usually in the early afternoon. The collected material must not be put into sealed containers or, even worse, plastic bags; it is best carried in a basket and should be dried as soon as possible. Whether a herb should be dried in the sun or in shade is indicated with the individual description. Rhizomes and roots must in most cases be washed and brushed before drying. Very thick or tough rhizomes are best cut in the fresh state before drying.

In order to avoid fermentation or the formation of mould, herbs must be dried quickly and always arranged in thin layers; fresh air is of paramount importance.

For succulent herbs, fruits or some seeds the initial drying process in the open is best finished by artificial heat (never exceed 60°C.). To test readiness for storage check that stems are brittle, leaves do not feel cold when held against the cheek, and berries, fruits or seed are hard throughout. Only a few medicinal plants are best dried in artificial heat for optimum effect. Special requirements are mentioned in the relevant description.

Storage of medicinal herbs

Dried herbs should always be kept in lidded containers which should be made of glass, or galvanized metal boxes; cardboard boxes can also be used if stored in a dry place. Some herbs require storage in the dark but in any case the herbs should not be exposed to direct sunlight. To avoid mould the drugs should only be stored after having been completely dried. Some herbs should be kept bundled in the open, in a well ventilated attic room (to keep them dust-free they can be hung in a coarse bag or inside a basket). However carefully stored, most herbs and herbal mixtures (especially those containing essential oils and saponins) lose their properties with time. Medicinal herbs and herbs for regular consumption as tea substitutes should therefore not be stored for much longer than a year.

The preparation of herbs for medicinal purposes
Herbal remedies can be applied in various forms — internally or externally — the nature of which is usually dictated by the structure of the plant or its ingredients. Processes which can only be used by the professional chemist and which demand the use of laboratory apparatus or detailed chemical knowledge (e.g. the preparation of essences, extracts, tinctures, embrocations, ointments, etc.) are excluded here. Such products are in many instances available from the chemists or specialized herbalist shops. For the layman the most important methods of preparation are maceration, infusion, and decoction. As a rule every ingredient should be cut into small pieces for optimum effect: rhizomes or roots are cut or shredded (in most cases this is best achieved before drying); herbs are cut with a sharp knife or crunched; fruits and seeds, especially those containing essential oils (e.g. *Carum, Foeniculum, Juniperus*, etc.) must be crushed on a hard surface (best with a mortar and pestle). Never use metal containers for any of the methods unless they are completely and faultlessly enamelled. Best are earthenware or heatproof glass vessels.

The application and method used for each herb included here is given at the end of the entry. Whichever method is used the preparation should always be freshly made and, if possible, kept for not longer than a few hours, otherwise the effects will be greatly diminished. For this reason the measures given for each plant are usually for one cup of water.

Maceration: this is the method used for plants with volatile or chemically delicately balanced ingredients. The drug is put into a vessel with the required quantity of cold water and left standing for 8–12 hours at room temperature. Before use the mixture can be heated to body temperature and strained. Whether or not the liquid can be sweetened is usually mentioned in the text.

Infusion: this is the most common method for the preparation of herbal teas and is applied mainly to drugs consisting of herbs, leaves, and flowers and those containing volatile oils which could be destroyed by boiling. The indicated amount of drug is placed in a warmed cup or non-metallic container and water at boiling temperature is added. The liquid should then be allowed to stand (covered with a lid or saucer) for the time given for each recipe; never exceed the indicated time because in some instances (e.g. *Mentha*) the infusion will acquire a foul taste. After straining it should be drunk immediately; whether it can be taken hot or cold, sweetened or not is usually mentioned. If sweetened one should use honey rather than sugar.

Decoction: this method is applied to plants or plant organs (bark, rhizomes, hard fruits, some seeds) which cannot be extracted by the above mentioned methods. Plants which contain essential oils are unsuited for this process, and since most drugs contain volatile oils it is rarely applied. Besides essential oils other compounds suffer damage when exposed to boiling (e.g. mucilage, glycosides, enzymes, some alkaloids, proteins, and others). Moreover, most decoctions should only be used under medical supervision unless their use has been described as safe. For domestic purposes (the pharmacist uses a more complicated method) the drug is placed with the indicated amount of cold water in a non-metallic saucepan or pot, heated to boiling point and then allowed to simmer gently for the indicated time. After straining the liquid should be consumed as soon as possible.

In some cases a combination of maceration and decoction is appropriate. After the drug has been steeped in cold water for the given amount of time the strained-off liquid is kept and the remaining material, with fresh water, brought to boiling point and, usually, simmered only for a very short time. Both liquids are then mixed and drunk. This method should only be applied where indicated.

Whereas macerations, infusions, and decoctions are unstable and cannot be kept, alcoholic extracts (essences, tinctures, etc.) usually have better keeping properties.

A few herbal remedies are more effective when taken in powdered form. This can be achieved by grinding them down with a mortar and pestle. They are taken with a little water, milk or soup.

External application: the most common external use of herbs takes the form of a herbal bath which can either be a full bath or a bath for a particular organ (footbath, bath for soothing haemorrhoids, eye-bath, etc.). For bathing the eye a specially shaped eye-bath is available at the chemist.

For skin disorders, slow-healing wounds and some painful conditions a herbal compress is most beneficial, especially when applied hot and left warm as long as possible by cloths or a bandage wrapped around it. After the herb is processed by one or other of the methods described above, gauze or cotton-wool is soaked with the liquid and applied to the diseased part, and allowed to remain until cold; this process can be repeated several times a day.

Occasionally, especially in folk medicine, plants are applied directly to the affected parts of the body. For this purpose mostly fresh herbs are used, rhizomes, fruits or succulent leaves and stems being bruised before application. In some instances freshly cut or pulverized parts of roots are mixed with lukewarm water into a paste which is directly spread on to the skin or applied with a piece of linen cloth.

Dried herbs are sometimes sewn into a linen bag which is soaked in hot water (a better method is to wet the bags by steaming them in a grate or sieve above a pot of boiling water; in this way no ingredients are lost) and then applied to the affected organ. If a bandage is then wrapped around the bag, the heat, which greatly assists the herbal effect, can be retained for some time.

Aromatic dried herbs, sewn into linen bags, are placed overnight under or next to the pillow as a remedy for nervous disorders and insomnia.

Steam treatment: this method is not only applied for cosmetic purposes but also for the relief of various ailments (nasal and bronchial catarrhs, ear disorders, inflamed eyes, etc.). The plants used for this purpose usually are rich in volatile oils (e.g. *Chamomilla* or *Rosmarinus*) which act either beneficially on the skin or, when inhaled, have a soothing effect on the mucous membranes. The indicated amount of the herb or herbal mixture is placed in a small enamel bucket or pan of water, which is brought to the boil and then removed from the heat source and put on to a chair; the head, covered with a large towel, is then exposed to the steam, which in the case of catarrh should be inhaled. Herbs or herbal mixtures suitable for gargling or for use as mouthwashes are mentioned in the appropriate plant description.

Key to symbols used in the text

Ⓜ   plant used for medicinal purposes (denoted by **M** in text)
Ⓔ   plant a part or parts of which are edible (denoted by **E** in text)
☠   plant a part or parts of which are poisonous
C   (used in text only)   drug which should be used only with extreme care or under medical supervision

Note   where months are given at the beginning of the botanical description these refer to the suggested collecting time of the useable parts, and not necessarily to the flowering or fruiting time of the plant.

Ⓜ *Lycopodium clavatum* L. Lycopodiaceae

Clubmoss (June/July – Sept.) A perennial herb with simple or dichotomously branched trailing stems; only the fertile branches are erect or nearly so. The leaves are up to 5mm long, dense, spirally arranged, appressed to the stem or curved inwards, linear, tapering to a long hair-like white point. The fertile branches are 8–25cm long and terminated by 1–3 long-stalked cones, the stalks covered with appressed scale-like leaves. The sporophylls are ovate to ovate-elliptic, with thread-like apices.

Habitat heath, coniferous woods, moors, mountain grassland. **Distribution** throughout the region. **Active ingredients** traces of alkaloids, about 50% fixed oils, resins. **Effect** stops inflammation and irritations of the skin (spores); mildly diuretic (the entire herb). **Parts used** mature spores and (rarely) the entire plant. Collect the cones and dry them on paper until all the spores have fallen out; keep in a dry dark place. **Application M:** the spores are used as a soothing and cooling dusting powder and as a treatment (nowadays disputed) taken internally against bladder complaints; in the past they were mainly used in the preparation of pills. The dried herb is used as an infusion against pyelitis and inflammation of the bladder: 1–2 teaspoons in 600ml water, bring to the boil and stand for 6–10 minutes. **Note** the related species *L. annotinum* and *L. alpinum* have the same properties.

Ⓜ *Huperzia (Lycopodium) selago* L. Lycopodiaceae

Fir Clubmoss (June – Aug.) A perennial species related to *L. clavatum* but with stems nearly erect, rooting only at the base; leaves up to 8mm long suberect or spreading not appressed; sporophylls not arranged in cones; sporangia appear in the axils of the leaves.

Habitat mountain grassland, heath, moors, amongst rocks. **Distribution** throughout the region. **Active ingredients** alkaloids, bitter principle of unknown composition, resin. **Effect** laxative; kills worms. **Parts used** whole plant. **Application M:** only used for homoeopathic preparations from fresh leaves.

Ⓜ *Equisetum arvense* L. Equisetaceae

Common Horsetail (July – Aug.) A perennial with a creeping, pubescent, tuber-bearing rhizome and aerial stems of two kinds, sterile and fertile. The sterile stems are 15–60cm (up to 80cm) tall, branched, erect or decumbent, green, rough to the touch, up to 5mm in diameter, with 6 to 19-toothed green sheaths; their branches are spreading, numerous, and arranged in whorls. The fertile stems, which appear before the sterile stems, are shorter, usually unbranched, pale brown, and die soon after spore dispersal; the sheaths number 4–6, pale brown with dark brown teeth.

Habitat open fields, arable land, waste ground, hedges, roadsides. **Distribution** throughout the region. **Parts used** the green sterile summer growth, collected in late summer (cut the entire plant just above ground) and dried quickly to avoid decolouring. Keep in a dry well-ventilated place. **Active ingredients** saponin, flavone-glycosides, resin, silicic acid (7–10%) equisetonine. **Effect** diuretic; checks bleeding, assists treatment of lung diseases, arthritis, chilblains, rheumatism, weak circulation and chronic cough. **Application M:** can be used in a hot bath (pour 1·5 litres boiling water over 125g of dried herb, keep hot and leave to stand for 1 to 1½ hours, strain and add to the bathwater). Also used in hot compresses: soak linen or cotton wool in above (or stronger) infusion and place on bruised or swollen part of body. The infusion can also be used for gargling and as a mouthwash. Can also be taken internally as a decoction: macerate 1–1½ tablespoons cut dried herb in 1 cup of cold water for 10–15 hours, add boiling water and keep for 45 minutes, strain. Drink 2–3 cups per day (rheumatic pains, swollen limbs, chronic cough).

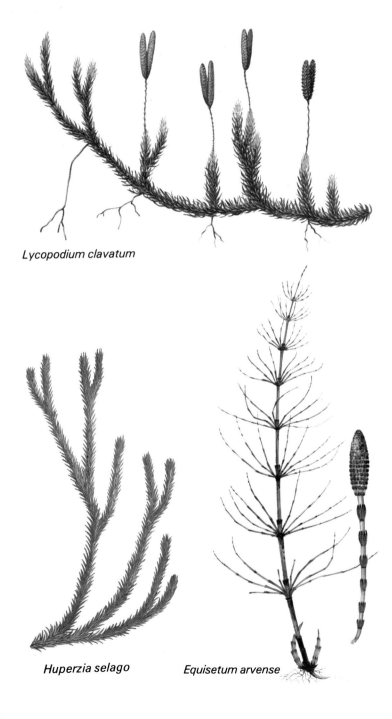

Lycopodium clavatum

Huperzia selago

Equisetum arvense

Ⓔ *Pteridium aquilinum* (L.) Kuhn Polypodiaceae

Bracken A perennial fern with a long, stout, tomentose, creeping rhizome. The fronds are large, 20–200cm (up to 400cm) tall, usually 3-pinnate, solitary and slightly drooping from an erect base, at first covered with fine brown scales, but later almost glabrous. The pinnae are oblong or oblong-lanceolate, the segments are up to 1·7cm long, sessile, entire or lobed in the lower half. They are usually pubescent beneath, with the sori arranged along the recurved margin. The petiole is about as long as the blade, stout, usually blackish-brown and tomentose at the base. The young fronds are rolled inwards.

Habitat heath, woods usually on acid soil, often covering large areas of former grassland. **Distribution** throughout the region. **Parts used** the young, 5–20cm long shoots, still unfolded. **Application E:** Bracken has no medicinal use but is the only fern which can be used for culinary purposes. The shoots are used either like spinach or asparagus. Since they are somewhat bitter they should be blanched in boiling water. The brown scales are brushed off and the stalks are peeled (if used like asparagus) and together with the softer fronds, boiled in water with a pinch of salt. Serve with butter and/or a white sauce (best spiced with capers). **Note** regular consumption of this plant is not advisable but its occasional use will do no harm.

Ⓜ *Phyllitis scolopendrium* (L.) Newm. Polypodiaceae

Hart's-tongue Fern (May–Oct.) A perennial fern with an erect, stout, densely scaly rhizome. The fronds are arranged in tufts, 8–61cm long, persistent: the petiole is shorter than the blade and covered with brownish scales; the blade is entire or slightly lobed, strap-shaped from a heart-shaped base, tapering above, usually blunt at first or covered with slender scales, later glabrous, with parallel venation. The sori are arranged in pairs on the veins.

Habitat woods, walls, along brooks, usually on rocks in shady and humid places. **Distribution** throughout the region. **Active ingredients** tannin, mucilage, sugar. **Effect** diuretic; stimulates perspiration. **Parts used** the fronds, fresh or dried; **Application M:** as an infusion: 1 tablespoon of herb to 2–3 cups of water 2–3 times a day against bronchitis, ailments of liver and spleen and chronic bowel disorders and diarrhoea. Also used in addition to other remedies in the treatment of lung diseases.

Ⓜ *Adiantum capillus-veneris* L. Polypodiaceae

Maidenhair Fern (June–Sept.) A delicate perennial fern, with a creeping rhizome. The fronds are 5–35cm long; the petiole and rachis are shiny black; the blade is 2 to 3-pinnate, ovate to ovate-elliptic ; pinnules are borne on thin black stalks, fan-shaped, up to 1·7cm long, without midrib, veins branched dichotomously. The sori are arranged on the veins of the recurved area of the lobes of the pinnules.

Habitat rock crevices and on cliffs near the sea, sometimes as an escape on walls. **Distribution:** Channel Islands, Isle of Man, N.W. and S.W. England, parts of Ireland; Switzerland and W. France. **Active ingredients** tannin, mucilage, gallic acid, capillarine, bitter substances of unknown composition. **Effect** diuretic, emollient, stimulates menstrual flow. **Parts used** the whole plant above ground. It should be collected in late summer and dried quickly but without heat, but best when used fresh. **Application M:** as an infusion: 1 tablespoon of finely cut leaves to 1–2 cups of water or hot milk to stimulate menstruation, against bronchitis and coughs. Not used for pharmaceutical purposes.

Phyllitis scolopendrium

Pteridium aquilinum

Adiantum capillus-veneris

☠ **_Dryopteris filix-mas_** (L.) Schott Polypodiaceae

Ⓜ **Male Fern** (Sept.–Oct.) A large perennial fern with an erect rhizome. The fronds grow up to 150cm long or more and usually die in the autumn; the petiole is up to half as long as the blade, thinly covered with light brown acuminate scales; the blade is usually suberect, rarely spreading, pinnate to 2-pinnate; rachis thinly covered with scales or glabrous; the pinnae go up to 35cm either side of the rachis, linear-lanceolate, up to 16cm long; the pinnules (or segments) are flat, numbering up to 25 on each side of the pinnae, almost entire or toothed. The sori are arranged in a line along each side of the pinnule-midrib.

Habitat forests, amongst rocks, in screes, hedge banks, mountains, river banks, in shade. **Distribution** throughout the region. **Active ingredients** filicin, filixid acid, tannins, phloroglucin derivatives, fixed oil, traces of essential oils, resin, starch, sugar. **Effect** kills worms (especially tapeworm), healing. **Parts used** the rhizome, freed of its roots; it should be dried in the sun or moderate heat. **Application C:** although one of the best remedies against tapeworm _Dryopteris_ should _only be used under medical supervision_ since even a small overdose can lead to poisoning or blindness.

Ⓜ **_Polypodium vulgare_** L. Polypodiaceae

Polypody (March–April or Sept.–Oct.) A smallish perennial fern with a rather stout creeping rhizome which is densely covered with red-brown scales. The fronds are solitary, pinnate or deeply pinnatifid, persistent; the petiole ranges from shorter than to almost as long as the blade and is usually glabrous; the blade may be up to 50cm long, oblong, ovate-lanceolate or linear-lanceolate, thinly leathery, erect to drooping. The pinnae are all in the same plane, oblong or linear-lanceolate from the wider base, rounded at the apex, the margins almost entire. The sori are circular to (rarely) elliptic, arranged halfway between the margins and the pinna midrib.

Habitat tree trunks, rocks and walls, also at ground level in forests, usually in humid situations in shade. **Distribution** throughout the region. **Active ingredients** sugar, resin, saponin, mucilage, bitter principles, fixed oil, traces of essential oils, tannins. **Effect** diuretic, expectorant, purgative, stimulates biliary secretion, kills worms, relieves female complaints. **Parts used** the rhizome, freed of its roots and cleaned and dried in the sun (or artificial heat); either cut into small pieces or pulverize. **Application M:** as an infusion: 3–5 teaspoons of cut rhizome with 1 litre of boiling water for the treatment of catarrh and other ailments of the respiratory tract, gall disorders, constipation, menstrual pain, intestinal worms. For the same purposes the powdered drug may be more effective (1 teaspoon 3–4 times a day with some water, tea or milk).

Ⓜ **_Pinus sylvestris_** L. Pinaceae

Scots Pine (April–May) A large tree with a flat crown and reddish-brown bark, darker on lower part of the trunk. The buds are oblong-ovate, up to 1·3cm long, resinous. There are 2 leaves (needles) on each short shoot up to 10cm long and 2mm wide, somewhat twisted, stiff, bluish-green; the long shoots only bear scale-like brownish leaves without chlorophyll. The cones are usually slightly asymmetrical, 3–7·5cm long, ovoid-conical, greyish-brown, with oblong scales.

Habitat forming large natural woods; also planted. **Distribution** throughout the region. **Active ingredients** tannin, resin, essential oil, terpenes, pinipricin. **Effect** expectorant, diuretic, antiseptic; causes skin redness. **Parts used** only the young shoots; these should be dried in shade. **Application M:** as an addition to bath for fatigue, nervous exhaustion, sleeplessness, circulatory disorders, slow-healing cuts or skin irritations: macerate 3 handfuls of dried or fresh twigs in 700ml water, boil for 1–2 minutes, keep for 30 minutes, strain and add liquid to hot bathwater. As an inhalant for relief of bronchial catarrh, asthma, blocked nose and similar complaints: bring 2–3 handfuls of twigs to the boil in 1·5–2 litres of water, allow to simmer, cover head with towel and inhale steam for 15 minutes 3 times daily. Internally an infusion or decoction: 1 tablespoon to 2 cups of water 3 times a day against bronchial catarrh, arthritic and rheumatic pain.

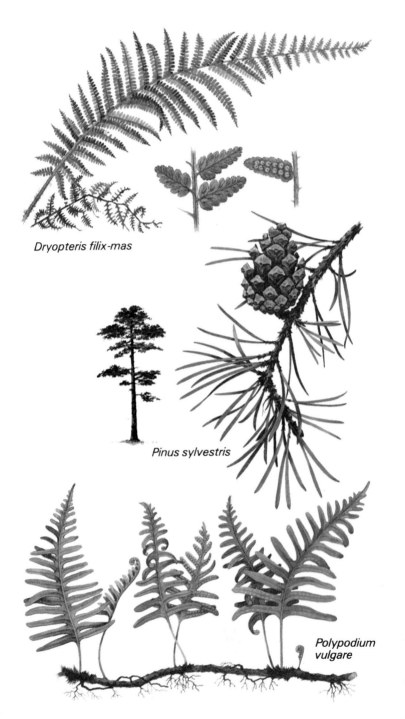

Dryopteris filix-mas

Pinus sylvestris

Polypodium vulgare

Juniperus communis L. Cupressaceae

 Juniper A shrub or (rarely) small tree with a reddish-brown bark. The leaves (needles) are arranged in whorls of 3, linear, 4–20mm long, sessile, spreading to ascending, sharply pointed, with a whitish stripe above, keeled on the lower surface. The flowers are dioecious. The male cones are solitary, 6–9mm long, with about 6 whorls of scales. The female cones are solitary, rather short at flowering time. The fruits are berry-like, globose, bluish-black, pruinose, containing up to 6 seeds.

Habitat woods, heath, scrub, mostly on chalk and limestone. **Distribution** throughout the region. **Active ingredients** aromatic essential oil, flavone, tannin, resin, glycoside, bitter principle, sugar. **Effect** strongly diuretic, digestant, antiseptic; causes redness, relieves flatulence, stimulates menstrual flow. **Parts used** the dried 'berries' and more rarely dried wood of the stem and roots. **Application M:** as a remedy for rheumatic conditions chew 1 berry 3 times on the first day, then increase dosage to up to 20 or 25 berries 3 times per day and decrease dosage in the same way down again to 1 berry; as a mixed infusion against dropsy and bladder and kidney disorders; externally an alcoholic extract is used on its own or as a mixture to alleviate rheumatic and similar pains. The juice of fresh juniper berries (available at chemists and health food shops on the Continent) can be used instead of the infusion. Juniper preparations should _not be taken during pregnancy._ **E:** the dried whole or bruised fruits give flavour to marinades and sauces and are indispensable in game dishes. They can also be rubbed into roasts of lamb, pork and beef and are essential for sauerkraut (3–6 berries season 4 servings). On the Continent the wood is added to fuel for smoking ham and bacon.

 Helleborus niger L. Ranunculaceae

 Black Hellebore A perennial herb with a stout rhizome. The basal leaves are pedate with usually 7–9 segments, persistent through the winter, dark green and often tinged reddish-brown; the stem leaves are undivided, bract-like, ovate, pale green. The flowers are 0·3–1cm in diameter, arranged in cymose groups of 2 or 3, showy. The perianth segments number 5, ovate, white or tinged pink, more or less spreading. The fruit consists of 6–8 follicles joined at the base, with several seeds.

Habitat woods, rocky grass banks and slopes, parks and gardens. **Distribution** S., C. and E. Europe; cultivated in the British Isles as a garden plant (Christmas Rose). **Active ingredients** hellebrin (a glycoside), helleborin (a saponin), aconitic acid, traces of essential oils. **Effect** strongly laxative, diuretic; causes watery purgation, influences cardiac function in the same way as strophanthin and digitalis, irritates mucous membranes. **Parts used** the dried rootstock. **Application C:** this drug should not be used without medical supervision. Today it is used only in few proprietary medicines. In homoeopathy the drug is used against headaches, psychic disorders, enteritis and spasms. Because of its effect on the mucous membrane the powdered rhizome is used in some Continental brands of snuff.

 Helleborus viridis L. Ranunculaceae

 Bear's-foot, Green Hellebore A perennial plant with a short ascending black rootstock. The stems are 15–40cm tall, erect, usually glabrous. The basal leaves are large, not overwintering, usually 2, digitate or somewhat pedate, with 7–11 (more rarely up to 13) segments; the stem leaves are sessile, digitate, and smaller. The flowers are slightly fragrant, in cymes in groups of 2–4, somewhat drooping, and up to 5cm in diameter. The perianth segments number 5, yellowish-green, spreading, broadly elliptical or ovate-acuminate. The fruit consists of 3-beaked follicles, slightly joined below.

Habitat woods and scrub, in most calcareous soil. **Distribution** in various subspecies in C., W. and E. Europe; S. and W. England (native) extending to N. Yorkshire (probably only naturalized). **Active ingredients** similar to _H. niger_ but containing other cardioglycosides. **Effect and application:** similar to _H. niger._

Juniperus communis

Helleborus niger

Ⓜ *Nigella sativa* L. Ranunculaceae

Small Garden Fennel (Aug.–Sept.) An annual herb with stems up to 55cm tall, erect and branched. The leaves are alternate, 3-pinnatisect, with linear segments, the lower ones petiolate, the upper ones sessile. The flowers are solitary, terminal, hermaphrodite and regular. The perianth segments number 5, ovate, shortly claw-shaped, white with greenish or bluish tips, usually persistent for some time. There are 5 nectaries, smaller than the perianth-segments and opposite them. The fruit consists of united follicles, warty on the back. The seeds are almost black, at first bitter, later tasting aromatic.

Habitat waste places, arable land, waysides. **Distribution** cultivated and frequently naturalized in C. Europe. **Active ingredients** fixed oil, essential oil, saponin, melanthine, tannin. **Effect** diuretic, digestive; aids menstrual flow, relieves flatulence. **Parts used** the mature seeds. **Application M:** an infusion (1 teaspoon per cup of water) is given 3–4 times a day against digestive and menstrual disorders. **Note** in the past these seeds were used to spice cakes and biscuits and in the near East they are sprinkled on freshly-baked bread.

☠ Ⓜ *Aconitum napellus* L. Ranunculaceae

Wolfsbane, Monkshood A robust perennial herb with a rather stout fleshy tuber-like stock. The stems are 45–150cm tall, erect, with leaves throughout, somewhat downy. The leaves are alternate with 3–5 palmate segments, the segments divided again over half their length, light green. The flowers are arranged in terminal-branched racemes, radially symmetrical, hermaphrodite, violet or blue. The perianth segments are spirally arranged, the posterior forming a showy, erect hood (helmet) up to 1·5cm long and 1·8cm wide. The fruit consists of usually 3 follicles. The seeds are winged.

Habitat woods, scrub, along watercourses, rich mountain pastures usually in calcareous soil. **Distribution** Europe; S.W. England. **Active ingredients** the highly poisonous alkaloid aconitine, traces of other related alkaloids, tannin, resin. **Effect** irritant, sedative, causes redness, alleviates fever, affects the central nervous system. **Parts used** the entire plant, fresh or dried, but usually the dried tubers. **Application C:** the toxicity of *A. napellus* is such that it should *not be used in any circumstances for domestic purposes*. The drug is contained in many brands of proprietary medicine; but even under medical supervision they have to be used with utmost caution. In homoeopathy preparations (usually tinctures) are given against feverish conditions, bronchitis, neuralgia, sciatica and internal haemorrhage.

Ⓔ Ⓜ *Ranunculus ficaria* L. Ranunculaceae

Lesser Celandine, Pilewort (March–May) A perennial with fibrous roots and spindle or club-shaped small tubers. The stems usually ascend from a rooting base, branched, up to 25cm tall. The basal leaves grow in a rosette, 0·8–4cm long, cordate, slightly angled or shallowly crenate, long petiolate, fleshy and glabrous; the stem leaves are smaller; the petiole is sheathed at the base. The flowers are up to 3cm in diameter, solitary. The sepals number 3 (sometimes more), green. The petals number up to 12, rarely absent, golden-yellow. The fruit consists of finely beaked and keeled achenes, 2–2·5mm long.

Habitat woods, scrub, meadows, banks, along streams. **Distribution** throughout the region. **Parts used** the leaves and young herb. **Application E:** the first leaves make an excellent salad or can be used in sandwiches. Leaves, stalks and buds are used in the same way as spinach; buds on their own, preserved in vinegar, make a substitute for capers. Both the bulbils which are formed in the leaf axils and the root bulbils are served with meat (stew in salted water until soft, strain and put in vinegar) or as a vegetable (stew briefly in salted water, strain, sauté in butter, thicken with cornflour, season and serve). **M:** although this plant is no longer used for medicinal purposes it has been used in the past as a remedy for both piles and scurvy.

Nigella sativa

Aconitum napellus

Ranunculus ficaria

☠ *Adonis vernalis* L. Ranunculaceae
Ⓜ **Spring Adonis** (April–May) A herb with a stout, fibrous, branched rootstock. The stems are 15–30cm tall, erect, simple or branched, scaly at the base. The stem leaves are alternate, small, finely 2-pinnatisect, linear, with entire lobes. The flowers are regular, hermaphrodite, terminal, very showy, 4–8cm in diameter. The sepals number 5–8, obovate, pubescent, greenish or petal-like. The petals number up to 20, twice as long as the sepals, bright yellow, elliptic. The stamens are numerous. The fruit consists of numerous, shortly beaked achenes, up to 3·5mm long.

Habitat sunny grassy hills on dry calcareous soil. **Distribution** C. and SE. Europe; cultivated in Britain. **Active ingredients** adonic acid, glycosides. **Effect** diuretic, sedative, cardiac stimulant. **Parts used** the entire plant at flowering time. Dry at temperatures not exceeding 40°C (the fresh herb is used for homoeopathic preparations). Application **C:** since the glycosides of this drug are in their effect similar to those of *Digitalis* and *Strophanthus, it cannot be used for domestic purposes*. In clinical medicine *Adonis* preparations are valuable in the treatment of cardiac malfunction, dropsy, chronic kidney failure, and certain forms of obesity.

Ⓜ *Hepatica nobilis* Mill. Ranunculaceae
(H. triloba; Anemone hepatica) (March–April) A delicate perennial, up to 15cm tall. The basal leaves are long petiolate, thickly fleshy or almost leathery, distinctly 3-lobed from a deeply heart-shaped base, intense green above, brownish or brownish-green and softly pubescent below; the stem leaves are entire, usually 3, and are situated beneath the flowers thus appearing like a calyx. The flowers are solitary on long, pilose pedicels and appear before the leaves in early spring; blue or rarely white or pinkish. The fruit is a cluster of achenes.

Habitat woods (mainly beechwoods), scrub and grassland. **Distribution** most of Europe; cultivated in Britain. **Active ingredients** saponins, enzymes, glycosides, resin, tannin. **Effect** diuretic, mildly astringent, aids formation of scar-tissue. **Parts used** fresh or dried leaves gathered in spring after flowering. **Application M:** the washed fresh leaves are turned into a pulp which is applied to slow-healing cuts, grazes or bruised skin. An infusion (2 teaspoons dried or freshly cut leaves to 1 cup of water) is taken 3–4 times a day against bronchitis and ailments of the liver or gall bladder; deep gargling soothes chronic irritation of the pharynx and throat.

Ⓜ *Aquilegia vulgaris* L. Ranunculaceae
Columbine (June–July) A perennial growing from an erect, stout, branched stock. The stems are 30–80cm (up to 110cm) tall, branched in the upper part. The basal leaves are biternate, on long petioles; the leaflets are on slender petioles, 3-lobed, with crenate margins, glabrous, greenish-blue above, green beneath; the stem leaves are similar but smaller and on shorter petioles. The flowers are regular, hermaphrodite, up to 5cm in diameter, drooping, usually blue, sometimes reddish or white. The sepals number 5, same colour as the petals, acute. The petals also number 5, with a long curved, knobbed spur. The stamens are numerous, exceeding the petals. The fruit consists of erect, beaked follicles, up to 2·7cm long.

Habitat woods, moist meadows and scrub. **Distribution** S. and C. Europe; moist parts of the British Isles. **Active ingredients** tannin, hydrocyanic glycosides and so far unknown substances. **Effect** mildly astringent. **Parts used** the fresh herb at flowering time. **Application M:** an infusion: 2 teaspoons per cup of water to be taken 3 times per day for disorders of the liver and gall bladder, chronic skin irritations and menopausal ailments. In the past this drug was used against scurvy and jaundice in allopathy, and in homoeopathy against nervous disorders, especially hysteria.

Adonis vernalis

Hepatica nobilis

Aquilegia vulgaris

Ⓜ️ *Delphinium consolida* L. Ranunculaceae
Forking Larkspur An annual, sometimes overwintering, with a slender tap-root. The stems are 25–50cm tall, thin, branched. The branches are somewhat ascending to spreading, long-petiolate, glandular-hairy. The lower leaves are deeply palmate; the segments are linear, narrow, acute; the upper stem leaves are similar but sessile. The flowers grow in few-flowered terminal racemes, up to 6mm in diameter, blue or rarely white or pink. The sepals number 5, petal-like, about 1·5cm long, one extended into a conical spur about as long as the petals. The nectaries number 4, blue to purple-blue, joined into a 3-lobed limb and producing 1 spur inside the sepal spur. The fruit consists of many-seeded, abruptly beaked follicles.

Habitat arable fields and waste places. **Distribution** introduced in Europe; casual in the British Isles. **Active ingredients** anthocyanglycoside (flower), alkaloids. **Effect** lowers blood pressure and pulse; mildly diuretic. **Parts used** the flower or the whole plant. **Application C:** a strong dose of flower preparations paralyzes breathing and is therefore no longer used. The herb and occasionally seeds are used as an infusion mixed with *Betula, Ononis, Herniaria* and given in addition to other drugs against disorders of the urinary tract.

Ⓜ️ *Berberis vulgaris* L. Berberidaceae
Ⓔ **Barberry** (Aug.–Sept: fruits; March–April: leaves) A deciduous shrub, 0·75–1·75m (up to 2·5m) tall, with grooved yellowish twigs and 3, usually 3-partite spines (representing the leaves of long shoots). The leaves are arranged in clusters on short axillary shoots, obovate to oblong-obovate, up to 4cm long, their margins minutely spiny-toothed, with short petioles. The flowers are arranged in pendulous racemes up to 6cm long, 6–8mm in diameter, yellow. The perianth segments are usually in 5 whorls, each with a basal nectary. The stamens are sensitive to the touch. The fruits (berries) are red, oblong, 1–1·2cm long.

Habitat hedges, clearings in woods, roadsides, usually in sun. **Distribution** throughout the region, often cultivated as an ornamental shrub. **Active ingredients** vitamin C, organic acids, pectin (fruits); berberine and traces of other alkaloids, tannin, resin. **Effect** digestant, purgative, stimulates peristalsis and bile flow. **Parts used** the dried root or root bark; the fruits, fresh or dried. The roots are dug up, cleaned, cut into small pieces or the bark peeled off and dried in moderate heat; the fruits are used fresh or dried carefully. **Application M:** the freshly pressed juice (or the bruised mature fruits) are given against ailments of the liver and gall bladder, kidney stones, menstrual pains, constipation, and all conditions which require the intake of vitamin C (colds, exhaustion). The dried fruits, mixed with rosehips, are used as an infusion (2 teaspoons per cup water). Infusions based on the root should only be used sparingly. **E:** the leaves can be used like *Rumex acetosella*; dried young leaves and branch-tips make an excellent refreshing tea (2 teaspoons per cup). The juice can be used like lemon juice or made into a fine jam; when fruits are pressed the stones must not be crushed.

Ⓜ️ *Nymphaea alba* L. Nymphaeaceae
White Waterlily (June–Sept.) An aquatic perennial with a stout rhizome. The leaves are always floating, large, up to 30cm in diameter, nearly circular, with a basal sinus, usually dark green on the upper surface, pale green tinged with red on the lower surface. The flowers are large and showy, up to 20cm in diameter, floating, with pedicels 2–3m long. The sepals number 4, lanceolate, green but white inside. The petals are numerous (up to 25 or more), white, the outer ones much longer than the sepals, the innermost shorter and often stamen-like. The stamens are numerous, arranged near the apex of the ovary, with linear filaments. The fruit is globose, up to 4cm in diameter.

Habitat lakes and ponds. **Distribution** throughout the region. **Active ingredients** several alkaloids, one glycoside, tannins, nymphalin, starch. **Effect** heart tonic; stimulates liver and spleen functions. **Parts used** the dried rootstock. **Application M:** this drug is not used medically. Older sources (e.g. Dioscorides) quote it as a remedy for dysentery.

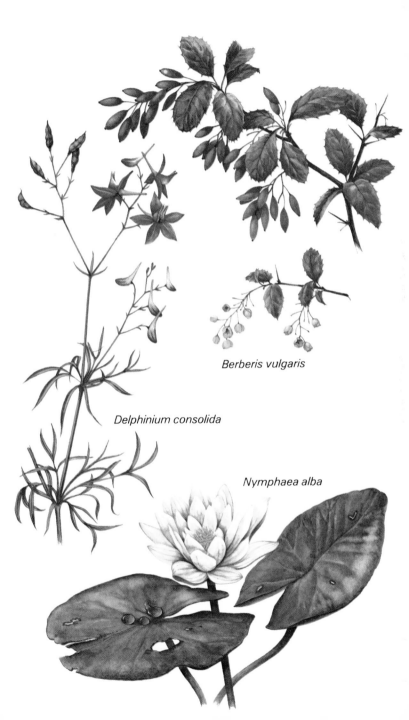

Berberis vulgaris

Delphinium consolida

Nymphaea alba

Ⓜ **Papaver rhoeas** L. Papaveraceae

Field Poppy (June–Aug.) A delicate annual with a slender tap-root. The stems are erect or ascending, branched, 15–60cm tall with stiff spreading hairs, rarely glabrous. The basal leaves are 1–2 pinnatifid, with segments ending in a fine bristle, petiolate; the upper leaves are sessile, usually only 3-lobed, with the terminal lobe elongated. The flowers are axillary, solitary, drooping in bud, up to 10cm in diameter (usually less). The sepals number 2, soon falling off, covered with stiff bristles. The petals number 4 (in 2 pairs), short-lived, up to 4cm wide, scarlet or rarely pink or white, with a blackish blotch at the base. The stamens are numerous, with bluish anthers. The fruit (a capsule) opens by pores. The seeds are small and numerous.

Habitat fields, waysides and waste places. **Distribution** throughout the region. **Active ingredients** tannin, mucilage, traces of alkaloids. **Effect** soothes cough; mildly expectorant. **Parts used** petals; collect on a dry day and dry in the sun or in a warm room. **Application M:** an infusion (1½ teaspoons per cup of water) to be taken 3 times a day against bronchial and nasal catarrh or coughs. The dried petals are also used to embellish herbal teas or potpourries.

Ⓜ **Chelidonium majus** L. Papaveraceae

Greater Celandine (May–Aug: flowers; Aug.–Oct: roots). A perennial with a branched woody rootstock. The stems are rather fragile, branched, 20–60cm (up to 90cm) tall, with scattered hairs, and contain an orange latex. The leaves are deeply pinnatisect, with up to 7 oblong or ovate leaflets, bluish-green beneath, the margins crenate-dentate. The flowers are up to 2·5cm in diameter, terminal. The sepals number 2, usually hairy. The petals number 4, broad-obovate, bright yellow. The stamens are numerous, yellow, with thickened filaments. The fruit (a capsule) is linear in outline, 1-celled, up to 5cm long. The seeds are black with a white appendage.

Habitat hedgerows, walls, on trees, mainly near human habitations. **Distribution** throughout the region. **Active ingredients** several alkaloids, traces of essential oils, saponin, enzymes. **Effect** relieves spasms, stimulates bile flow; mildly sedative. **Parts used** the fresh or dried herb at flowering time; the root. Both must be dried quickly in a warm and shaded place and kept dark (protect hands with gloves). **Application M:** An infusion (½–1 tablespoon to 1 litre of water) or decoction (1–2 teaspoons finely cut herb to 1 litre of water, simmer for 3–5 minutes, keep for fifteen minutes) 3 times daily against stomach pain, indigestion or gallstones. *A stronger dose will be harmful.* This drug is contained in many proprietary medicines.

Ⓜ **Corydalis bulbosa** (L.) DC. Fumariaceae

(C. cava) (March–April) A perennial with a short, tuberous, more or less hollow · rootstock and wiry roots. The stem is 10–35cm tall, erect, without scales below the lowest leaf. The leaves are alternate. 2–ternate, petiolate, light green on the upper surface and bluish-green on the lower surface. The flowers are arranged in a terminal, 10–20 flowered, usually dense raceme. The bracts are entire, ovate, green. The sepals number 2 or may be absent, free. The petals number 4, reddish-blue to blue-violet, up to 3cm long, the outer 2 unequal and the upper one drawn out from the base into a distinct, apically curved spur. The fruit is a 2-valved capsule up to 2.5cm long, pendent when mature; the seeds are minute.

Habitat woods, hedgerows. **Distribution** all over Europe (in the British Isles only as a garden escape). **Active ingredients** corydaline and bulbocapnine (both alkaloids). **Effect** Hallucinogenic; slows pulse, relieves spasms. **Parts used** the tuber; dig up in spring before flowering, clean, dry in the sun or in moderate heat. **Application M:** used clinically for the control of Parkinson's disease and other neurological disorders and also contained in preparations for post and pre-anaestheric treatment. Not suitable for domestic use.

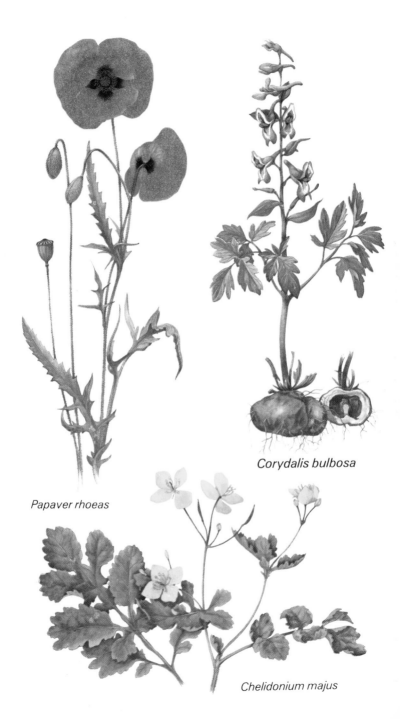

Papaver rhoeas

Corydalis bulbosa

Chelidonium majus

Ⓜ *Fumaria officinalis* L. Fumariaceae

Common Fumitory (June–Sept.) A fairly robust, often climbing annual herb, 5–30cm (up to 40cm) tall. The leaves are alternate, deeply 2–4 pinnatisect or pinnate; the leaflets or lobes are flat, lanceolate to linear-oblong, bluish-green, all borne on the stem. The flowers are arranged in axillary, many-flowered racemes, at first dense and contracted, later elongated. The sepals number 2, ovate to ovate-lanceolate, up to 3·5mm long, green, acuminate. The petals number 4, up to 9mm long, pink with dark red tips, the upper one spurred and dorsally compressed. The fruit is a nutlet, truncate or notched at the apex, somewhat keeled and a little compressed.

Habitat arable land and as a garden weed, usually on light soil. **Distribution** throughout the region. **Active ingredients** several alkaloids, fumaric acid, mucilage, aminoacids, resin, bitter principles. **Effect** mildly diuretic and laxative; stimulates bile secretion. **Parts used** the entire plant (without the roots) either fresh or dried. Application **M:** in folk medicine fumitory is used as a purgative and as a remedy for painful gall disorders, dropsy, against constipation and abdominal pain, piles, migraine and for certain ailments of the skin (mainly eczema). An infusion (1 teaspoon dried or fresh herb per cup of water) is taken 3 times a day *(higher doses may cause diarrhoea)*. This drug is used in several proprietary medicines.

Ⓔ *Sinapis arvensis* L. Cruciferae

Wild mustard, Charlock (April–May/June; Sept.–Oct: seeds) An annual, 15–80cm tall, usually erect, glabrous or hairy in the lower part. The leaves are 5–20cm long, usually with stiff hairs; the lower ones lyre-shaped with a toothed apical lobe and smaller lateral lobes; the upper leaves are usually undivided and sessile, lanceolate. The flowers are regular, hermaphrodite. The sepals number 4, spreading. The petals number 4, yellow, claw-shaped. The fruit is a siliqua, up to 4·5cm long, 1·5–4mm wide, glabrous or with stiff deflexed hairs. The seeds number 7–14, reddish-brown to almost black.

Habitat weed in fields, sometimes on waste land. **Distribution** throughout the region. **Parts used** young leaves and shrubs, before the plant comes into flower (older leaves are bitter); flower buds, mature seeds. **Application E:** a few leaves, finely chopped, lend a piquant flavour to salads, cottage cheese, paté, omelettes and sandwiches. Larger quantities can be served as a vegetable: boil for at least 30 minutes in salted water, strain, add finely chopped onions, some lemon juice and season according to taste. The flower buds are used like broccoli (boil for 2–5 minutes only, strain, sauté in butter with thinly sliced spring onions. The seeds can be used to make mustard: put dry plant on linen or sheets of paper before the seed pods open; beat gently until all the seeds have fallen out.

Ⓔ *Raphanus raphanistrum* L. Cruciferae

White Charlock, Wild Radish (March–April/May; Sept.–Oct: seeds) An annual 12–150cm tall, usually erect, branched, stiffly hairy. The basal and lower stem leaves are lyre-shaped, the upper stem leaves are entire. The flowers are regular, hermaphrodite, arranged in racemes, without bracts. The sepals number 4, erect, elliptic-lanceolate, obtuse, up to 1cm long. The petals number 4, twice as long as the sepals, white, yellow or (rarely) violet. The fruit is a siliqua, up to 9cm long and 4mm wide, with several shallow constrictions; the segments are longer than they are wide, with strong venation and a seedless 0·8–3cm beak above.

Habitat weed in fields and pastures, on waste land. **Distribution** throughout the region. **Parts used** the young leaves and shoots (best collected before flowering time); the seeds. **Application E:** as for *Sinapis arvensis*. **Note** this plant can be mistaken for the yellow-flowering *S. arvensis*.

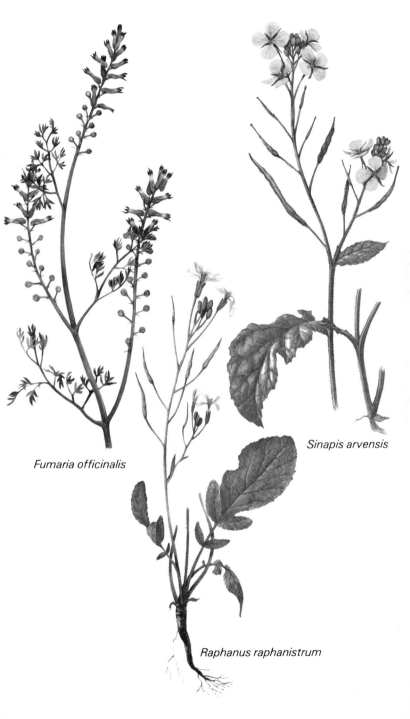

Fumaria officinalis

Sinapis arvensis

Raphanus raphanistrum

(E) *Lepidium campestre* (L.) R. Br. Cruciferae

Pepperwort (April–May) An annual or biennial, up to 60 cm tall, densely covered with short hairs. The basal leaves are entire or somewhat lobed, ovate to obovate, obtuse; the stem leaves are usually numerous, ovate to oblong, auriculate, the margins toothed. The flowers are very small, regular, hermaphrodite, arranged in dense racemes. The sepals number 4, not pouched, about 1·5 mm long. The petals number 4, usually white, slightly longer than the sepals, with yellow anthers. The fruit is a single-seeded silicula, up to 6 mm long, covered with tiny blisters; the valves are winged (the wing joined with the basal part of the style) and keeled.

Habitat meadows, pastures, in arable land, waste places, on walls etc. **Distribution** throughout the region. **Parts used** the fresh young shoots and early leaves; the pods and seeds, fresh or preserved in vinegar and salt. **Application E:** leaves and shoots, finely chopped, give a watercress-like peppery taste to salads, omelettes, soups, and sauces. Fish can be served with a white sauce made of 3 measures finely chopped pepperwort, 1–2 measures chopped gherkins, 2 measures capers, 2 measures chopped green olives, 1 measure mildly pickled onions, 5 measures mayonnaise, small clove of garlic, some freshly ground pepper. The much stronger-flavoured seed pods can be served with strong meats (mutton, game) or added to salads.

(E) *Lepidium densiflorum* Schrad. Cruciferae

(May–July) An annual or biennial with erect stems, branched in the upper part, papillose. The basal leaves are elliptical, with toothed margins, long petiolate, the stem-leaves linear-lanceolate, sparsely toothed, ciliate, with visible lateral nerves. The flowers are rather small, regular, hermaphrodite, arranged in dense terminal racemes. The sepals number 4, about 1 mm long. The petals are shorter than the sepals or sometimes not developed, usually white. The fruit, a silicula up to 4 mm long and 3 mm wide, circular-ovate, is winged in the upper part (the wing not joined with the very short style); the pedicel is up to 5·5 mm long.

Habitat as for *L. campestre*. **Distribution** native to N. America, introduced in Europe including the British Isles. **Parts used** the whole plant **Application E:** as for *L. campestre*. **Note** both species are related to the garden cress (*L. sativum*) which is cultivated as a popular salad plant all over Europe, including the British Isles.

(E) *Thlaspi arvense* L. Cruciferae

Field Pennycress A glabrous annual herb, 5–51 cm (up to 65 cm) high, normally erect. The basal leaves are obovate to oblanceolate, petiolate; the upper stem leaves are oblong, with a clasping, arrow-shaped base, the margins entire or wavy to toothed. The flowers are arranged in a raceme, hermaphrodite, regular. The sepals number 4, up to 2 mm long, free. The petals number 4, white. The stamens have yellow anthers, and are shorter than the petals. The fruit is a silicula, almost circular, flat, 0·8–1·5 cm wide; the pedicels are 0·5–1·1 cm long, ascending. The seeds number 5–8 in each cavity.

Habitat waste places, as a garden weed, arable land, roadsides. **Distribution** throughout the region. **Parts used** the leaves and young shoots (always collect the leaves before flowering). **Application E:** field pennycress is edible but on account of its bitter aroma it is not to everyone's taste. A small amount of the finely chopped leaves adds a distinctive flavour to salads, sandwich spreads, scrambled eggs, soups, sauces, etc.

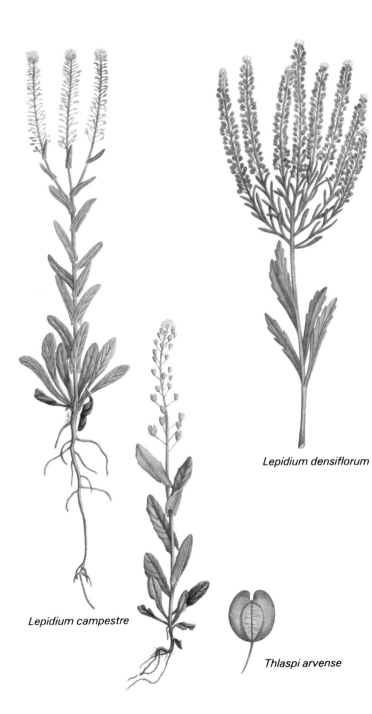

Lepidium densiflorum

Lepidium campestre

Thlaspi arvense

Ⓜ *Capsella bursa-pastoris* (L.) Medic. Cruciferae

Ⓔ **Shepherd's Purse** (March – Oct.) An annual or biennial 3 – 35cm tall or more, usually erect, somewhat hairy or glabrous. The basal leaves are pinnatifid or undivided, the stem leaves clasping, arrow-shaped at the base. The flowers are arranged in a terminal raceme without bracts, regular, hermaphrodite. The 4 petals are white, up to 3mm long, twice as long as the sepals, sometimes absent. The fruit is a silicula, 6 – 9mm long and 4 – 9mm wide, triangular-heart-shaped, sometimes notched; the valves are keeled, with a network of veins.

Habitat arable land, gardens, waste places, roadsides, rubbish tips, etc. **Distribution** throughout the region. **Active ingredients** choline, acetylcholine, tyramine, diosmin (a glycoside), traces of tannin, resin. **Effect** diuretic; checks bleeding. **Parts used** the entire herb without roots, best collected in summer, quickly dried and stored away from light (not effective when left too long). **Application M:** as an infusion (2 teaspoons per cup of water) 3 – 4 times a day against nosebleed, uterine bleeding, inflammation of the urinary tract and, as a compress, applied to open bleeding cuts and sores. The drug is also contained in some proprietary medicines. **E:** the young leaves of the basal rosette (before flowering) make a fine addition to salads or — sautéd in flour and butter — sauces and soups.

Ⓜ *Cochlearia officinalis* subsp. *officinalis* L. Cruciferae

Ⓔ **Scurvy-grass** (May – June/July) A biennial or perennial with a long tap-root and shoots up to 51cm long, ascending or trailing, usually somewhat fleshy. The basal leaves are kidney-shaped or ovate-cordate to ovate-truncate, long-petiolate, arranged in a loose rosette; the stem leaves are usually sessile and clasping the stem. The flowers are up to 1cm in diameter, regular, hermaphrodite. The sepals number 4, green, erect to spreading. The petals number 4, white, rarely lilac, 2 – 3 times as long as the sepals. The fruit is a silicula, globose to ovoid-ellipsoid, rounded at both ends, 3 – 7mm long; the valves are strongly convex, with a conspicuous network of veins.

Habitat coastal marshes, cliffs, etc. **Distribution** coastal areas of Europe; inland near salt mines or saline springs. **Active ingredients** bitter principles, tannin, mustard-oil glycoside, essential oil, vitamin C, mineral salts. **Effect** diuretic, disinfectant; stomach stimulant; causes redness, prevents scurvy. **Parts used** the leaves and flower stalks, fresh (preferably) or dried in moderate heat. **Application M:** the bruised fresh leaves are put on slow-healing ulcers, etc. An infusion (1 – 2 tablespoons per cup of water, can be taken 3 times daily against dropsy, arthritis, scurvy and chronic skin ailments, used as a spring tonic and as a mouthwash against mouth ulcers and bleeding gums. **E:** on account of its high vitamin C content the leaves (also collected after flowering) are valuable for salads, soups, sauces and sandwiches.

Ⓜ *Cardamine pratensis* L. Cruciferae

Ⓔ **Lady's Smock** (April – May) A perennial with a short prostrate rhizome, sometimes producing stolons. The stems are erect or ascending, 10 – 61cm long, glabrous. The basal leaves are arranged in a rosette, pinnate, with rounded leaflets and a large, kidney-shaped terminal lobe, long-petiolate; the stem leaves are shortly petiolate, lanceolate, entire or with a toothed terminal lobe. The flowers grow in a raceme, without bracts, regular, hermaphrodite. The sepals number 4, the inner ones slightly pouched with scarious margins and lilac apex. The petals number 4, claw-shaped, lilac or sometimes white, three times as long as the sepals. The anthers are yellow. The fruit is a siliqua, 2·5 – 5cm long and 1 – 1·5mm wide; the pedicels are up to 2·5cm.

Habitat moist grassy places along streams, usually in acid soil. **Distribution** throughout the region. **Active ingredients** mustard-oil glycoside, vitamin C. **Effect** diuretic; relieves spasms, prevents scurvy. **Parts used** the fresh flowering herb. **Application M:** ½ teaspoon juice or an infusion (1 teaspoon per cup of water) is given 3 – 4 times a day against scurvy, dropsy, spasms (also when caused by hysteria) and chronic skin ailments. **E:** the young leaves, shoots, and buds taste like watercress and make a fine addition to salads or sandwich spreads. **Note** the related *C. amara* (recognized by its purple anthers) can also be used for salads but is rather bitter.

Cardamine pratensis

Capsella bursa-pastoris

Cochlearia officinalis

Ⓜ **Armoracia rusticana** (Gaertn.) Mey. & Scherb Cruciferae
Ⓔ **Horseradish** (Sept.–Oct.) A perennial up to 100cm tall or more, with a stout simple or branched rootstock and fleshy roots. The basal leaves are ovate-oblong or ovate, up to 50cm long, margins crenate or finely toothed; the petiole is 10–31cm long; the stem leaves are sessile or shortly petiolate, entire or pinnatifid. The flowers are regular, hermaphrodite. The sepals number 4, not pouched. The petals number 4, white, 4–7·5mm long. The fruit is a silicula, up to 6·5mm long, globose or ovoid.

Habitat arable land, waste places, railway embankments, along streams, etc. **Distribution** as an escape throughout the region. Widely cultivated for culinary purposes. **Active ingredients** essential oil with mustard oil glycoside, sinigrin, enzymes. **Effect** diuretic, slightly laxative; causes redness. **Parts used** the tap-root; collect during the winter and store in sand (preferably in a cellar). **Application M:** the drug is rarely used on its own but is contained in a few proprietary medicines against influenza and inflammation of the urinary tract. Some people are allergic to it. **E:** the tap-roots, as long as they are not already woody, make an excellent pungent salad or can be eaten thinly sliced on bread and butter.

Ⓔ **Barbarea vulgaris** R.Br. Cruciferae
Yellow Rocket, Winter Cress (Dec.–Jan.) A biennial or perennial with a yellowish tap-root. The stems are erect, up to 90cm tall, glabrous, branched. The basal leaves are in a rosette, petiolate, lyre-shaped and pinnatisect, with rounded terminal lobe and 6–9 lateral lobes, widest below the terminal lobe; the stem leaves pinnatisect, the uppermost undivided. The flowers are arranged in a usually dense raceme, about 8mm in diameter. The sepals number 4, the inner pair slightly pouched. The petals number 4, twice as long as the sepals, bright yellow. The siliquae are up to 2·6cm long and 2mm wide, more or less erect on up to 5mm pedicels; the style is persistent, up to 3mm long.

Habitat moist places, roadsides, stream banks, hedges. **Distribution** throughout the region. **Parts used** leaves of the basal rosette. **Application E:** fresh young leaves collected in early spring make a fine salad (toss in olive oil and lemon juice and mix with finely cut onions). Leaves collected in winter are used like spinach: boil in salted water until soft, strain, add pork dripping or butter, season with pepper and 1–2 cloves of garlic according to taste, add a little nutmeg before serving.

Ⓜ **Rorippa nasturtium-aquaticum** (L.) Hayek **(Nasturtium officinale)**
Ⓔ Cruciferae
Watercress (May–Oct.) A perennial that remains green in autumn, with angular hollow shoots, up to 65cm long, setting roots below, ascending or floating. The leaves are lyre-shaped, pinnate, the lower ones petiolate, the upper ones sessile and auricled; the lateral leaflets number 5–11, elliptical or ovate; the terminal leaflets are usually broadly heart-shaped. The flowers are arranged in a raceme, about 5mm in diameter. The sepals number 4, the inner pair pouched. The petals number 4, white, about twice as long as the sepals. The stamens number 6. The siliquae are 1·2–1·8cm long, ascending from usually horizontal pedicels. The seeds are ovoid, about 1mm wide, arranged in 2 rows in each cell, with about 25 depressions on each side.

Habitat running water. **Distribution** throughout the region. **Active ingredients** mustard oil glycoside, gluconasturtiin, vitamin C, essential oils, iodine, mineral salts including iron compounds. **Effect** diuretic. **Parts used** the whole plant above ground at or before flowering time, fresh or dried. **Application M:** this drug is contained in several proprietary medicines. For domestic purposes the freshly pressed juice (½ teaspoon 3 times a day) or an infusion (2 teaspoons per cup of water) is used against bronchial catarrh, chronic irritations and inflammation of the skin, rheumatism, bladder and kidney complaints (stones); also as a spring tonic. *Excessive use of the drug may lead to stomach upset.* **E:** the fresh plant is an ideal addition to salads **Note** freshly collected plants must be thoroughly washed to remove insect larvae or snails.

Armoracia rusticana

Barbarea vulgaris

Nasturtium officinale

Ⓜ **Alliaria officinalis** Bieb. **(A. petiolata)** Cruciferae

Ⓔ **Garlic Mustard, Hedge Garlic** (April/May – June) A biennial with a strong-smelling tap-root. The stem is 15 – 120cm tall, usually erect and unbranched. The basal leaves are arranged in a rosette, kidney or heart-shaped, long-petiolate; the stem leaves are shorter petiolate, triangular-ovate from a heart-shaped base, with the margins wavy to toothed, giving off a scent of garlic when crushed. The flowers are arranged in terminal racemes, 5 – 6mm in diameter. The sepals number 4, not pouched. The petals number 4, white, shortly claw-shaped, twice as long as the sepals. The siliquae are up to 6cm long and 2mm wide, erect or curved at the base, 4-angled, with blackish seeds.

Habitat hedges, woods, along walls and fences, as a weed in pastures. Distribution throughout the region. Active ingredients essential oils, a glycoside. Effect diuretic, anti-asthmatic; kills worms. Parts used the leaves and stem (without flowers and fruits), fresh or dried. Application M: internally as an infusion: 2 teaspoons per cup of water, macerate in cold water for 5 hours, bring just to the boil, allow to stand for 5 – 10 minutes and strain, taken 3 times a day against bronchitis, eczema and disorders of the mouth; externally as a herbal compress for skin ailments and slow-healing cuts. E: a few shredded young leaves mixed with a salad will lend it a garlic-like flavour without having the lasting effect of garlic itself. Some people recommend blending the leaves with mint sauce to serve with lamb or mutton dishes.

Ⓜ **Sisymbrium officinale** (L.) Scop. Cruciferae

Ⓔ **Hedge Mustard** (March – May) An annual, sometimes overwintering, with a thin tap-root. The stem is up to 90cm tall, erect, branched above, with downward pointing, stiffish hairs. The basal leaves are arranged in a rosette, pinnatifid, with 3 – 5 lateral lobes on either side and a roundish terminal lobe; the stem leaves have 1 – 3 lateral lobes and a hastate terminal one. The flowers are 2 – 3mm in diameter, in dense racemes, later elongated, shortly pedicelled. The sepals number 4, green. The petals number 4, yellowish, longer than the sepals, claw-shaped. The siliquae are up to 1·6cm long and 1mm wide, stiff, erect and usually appressed to the axis, hairy or glabrous. The seeds are brownish or orange-brown, ovoid, about 1mm wide.

Habitat roadsides, hedges, waste land, as a weed in arable land. Distribution throughout the region. Active ingredients lactones, tannins, a glycoside similar to digitalin. Effect bronchial sedative; mild heart tonic. Parts used the entire plant above ground. Application M: no longer commonly used, but still contained in some proprietary cough medicines. An infusion (2 teaspoons per cup of water) is supposed to have a similar effect. In France it is still used as a spring tonic, against colds and as an expectorant (effective in case of coughs). E: the leaves are a welcome addition to salads, sauces, soups and omelettes.

Ⓔ **Crambe maritima** L. Cruciferae

Seakale (Feb. – May) A perennial with a branched fleshy rhizome. The stem is 20 – 60cm long, 2 – 3cm wide, usually erect, branched from below. The leaves are large (the upper ones much smaller), up to 30cm long, ovate, bluish-green, glabrous, usually pinnately lobed, with wavy margins. The flowers grow in corymbose inflorescences up to 1·6cm in diameter. The sepals number 4, spreading. The petals are nearly 1cm long, claw-shaped, white (the claw green). The fruit is not dehiscent, dispersed by the sea, up to 1·5cm long and 6 – 8mm wide, ascending from its spreading pedicel.

Habitat coastal areas, on dunes, cliffs, walls, rocks, shingle, etc. Distribution most of the coastal areas of N. Europe. Parts used mainly the young shoots but also the first leaves as long as they are very young. Application E: blanch the shoots after harvesting, cut into pieces and use like asparagus (boil in salted water for 15 – 25 minutes, or boil for 10 minutes, pour away water and sauté in butter or olive oil until tender). The leaves are boiled until soft, minced, seasoned with 1 – 2 cloves of garlic and served as, or mixed with, spinach.

Sisymbrium officinale

Alliaria officinalis

Crambe maritima

ⓂⒺ *Viola odorata* L. Violaceae

Sweet Violet (March–April/May: herb; July–Oct: roots) A perennial with a short stout rhizome and long rooting stolons. The leaves are long-petiolate (the petioles with deflexed hairs), up to 6cm long, ovate-circular to broad-ovate from a heart-shaped base, dark green, sparsely hairy to glabrous, margins crenate or finely toothed. The flowers are solitary on long pedicels, fragrant. The sepals extend into basal, spreading appendages. The corolla is bilaterally symmetrical, up to 1·6cm long, usually deep violet, rarely purplish, white or pink; the lower petals are spurred, the upper ones obovate-oblong. The fruit is a 3-valved capsule, globose, pubescent.

Habitat woods, hedgerows, scrub, parks. Distribution throughout the region. Active ingredients saponin, essential oil, methyl salicyatate, glycoprotein. Effect expectorant; stimulates glandular secretion. Parts used mainly the rootstock but also leaves and flowers, fresh or dried. Application M: as an infusion: 1 tablespoon leaves and flowers per cup of water; or decoction: 1 tablespoon finely cut rootstock, 2 cups of water, steep for 10 hours, bring to the boil, strain, 3–4 times a day against cough, bronchitis (especially dry bronchitis), catarrh, whooping cough; as a mouthwash or for gargling against sore throat and inflammation of the mouth. E: sprinkle fresh flowers on fruit salads, puddings, ice-cream and some salads (e.g. Spanish beans with oil, lemon and orange juice) for flavour and decoration.

Ⓜ *Viola tricolor* L. Violaceae

Wild Pansy (June–Aug.) An annual or perennial with tufted stems, ascending or erect, usually branched, 15–30cm tall, hollow, sometimes having a short rhizome. The lower leaves are ovate or heart-shaped, obtuse, crenate; the upper leaves are ovate to lanceolate from a usually cuneate base; the stipules are often deeply pinnately lobed. The flowers are axillary, long-pedicelled, showy, not scented, 1–3cm in diameter. The sepals are triangular-lanceolate, acute. The corolla is longer than the sepals, usually 3-coloured (violet, yellow, blue-violet); the petals are longer than they are wide, flat, the spurs variable, longer than the appendages.

Habitat arable land, waste ground and grassland, margins of woods. Distribution throughout the region. Active ingredients saponins, the glycoside gaultherine, salicylic compounds, tannin, mucilage, flavonoids. Effect diuretic; alleviates fever, stimulates perspiration. Parts used the entire plant, including roots, dried away from direct sun, or in low artificial heat. Application M: effective against skin diseases (acne, pruritus, eczema, etc.), also against rheumatic conditions, dropsy, bedwetting and intestinal disorders. It can be used as an infusion taken internally (2 teaspoons per cup) 2–3 times a day and externally applied to the skin by means of a compress.

Ⓜ *Polygala amara* L. Polygalaceae

(June–Aug.) A perennial herb with stems 4–15cm (up to 20cm) tall, erect or ascending, usually simple, stout, woody at the base, numerous. The basal leaves form a dense rosette, obovate to elliptic, 4mm to 3cm long, obtuse, glabrous; the stem leaves are smaller, oblong or lanceolate. The flowers are arranged in many-flowered lateral inflorescences up to 6mm long, blue, pink or purplish, hermaphrodite, bilaterally symmetrical. The sepals number 5, free, the 2 inner ones being longer than the outer ones. Petals number 3, the outer one fused with the lower and joined to a staminal tube. The stamens have anthers opening by pores. The fruit is a capsule, up to 5·5mm long.

Habitat grassland and damp mountain pastures, usually on chalk. Distribution uneven throughout the region. Active ingredients saponin, bitter principles, tannin, essential oil, traces of glycosides. Effect mildly expectorant, diuretic, emollient. Parts used the dried herb, collected at flowering time and dried in the sun. Application M: taken as an infusion (1½–2 teaspoons per cup) 3 times daily against stomach upsets, disorders of the bladder and kidneys, rheumatic pains and arthritis. The drug is sometimes used in dispensed cough mixtures.

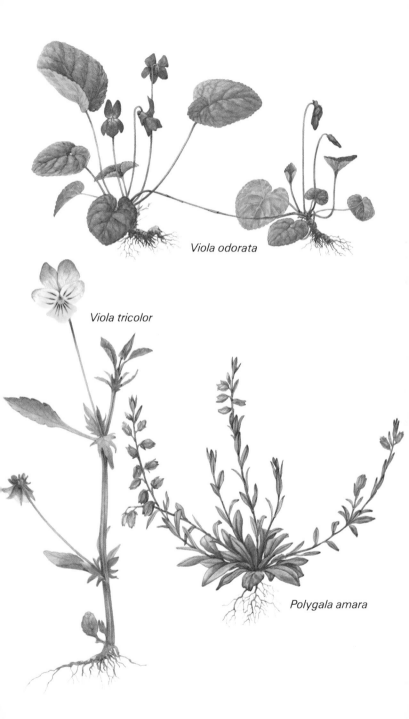

Viola odorata

Viola tricolor

Polygala amara

Ⓜ️ *Hypericum perforatum* L. Guttiferae

Common St John's Wort (June–Aug.) A perennial with a stout creeping rhizome. The stems are up to 90cm tall, woody at the base, with 2 raised longitudinal lines. The leaves are opposite, sessile, up to 2cm long, oblong, linear or elliptic, obtuse, with numerous translucent glandular dots (visible against the light). The flowers are arranged in many-flowered terminal cymes, regular, showy, 1·7–2cm in diameter. The sepals number 5, lanceolate, entire, glandular. The petals number 5, are much longer than the sepals, and yellow. The stamens are numerous. The fruit is a capsule.

Habitat grassland, hedge banks, open woods, usually on calcareous soil. **Distribution** throughout the region. **Active ingredients** essential oil, tannins, hypericine, flavonoids, resin. **Effect** mildly sedative, astringent, antidepressant, relieves spasms, stimulates intestine secretion and bile flow. **Parts used** mainly the fresh flowers, but also fresh or dried flowering shoots. **Application M:** used as an infusion (2 teaspoons fresh or dried herb per cup of water) twice daily against menstrual disorders, and gastric and intestinal disorders. When taken over a long period it relieves depression, melancholia and migraine. As a lint it is applied to cuts and bruises, especially those that heal slowly. The drug is contained in several proprietary medicines.

Ⓔ *Silene vulgaris* (Moench) Garcke Caryophyllaceae

Bladder Campion (June–Sept.) A perennial with a woody branched rhizome. The shoots are erect, 20–60cm (up to 90cm) tall, sometimes branched, usually glabrous. The leaves are opposite, without stipules, up to 4·5cm long and 1·3cm wide, ovate or elliptic-lanceolate, acute, the lowest petiolate, the upper ones sessile, bluish-green. The flowers are arranged in cymose inflorescences. 1·5–1·8cm in diameter, regular, polygamous, usually drooping. The calyx is almost globular, with a narrow mouth, light green or reddish, with a network of 20 distinct longitudinal veins; the lobes number 5, triangular. The petals are deeply bifid, white. The fruit is a capsule, enclosed by the calyx, opening with 6 teeth.

Habitat grassy slopes, arable land, roadsides and broken ground. **Distribution** throughout the region. **Parts used** the leaves and young shoots. **Application E:** the leaves and young shoots (cut before flowering) can be used either on their own or as an addition to salads. Finely cut and boiled for 5–10 minutes they are added to soups or sauces. As a leaf vegetable they can be used like spinach or mixed with other plants.

Ⓜ️ *Stellaria media* (L.) Vill. Caryophyllaceae

Ⓔ **Chickweed** (Feb.–Nov.) An annual or biennial with a fine tap-root, forming loose mats. The stems are 3cm to over 40cm long, frequently branched, ascending (often only at the tip), leafy, with a single line of hairs on each internode. The leaves are usually glabrous but sometimes ciliate near the base, 0·3–2·5cm long, ovate to broadly elliptical, acute to acuminate. The flowers are arranged in terminal inflorescences, numerous, regular; the pedicel usually has a line of hairs. The sepals number 5, ovate-lanceolate, about 5mm long, with narrow membranous edges. The petals number 5 (rarely absent), white, not longer than the sepals, deeply bifid. The stamens number 3–8, with reddish anthers. The fruit is a capsule, exceeding the calyx. The seeds are reddish-brown.

Habitat cultivated and waste areas. **Distribution** throughout the region. **Active ingredients** saponin, mineral salts. **Effect** diuretic; assists formation of scar-tissue. **Parts used** the entire flowering plant, dried or fresh. **Application M:** internally as an infusion (1 teaspoon per cup water) 3–4 times a day to cure dropsy, rheumatism, arthritis, inflammation of the joints. The fresh bruised herb is applied to slow-healing cuts or skin irritations. **E:** for culinary purposes the plant, which is available in abundance for most of the year, can be used like *Silene* but because of its bitter taste and fibrous nature it cannot be recommended for salads. As a vegetable it is best minced after boiling.

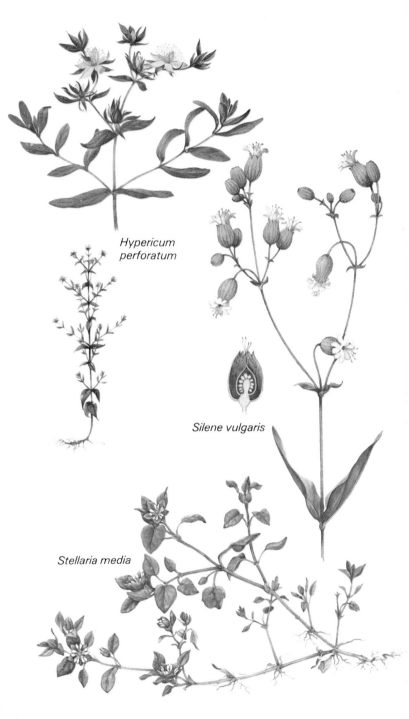

Hypericum perforatum

Silene vulgaris

Stellaria media

Ⓜ️ *Herniaria glabra* L. Caryophyllaceae
Glabrous Rupturewort (June–Aug.) An annual or biennial mat-forming herb with a tap-root. The shoots are numerous, prostrate, 5–30cm long, green, slightly hairy but usually glabrous, much-branched. The leaves are up to 1cm long (usually much shorter), ovate-lanceolate, acute, sometimes ciliate. The flowers are tiny, 1·8–2·2mm in diameter, regular, arranged in dense axillary clusters, these occasionally forming a spike. The sepals number 5, ovate, obtuse. The petals number 5, minute and shorter than the sepals, white. The stigmas are longer than the sepals. Fruit is a nutlet, glossy, at first reddish then black, 5–6mm long, not opening.

Habitat dry, sandy areas. Distribution unevenly in Britain; throughout the rest of Europe. Active ingredients saponin, the glycoside herniarin, essential oil, tannins. Effect disinfectant (urinary tract), very mildly diuretic; gives mild relief from spasms. Parts used the entire flowering herb, dried. Application M: internally as infusion (2 teaspoons per cup) 3–4 times daily against disorders of the bladder and kidney (urethritis, chronic cystitis, etc.); also recommended against bronchial catarrh.

Ⓜ️ *Saponaria officinalis* L. Caryophyllaceae
Soapwort, Bouncing Bett (March–Sept: roots) A perennial with a creeping rhizome and stolons. The shoots are up to 70–90cm tall, erect or ascending, glabrous. The leaves are opposite, ovate to elliptical, 3–10cm long, acute, glabrous. The flowers grow in open or dense terminal inflorescences, 2–2·5cm in diameter, regular. The sepals are united at the base to form a cylindrical calyx tube 1·8–2·1cm in length and crowned by 5 teeth. The petals number 5, claw-shaped, pink or flesh-red (the claw longer than the calyx tube), obovate, entire or notched, the base with 2 scales. The fruit is a capsule, opening with 4 or 5 teeth. The seeds are blackish.

Habitat away from cultivation, by streams, hedge banks, etc. Distribution throughout the region. Active ingredients saponins. Effect mildly diuretic, laxative, expectorant; causes glandular secretions. Parts used the rootstock with roots; to be dug up, brushed clean and dried in the sun or moderate heat; the flowering plant can also be used but is much less effective. Application M: best used as a decoction: put 2 tablespoons finely chopped rootstock or 3–4 of dried herb into 1 litre cold water, let stand for 5–8 hours, bring to the boil, cool, strain; take 2–3 times daily against bronchitis, dry coughs, and gall disorders. A stronger decoction is effective against constipation but *may cause stomach irritation*. It can also be added to the bathwater as a remedy for eczema and other skin eruptions.

Ⓔ *Portulaca oleracea* L. Portulacaceae
(May–Oct.) A fleshy annual with prostrate or ascending branched stems up to 35cm long. The leaves are almost opposite, up to 2cm long, obovate-oblong from a cuneate base, obtuse, glossy, usually crowded in the upper part of the stem. The flowers are axillary or terminal, numbering 1–3, regular, hermaphrodite, 0·9–1·2cm in diameter. The sepals number 2, hooded at apex. The petals number 4–6, usually free, yellow, falling early. The stamens number up to 15. Style is divided into 3–6 branches. The fruit is a capsule, opening by a transverse lid, up to 7mm wide.

Habitat warm positions in fields, vineyards, railway embankments, waste places. Distribution various parts of the British Isles; throughout the rest of Europe. Parts used the fresh leaves and shoots before flowering (the plant flowers for several months). Application E: only fresh plants should be used: once dried they lose their spicy and slightly salty taste. They can be added to salads or finely chopped to sandwich spreads, and sautéd in butter to soups, omelettes, and sauces. As a vegetable the plant is treated and served in the same way as spinach. The leaves or small parts of the shoot can also be added to capers or their substitutes and to olives. To preserve the plant for the winter put it into salt and dry white wine. Note the variety *sativa* is a long-established cultivated plant used as a pot herb.

Saponaria officinalis

Herniaria glabra

Portulaca oleracea

Ⓔ ***Chenopodium album*** L. Chenopodiaceae

Fat Hen (March–Oct.) An annual, 40–100cm tall, usually erect, with short branches, green and greyish-white, mealy. The leaves are ovate-lanceolate, ovate or rhomboid, usually toothed. The flowers grow in dense small groups which are arranged in a dense spike-like inflorescence, the axis of which is distinctly mealy. The perianth has 2–5 keeled segments; the stamens number 2–5; the seeds are up to 1·8mm diameter, often radially marked, sometimes with a criss-cross pattern.

Habitat cultivated land and waste areas. **Distribution** throughout the region. **Parts used** fresh young leaves and shoots, available in abundance during spring, summer and autumn. **Application E:** this is the best spinach substitute amongst all wild plants. The taste may be a little bland but can be improved by the addition of *Portulaca*, a little *Lepidium*, very little *Alliaria*, garlic or chopped onions sautéd in butter or olive oil. Finely chopped it may be added to soups and sauces. The plant cannot be recommended for salads, and the use of the mature seeds for making flour, although possible, is extremely cumbersome. **Note** none of the other annual species is edible. *C. album* can be recognized by the mealy axis of the inflorescence, the toothed leaf-margins and the fact that the inflorescence is leafless in the upper part. If in doubt rub leaves: other species smell and/or taste bad.

Ⓔ ***Chenopodium bonus-henricus*** L. Chenopodiaceae

Good King Henry, All Good (April–July) A perennial with 30–60cm tall erect stems. The leaves are 5–11cm long, triangular-hastate, acute or obtuse, entire with wavy margins, at first with a mealy surface, later dull green. The flowers are arranged in small groups in a usually terminal, pyramidal inflorescence, not interspersed with leaves. The perianth segments are 4–5, not keeled. The stigmas number 2–3, long and protruding. The seeds are *c.* 2mm long, reddish-brown, with a persistent pericarp. They are not enclosed by the perianth and have a rough surface.

Habitat pastures, near farmyards, roadsides, along fences, in nitrogen-rich soils. **Distribution** throughout the region. **Parts used** the young leaves and shoots. **Application E:** no longer used for medicinal purposes. Like *C. album* this plant makes a fine addition to vegetable soups or is used as a vegetable either on its own or mixed with others. The young shoots can be prepared and served like asparagus. Its use for salads is a matter of taste. **Note** this species can be distinguished from the rest of the genus by its perennial habit and the hastate base of the typically triangular leaves.

Ⓜ ***Atriplex hortensis*** L. Chenopodiaceae

Ⓔ **Orache** (April–Oct.) An annual with erect stems, 30–60cm tall, green but often tinged red in young plants. The lower leaves are petiolate, heart-shaped to triangular, usually glabrous, the margins toothed; the middle stem leaves are hastate with coarsely toothed margins; the upper leaves are lanceolate, with entire margins; the young leaves have a mealy surface. The flowers are arranged in yellowish or red groups in spike-like panicles, some with perianth but no bracteoles, the rest without perianth but with non-fused bracteoles.

Habitat arable land, waste and disturbed ground, shingle, etc. **Distribution** cultivated and found naturalized throughout the region. **Active ingredients** saponins. **Effect** stimulates metabolism. **Parts used** fresh or dried leaves gathered before flowering. **Application M:** as an infusion (2–3 teaspoons per cup) 2–4 times daily against nervous exhaustion, tiredness or as a spring tonic. **E:** in parts of Europe this plant is cultivated as a vegetable. The wild plant can be used for the same purpose and should be prepared like spinach. It can be used on its own, or mixed with spinach or *Chenopodium album, C. bonus-henricus, Atriplex hastata* or *A. patula.*

Atriplex hortensis

Chenopodium album

*Chenopodium
bonus-henricus*

(E) **Atriplex hastata** L. Chenopodiaceae

Hastate Orache (April– Oct.) An annual, 20–80cm (up to 100cm) tall, usually erect or ascending, more or less branched, deeply rooted, almost glabrous and often somewhat mealy in appearance. The leaves are triangular-hastate, often broad-cuneate at the base and contracted into the petiole (the uppermost ones usually tapering towards the base). The flowers are arranged in inflorescences similar to *Chenopodium*, unisexual; the male ones have 3–5 perianth segments; the female ones are enclosed by 2 bracteoles which are united at the base, up to 1·2cm long (in fruit), usually ovate and acute. The seeds are up to 2·5mm in diameter.

Habitat waste or disturbed ground, along roads and canals near the coast, on mud and shingle. **Distribution** throughout the region. **Parts used and application** as for *Chenopodium album*. **Note** the species of *Atriplex* differ from those of *Chenopodium* in having unisexual flowers, and their fruit is enclosed by 2 upright bracteoles (by 2–5 perianth segments in *Chenopodium*).

(E) **Atriplex patula** L. Chenopodiaceae

Common Orache, Iron-root (April– Oct.) An annual species similar to *A. hastata* but with leaves which are long-cuneate at the base and taper into the petiole; both differ from other species of *Atriplex* in having bracteoles only fused at the base, and from the inedible *A. littoralis* in not having linear or linear-oblong leaves below. If in doubt rub the leaves: inedible species smell and taste unpleasant.

Habitat waste ground, arable land, along the coast. **Distribution** throughout the region. **Parts used and application** as for *Chenopodium album*.

(M)
(E) **Fagopyrum esculentum** Moench Polygonaceae

Buckwheat (Sept.– Oct.) An annual herb 15–65cm tall with hollow stems, often tinged with purple or red. The leaves are triangular to arrow-shaped, up to 7cm long and 6cm wide, dark green, the lower leaves petiolate and the upper leaves sessile, the margins entire or wavy. The flowers are arranged in terminal and axillary panicles; the axillary ones are long-pedunculate, short and dense. The perianth is bell-shaped; the segments number 5, greenish-white with pinkish tops, 3–4mm long. The stamens number 8. The fruit is a nut, 5–6mm long, dull-brown, smooth.

Habitat waste ground, clearings in woods on sandy soil, roadsides. **Distribution** rare as an escape in the British Isles but cultivated as a crop in parts of England; widely cultivated and as an escape in the rest of Europe. **Active ingredients** rutin (a bioflavonoid). **Effect** stimulant, compensating mineral deficiency. **Parts used** leaves and shoots of fruiting plants (M); the mature fruits (E). **Application M:** in homoeopathy this drug is used in the form of a tincture against eczema and liver disorders. **E:** buckwheat, in the past regarded as a poor man's food, is increasingly cultivated again. From the mature grains an excellent and tasty flour is produced and used like ordinary flour for baking bread, making porridge and for pancakes. The wild plant can be utilized but this is only worthwhile where it is abundant.

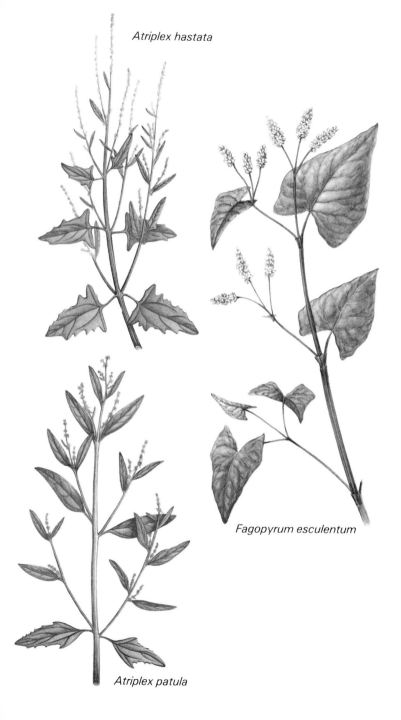

Atriplex hastata

Fagopyrum esculentum

Atriplex patula

Ⓔ *Salsola kali* L. Chenopodiaceae

Saltwort (May – Sept.) A usually decumbent or completely prostrate annual, rarely erect. The stems are 10 – 60cm long, much branched, pale green, usually with reddish longitudinal stripes. The leaves are sessile, succulent, up to 4cm long, almost round in cross-section, spine-tipped. The flowers are tiny, solitary in the leaf axils, with 4 – 5 perianth segments, enveloped by 2 leafy bracteoles. The stamens usually number 5, more rarely 3. The fruit is about 3·5mm wide, enclosed by the persistent perianth.

Habitat sandy beaches. Distribution coasts throughout the region. Parts used the entire plant without the roots. Application **E:** recommended for use on its own prepared like spinach, or mixed with other vegetables. It can also be eaten raw.

Ⓔ *Salicornia europaea* L. Chenopodiaceae

Glasswort, Marsh Samphire (Aug. – Sept.) A fleshy and rather brittle annual with much-branched erect, 15 – 35cm long stems, the lower branches usually as long as the stem. At first it is dark green, later green-yellow and often tinged with pink or red. The leaves are fleshy, translucent, opposite, fused at the base, free above. The flowers are arranged in groups of 3 on a terminal spike up to 5cm long, the central one much longer. The perianth is usually 3-lobed, obscured by bracts. The stamens usually number 1, often not protruding. The seeds are about 1·75mm wide, with hooked or curved hairs.

Habitat coastal sand. mud flats, salt-marshes. Distribution S. and W. coasts of England and most European coasts. Parts used the entire plant. Application **E:** for soups (add shortly before serving and allow to boil for only 1 – 2 minutes) and as a vegetable. Because of its habitat the plant must be thoroughly rinsed (*never* collect on polluted beaches). Serve on its own or mixed with other vegetables.

Ⓜ *Tilia cordata* Mill. Tiliaceae

Small-leaved Lime (June – July) A large tree, over 25m tall, with a smooth darkish bark, young twigs usually pubescent. The leaves are 5 – 12cm wide, broad-ovate from an obliquely heart-shaped base, abruptly acuminate at the apex, dull green and glabrous on the upper surface, pale green and pubescent as well as with tufts of whitish hairs in the axils of the veins on the lower margins, toothed; the petioles are up to 5cm long. The flowers are arranged in usually 3-flowered erect or spreading cymes, fragrant, yellow-ish-white; over half the length of the pedicel is joined to a large membranous bracteole. The sepals number 5, free. The petals number 5, free. The stamens are numerous, exceeding the petals. The fruit is nut-like, pubescent, almost globular, up to 1cm wide, with 3 – 5 pronounced ribs.

Habitat woods, copses, limestone cliffs. Distribution England and throughout Europe. Active ingredients essential oil, flavonoids, mucilage, tannin, traces of saponin, sugar. Effect laxative, mildly sedative; causes perspiration. Parts used the dried flowers (with the 'wing'), gathered when in full bloom and dried in a ventilated place in shade; rarely the bark. Application **M:** as an infusion (1 – 2 teaspoons per cup; never allow to boil) for colds, influenza and other infectious ailments where sweating is advised as part of the treatment. A 1 : 1 mixture of *Tilia* and *Sambucus nigra* is even more effective. The infusion should be drunk as hot as possible. It is also recommended against diarrhoea and as a mouthwash.

Ⓜ *Tilia platyphyllos* Scop. Tiliaceae

Large-leaved Lime Closely related to *T. cordata* but the leaves are only up to 6cm wide, glabrous on the lower surface except for rust-coloured tufts of hairs in the axils of the veins; the cymes are pendulous; the fruit is weakly ribbed or smooth, not thick-shelled.

Habitat woods and on wooded limestone cliffs. Distribution throughout the region. Parts used, effect and application **M:** as for *T. cordata*.

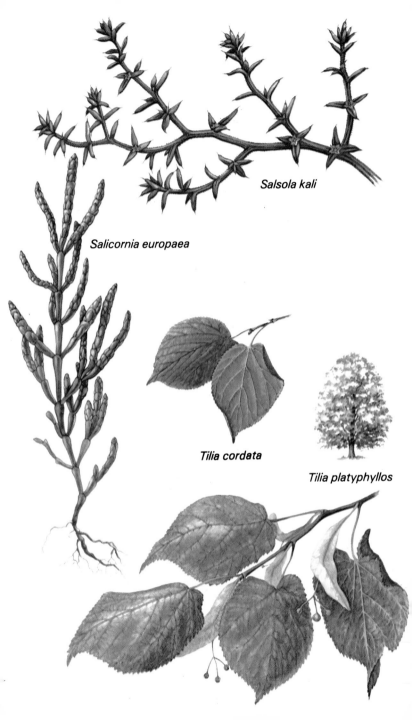

Salsola kali

Salicornia europaea

Tilia cordata

Tilia platyphyllos

(M) *Althaea officinalis* L. Malvaceae

Marsh Mallow (July–Aug: leaves, flowers; Oct: roots) A perennial with a thick rootstock. The stem is up to 125cm tall, erect, usually simple, densely covered with stellate hairs. The leaves are up to 8cm wide, mostly with 3–5 lobes, irregularly toothed, folded fan-like, with velvety hairs. The flowers are arranged in an irregular raceme, usually 1–3 together in a leaf axil, 3–5cm in diameter, regular, shortly pedicelled. The epicalyx is below the flower and consists of 8–9 narrowly triangular segments, up to 8mm long. The sepals number 5, ovate, acuminate, up to 1cm long, velvety-hairy. The petals are up to 3 times as long as the sepals, ovate, often slightly notched, pinkish. The fruit is a capsule, dividing into 1-seeded green-brown nutlets.

Habitat edges of brackish marshes, banks by sea, in moist meadows, in humus-rich and saline soils. **Distribution** British coastline (not Scotland), C. and S. Europe as far north as Denmark. **Active ingredients** mucilage, starch, pectin, traces of essential oil, tannin, sugar. **Effect** soothing. **Parts used** mainly the dried root, washed, peeled, cut and dried in a warm room, but also the leaves, and the flowers, dried in shade. **Application M:** as a mouthwash or for gargling against inflamed or bleeding gums, pharyngitis and similar ailments (2 teaspoons of root finely cut, macerated in 4 cups of cold water for 5 hours, brought to the boil and strained); as an infusion (1–2 teaspoons of leaves or flowers per cup) internally against bronchitis and intestinal disorders (also diarrhoea); as a herbal compress on slow healing cuts and minor burns. This drug is contained in several proprietary medicines and herbal preparations. **Note** the flowers of the related Hollyhock (*A. rosea*) are sometimes used as an infusion with similar effect.

(M) *Malva sylvestris* L. Malvaceae

Common Mallow (April–July: leaves) A perennial herb with a stem 30–90cm tall, erect, ascending, sometimes only at the tip, sparsely hairy. The basal leaves are almost circular, 4–10cm in diameter, shallowly lobed, slightly folded, with long petioles; the stem leaves are deeply 5–7 lobed, somewhat hairy. The flowers are regular, pedicel-led, appearing in dense groups in leaf-axils, up to 4cm in diameter. The epicalyx is beneath the flower, which consists of 3 free oblong-lanceolate segments. The calyx of 5 lobes is enlarged in fruit. The petals number 5, free, up to 4 times as long as the calyx, rose-purple, dark striped, notched. The fruit consists of several unbeaked 1-seeded green-brown nutlets.

Habitat roadsides, waste areas, margins of woods, fields. **Distribution** throughout the region. **Active ingredients** mucilage, essential oil, traces of tannin. **Effect** anti-inflammatory, astringent, expectorant, mildly purgative. **Parts used** the leaves and flowers; the flowers should be gathered on a warm dry day when fully open (around mid-day) and quickly dried on paper. Fresh flowers and leaves are only used for homoeopathic preparations. **Application M:** as a decoction (2–3 tablespoons dried herb per 4–5 cups water, boiled for 3–4 minutes and strained) added to the bathwater against abscesses, boils, minor burns etc., or applied as a compress; as an infusion (2 teaspoons per cup water) taken 3 times a day against bronchitis, catarrh, laryngitis, pharyngitis and gastritis; also used for eczema. **E:** young leaves and shoots make a fine salad or can be used for soups and as a vegetable.

(M) *Malva neglecta* Wallr. Malvaceae

(E) **Dwarf Mallow** (June–Sept.) Similar to *M. sylvestris* but an annual and having petals which are usually only twice (rarely 3 times) as long as the calyx, white with lilac venation, or pale lilac.

Habitat roadsides, waste areas, arable land, margins of woods, etc. **Distribution** throughout the region. **Note** this plant has similar properties and is applied as the species above.

Malva sylvestris

Althaea officinalis

Malva neglecta

Ⓜ *Linum catharticum* L. Linaceae

Purging Flax (June–Sept.) A delicate annual herb 3–25cm tall with erect, wiry, simple stems. The leaves are opposite, sessile, distant, up to 1·2cm long, obovate or oblong, 1-nerved. The flowers are small, arranged in loose or condensed cymes, the pedicels wiry, up to 1cm long. The sepals number 5, ovate-lanceolate. The petals number 5, longer than the sepals, white, up to 6mm long, narrow-obovate. The 5 stamens are fused into a tube below, the stigmas are head-like. The fruit is a capsule, globose, about 3mm in diameter, opening by 10 valves. The seeds are tiny and flat.

Habitat grassland, dunes, moors, etc. **Distribution** throughout the region. **Active ingredients** fatty oil, resin, tannin, bitter principle. **Effect** purgative, diuretic, emetic; kills worms. **Parts used** the entire plant fresh or dried. **Application M:** in homoeopathy a tincture from fresh plants is used against bronchitis, piles and amenorrhoea. In folk medicine an infusion (1–2 teaspoons per cup water) is taken against constipation, rheumatic pains and disorders of the liver.

Ⓜ *Geranium robertianum* L. Geraniaceae

Herb Robert (April/May–Oct.) An annual or biennial branched from below, 5–50cm long, fragile, green and usually tinged red, unpleasant smelling, hairy in lower parts. The stems are ascending sometimes only at the tip. The leaves are palmately divided, each up to 6·5cm long; the segments are pinnatisect; the basal leaves are long, usually with 5 leaflets; the upper leaves are shortly petiolate, usually with 3 leaflets. The sepals number 5, oblong-ovate, and glandular, spine-tipped. The petals number 5, claw-shaped, up to 1·2cm long, obovate to wedge-shaped, pink or rarely white. The stamens number 10; the anthers are purple or orange. The fruit has a 1–2cm beak. The seeds are smooth.

Habitat rocks and walls, moist woods and hedge banks, roadsides, waste places. **Distribution** throughout the region. **Active ingredients** tannins, essential oils, the bitter principle geraniin. **Effect** mildly diuretic, astringent, arrests bleeding and di-arrhoea. **Parts used** the entire plant, preferably with roots; collect on a dry day and dry in shade and fresh air. **Application M:** in homoeopathy an essence is prepared from the fresh herb. For stomatic purposes on infusion (1–2 teaspoons per cup water), is given 3–4 times a day against diarrhoea, dropsy and (questionably) disorders of the kidney and bladder. A decoction (1–2 tablespoons per 4 cups water, simmered for 1 minute) can be added to bathwater or used for a herbal compress against bruises, boils, septic cuts, etc. The fresh leaves are chewed to soothe or heal inflammation of the gums or oral bleeding.

Ⓜ Ⓔ *Erodium cicutarium* (L.) L'Hérit. Geraniaceae

Common Storksbill (May/June–Sept./Oct.) A rather variable annual. The stems are trailing, ascending or erect, 5–60 (rarely 100)cm long, sparsely to densely hairy, sometimes somewhat glandular. The leaves are 3–16cm long, pinnate; the leaflets are pinnatifid to pinnate, always cut more than halfway to the midrib. The flowers are arranged in terminal 2–12 flowered umbels, more or less regular, without a spur. The sepals number 5, free, up to 8mm long. The petals number 5, free, up to 1·2cm long, purplish-pink, lilac or rarely white, sometimes with a blackish spot at the base of the upper two. The fruit consists of mericarps, separating from below upwards, the outer part of the style being a beak, up to 7cm long, twisted at maturity.

Habitat sandy soils (dunes), grassland, arable land, waste areas, roadsides, railway embankments, etc. **Distribution** British Isles coastline and inland, very rare in Ireland; most of the rest of Europe. **Active ingredients** not known. **Part used** the young leaves (E) or the whole plant (M). **Effect** arrests bleeding. **Application M:** A medicinal preparation has been used against uterine and other bleeding. **E:** the young leaves are added to salads, sauces, omelettes, sandwiches or soups.

Erodium cicutarium

Linum catharticum

Geranium robertianum

ⓂⒺ *Oxalis acetosella* L. Oxalidaceae

Wood-sorrel (April–May) A perennial with a slender creeping rhizome. The petiole is up to 17cm long and rises from a swollen scale-clad base. The leaves are clover-like; the leaflets are 0·9–2·1cm long, broadly obcordate from a wedge-shaped base, fringed with scattered appressed hairs, pale green or light yellow-green. The flowers are hermaphrodite, regular, solitary on long bracteate pedicels. The sepals number 5, usually overlapping like tiles, oblong-lanceolate, obtuse. The 5 petals are up to 1·7cm long, white, rarely purple or lilac, with lilac venation, obovate. The stamens number 10. The fruit is a capsule, up to 4·5mm long, 7-angled, almost globose.

Habitat woods, scrub; shady, usually moist places. **Distribution** throughout the region. **Active ingredients** mucilage, Vitamin C, oxalic acid. **Effect** diuretic, analgesic, (supposedly counteracting arteriosclerosis); alleviates fever and scurvy, aids menstrual flow. **Parts used** fresh leaves and flowers. **Application M:** bruised fresh leaves were in the past applied to cuts and bruises. An infusion (1–2 tablespoons per cup water) sweetened with sugar or honey can be used as a laxative. **E:** can be used as an addition to spring salads, soups and sauces, all of which will be enhanced by the pungent taste. On account of its high oxalic acid content it should be used sparingly (¼ cup leaves make 4–6 helpings) and not too often.

Ⓔ *Oxalis corniculata* L. Oxalidaceae

Procumbent Yellow Sorrel (June–Sept.) A non-rhizomatous annual or biennial. The stems are numerous, trailing or ascending, rooting at the nodes, with leaves over their entire length, densely hairy below. The leaves are alternate, clover-like, more or less long-petiolate; the leaflets are 0·7–1.6cm long, broadly heart-shaped from a wedge-shaped base, with 2 lobes at the apex. The flowers number 1–7, arranged in axillary pedunculate umbels, nodding after flowering (umbels usually exceeding the leaves). The sepals number 5, lanceolate, acute. The petals number 5, up to 1·1cm long, narrowly wedge-shaped, yellow. The fruit is a capsule, cylindric, up to 1·6cm long, pubescent.

Habitat a common garden weed, on arable land and in waste places. **Distribution** throughout the region; in the British Isles more common in the South **Parts used** leaves and shoots (without the flowers). **Application E:** as for the above species.

Ⓜ *Impatiens noli-tangere* L. Balsaminaceae

Touch-me-not (June/July–Sept.) An annual with erect stems, swollen at the nodes, glabrous, somewhat translucent. The leaves are alternate, petiolate, up to 13cm long, ovate-oblong or ovate-elliptic from a wedge-shaped base, margins with up to 15 pointed teeth on either side. The flowers are arranged in few-flowered axillary cymes, bilaterally symmetrical, the pedicel twisted through 180°, 3–3.7cm long, yellow with brown dots. The lower sepal is conical, extended into a slender tapering curved spur. The lower petals are fused into a pair; the lateral ones are claw-shaped. The stamens number 5; the anthers are fused together around the ovary. The fruit is a capsule, opening elastically and catapulting seeds over a distance.

Habitat damp places in woods, along streams, in shade or semi-shade. **Distribution** Europe, in parts common; rare in the British Isles. **Active ingredients** bitter principle, resins, tannin, sugar. **Effect** strongly emetic, diuretic. **Parts used** leaves and young shoots. **Application M:** *rarely* used as a decoction, 2 tablespoons to 250ml cold water, heat, boil for 1 minute, leave for 10 minutes, strain; against haemorrhoids and as a diuretic and laxative take twice a day after meals. **Note** *a stronger decoction may lead to vomiting.*

Oxalis acetosella

Oxalis corniculata

Impatiens noli-tangere

Ⓜ *Aesculus hippocastanum* L. Hippocastanaceae

Horse-chestnut A large deciduous tree with a finely scaly, grey-brown bark. The leaves are opposite, palmate with 5–7 leaflets; these are obovate-lanceolate, up to 22cm long, tapering to a wedge-shaped base, strongly ribbed; the petioles are long; the leaf-buds rather sticky. The flowers are *c.* 2cm in diameter, bilaterally symmetrical, arranged in showy panicles up to 30cm long. The sepals number 5, green. The petals number 4, claw-shaped, white with yellow to pinkish basal dots. The stamens are long, protruding downwards; the anthers have red pollen. The fruit is a leathery prickly capsule. The seeds number 1 to 2, large, nut-like, shining brown, with large whitish scar.

Habitat widely cultivated as an ornamental tree. **Distribution** throughout the region. **Active ingredients** saponin and fatty oil (mainly in the seed), glycoside (aesculin, fraxin), tannin, flavones. **Effect** astringent (bark); arrests bleeding, prevents spasms. **Parts used** mainly the seed but also the flower and bark of young trees. **Application M:** for domestic purposes a wine based on the dried or fresh flowers (1 liqueur glass 3 times a day) is taken against neuralgia, rheumatic pain, arthritis; a decoction or infusion of bark is used internally against uterine and haemorrhoidal bleeding, chronic bronchitis, intestinal or stomach inflammations, arthritis, neuralgia, rheumatism; can be used externally as a compress (or added to bathwater) against eczema, cuts and grazes, boils, eruptions of the skin and chilblains, etc. the powdered seed is occasionally added to snuff.

Ⓜ *Ilex aquifolium* Aquifoliaceae

Holly An evergreen shrub or tree up to 15m tall (usually much smaller), with smooth grey bark and greenish twigs. The leaves are alternate, simple, leathery, ovate to oblong, dark green and glossy, paler beneath, margins entire or wavy and toothed, the teeth spiny, the petioles short. The flowers are arranged in axillary cymes, regular, hermaphrodite, usually dioecious, 5–6mm in diameter. The sepals number 4 and are very small. The petals number 4, united at the base; there are as many stamens as petals. The fruit is a drupe, 0·8–1·8cm wide, globose, scarlet, *poisonous*.

Habitat woods, scrub, hedges, usually on dry soils. **Distribution** throughout the British Isles, W. and C. Europe. **Active ingredients** tannin and bitter principle, ursolic and ilexic acid. **Effect** mildly diuretic; alleviates fever, stimulates sweating. **Parts used** the young leaves, fresh or dried (can be gathered most of the year; dry in shade). **Application M:** as an infusion (2 teaspoons per cup water) or a decoction (1 teaspoon per cup water, boil for 5–8 minutes), 2–3 times a day internally against common cold, influenza, bronchitis, rheumatism and arthritis. **Note** *the fruits are poisonous.*

Ⓜ *Euonymus europaeus* L. Celastraceae

Spindle-tree A deciduous, profusely branched shrub, up to 6·5m tall; the bark is smooth, greyish. The twigs are 4-angled, green. The leaves are opposite, 2·5–10cm (up to 13·5cm) long, ovate-lanceolate, elliptic or oblong-lanceolate from a wedge-shaped base, green but later turning reddish, shortly petiolate. The flowers number 2–10, regular, up to 1·1cm in diameter, arranged in axillary cymes. The sepals number 4, overlapping like tiles. The petals number 4, green, oblong. The fruit is a fleshy, pinkish capsule, 1·1–1·5cm wide, splitting lengthways. The seeds are exposed at maturity and have a bright orange aril.

Habitat woods and scrub, hedges; sometimes planted. **Distribution** throughout the region. **Active ingredients** bitter principles, pigments, tannin, alkaloids (not yet properly analyzed), vitamin C. **Effect** stimulates bile flow; emetic. **Parts used** the fruits, leaves and bark. **Application M:** not used in domestic medicine but contained in some proprietary medicines against disorders of the liver and gall bladder, and dyspepsia; externally unctions are used for abscesses, chilblains, acne and wounds. The fruits are *toxic in large quantities.*

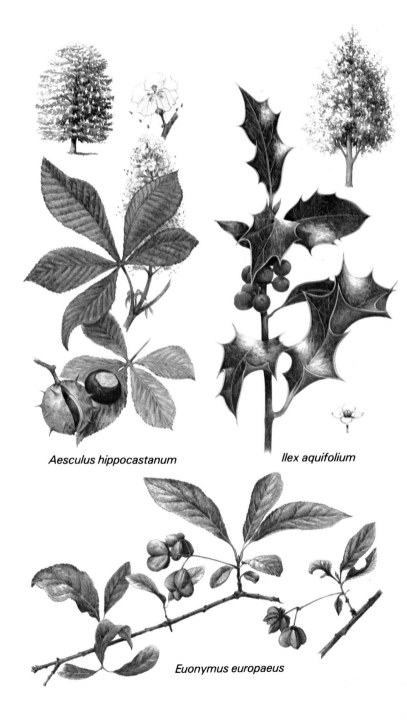

Aesculus hippocastanum

Ilex aquifolium

Euonymus europaeus

☠ *Buxus sempervirens* L. Buxaceae
Ⓜ **Box** An evergreen shrub or rarely a small tree, usually 1–5m tall with 4-angled pubescent twigs. The leaves are opposite, entire, glabrous, up to 2·5cm long, oblong or elliptic, obtuse, leathery; the petioles are rather short. The flowers are arranged in axillary groups, with one terminal female and several lateral male ones, white-green, small. The male flowers have 4 sepals and 4 protruding stamens with thickened filaments. The female flowers have several petals and a 3-chambered ovary. The fruit is a 3-horned, ovoid capsule, 6–8mm wide. The seeds are black, glossy.

Habitat in woods and scrub on chalk or limestone, frequently planted as an ornamental tree. **Distribution** S.W. Germany, France, Britain; planted elsewhere. **Active ingredients** buxin and secondary alkaloids, vitamin C, tannin, essential oil. **Effects** laxative, stimulates sweating, alleviates fever. **Parts used** the leaves; bark of flowering shoots and roots. **Application C:** although this drug has been used against epilepsy, baldness, malaria and infections, and even as a spring tonic, it is too toxic for domestic use. In homoeopathy it is occasionally used in preparations against rheumatism, diarrhoea, and ailments accompanied by fever.

Ⓜ *Frangula alnus* Mill. Rhamnaceae
Alder Buckthorn, Black Dogwood (May–July) A small deciduous tree or shrub, up to 5m tall, with almost opposite ascending branches. The twigs are at first green, later grey-brown. The bark is usually smooth; the winter buds are naked, brownish, hairy. The leaves are up to 7cm long, obovate, pointed at the apex, entire, brownish-pubescent beneath when young, green becoming yellow or red in autumn; with 7–9 pairs of lateral veins. The flowers are rather small, 2·5–3mm in diameter, solitary or arranged in axillary bundles, hermaphrodite. The calyx is 5-lobed, green. The petals number 5, rather small. The fruit is a drupe, up to 1cm wide, at first green, then red and almost black at maturity.

Habitat scrub, near bogs, moist heaths, in open woods, mostly in damp and peaty soil. **Distribution** most of England and Wales; all over Europe. **Active ingredients** anthraquinone derivatives, bitter principle, traces of alkaloids, tannin, glucofrangulin. **Effect** laxative. **Parts used** the dried bark. **Note** the drug must be stored for *at least 1 year* before being used; fresh bark causes *violent vomiting and abdominal pain*. **Application M:** this drug is not recommended for domestic purposes.

Ⓜ *Rhamnus catharticus* L. Rhamnaceae
Buckthorn A deciduous shrub or small tree, thorny and with opposite branches arranged almost at right angles to the stem and ending in a thorny point; the bark is fissured and scaling, usually orange coloured. The buds are covered by dark scales. The leaves are ovate or elliptic, with toothed margins, green but turning yellow or brown in the autumn, 2·5–6cm long; the lateral veins are 2–3, curved upwards and almost parallel. The flowers are small and inconspicuous, about 4mm in diameter, pedicelled, single or in bundles on the previous year's short shoots. The calyx has 4 lobes. The petals number 4, very small, greenish. The fruit is 0·5–1cm in diameter, black when ripe, with 3–4 seeds.

Habitat hedges, scrub, woods, fens, usually on calcareous soil. **Distribution** in most parts of England and Wales and all over the rest of Europe. **Active ingredients** vitamin C, anthraquinone derivatives (e.g. rhamnocarthrin). **Effect** laxative, diuretic; purifies the blood. **Parts used** the fruits fresh or dried. **Application M:** the mature fruits (8–15) chewed before breakfast are an effective laxative *for adults only*. Not quite mature fruits are used as an infusion (2 teaspoonsful per cup), taken internally as a mild laxative. *Large doses may lead to vomiting and violent diarrhoea.* **Note** *Rhamnus catharticus* can be distinguished from the related *Genista tinctoria* by its thorns and scaly buds.

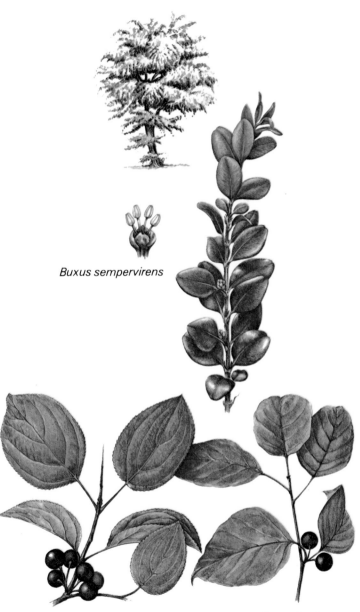

Buxus sempervirens

Rhamnus catharticus

Frangula alnus

Ⓜ *Genista tinctoria* L. Papilionaceae

Dyer's Greenweed (June–July) An erect or ascending shrub, 20–80cm tall, without spines. The stems are branched, slender, usually brown except for the young green twigs. The leaves are almost sessile, 1–3cm long, oblong-lanceolate, acute, fringed with hairs. The flowers are solitary, axillary, bilaterally symmetrical, 1·2–1·5cm long; the pedicels are up to 3·5mm long. The calyx is 2-lipped, green, the upper lip divided, the lower 2-toothed, green. The corolla is yellow, glabrous; the standard up to 1·6cm long, broad-ovate. The fruit is a pod, up to 3·2cm long, flat, 2-valved, splitting, with several seeds.

Habitat grassy places. **Distribution** throughout the region except Ireland and N. Scotland. **Active ingredients** alkaloids, essential oil, traces of tannin, luteolin, bitter principle. **Effect** diuretic, laxative; stimulates sweating. **Parts used** the young flowering shoots, fresh or dried. **Application M:** an infusion (2 teaspoons per cup water) is taken 2–3 times a day against rheumatism, arthritis, dropsy and chronic skin disorders. In homoeopathy essences prepared from fresh shoots are prescribed for these ailments. In the past the flowers were used for dying fabrics.

Ⓜ *Sarothamnus scoparius* (L.) Wimm. Papilionaceae

Broom (May–June: flowers; April–Sept: shoot tips) A deciduous unarmed shrub, 50 to over 180cm tall, much-branched, erect, ascending or trailing; the twigs are green, 7-angled, stiff. The leaves are petiolate to almost sessile, 0·5–2cm long, elliptic-oblong to obovate, hairy or glabrous. The flowers are axillary, solitary or sometimes in pairs, on pedicels twice as long as the calyx. The calyx is herbaceous, glabrous, 2-lipped; the lower lip finely 3-toothed, the upper 2-toothed. The corolla is golden-yellow; the standard is up to 2cm long. The fruit is a pod, up to 4cm long, black, with brown hairs along the margins, strongly compressed.

Habitat open woods, heaths, banks, waste places; not on calcareous soils. **Distribution** throughout the region. **Active ingredients** the alkaloid spartein, traces of essential oil, bitter principle. **Effect** diuretic; dilates the vessels. **Parts used** tips of flowering branches and/or flowers. **Application M:** because of the changing composition of its active ingredients (especially alkaloids) the drug is unreliable and rarely used. All preparations based on it must *only be used under medical supervision.*

Ⓜ *Ononis spinosa* L. Papilionaceae

Rest-harrow (Sept.–Nov: roots; June–Aug: herb) An erect or sometimes ascending perennial herb without a rhizome. The stems are 20–60cm tall, armed with spines, with 2 longitudinal lines of hairs, not rooting at the often woody base. The leaves have 3 leaflets, up to 2·2cm long, with stipules clasping the stem; the leaflets are narrowly obovate to obovate-elliptic, toothed, pubescent and glandular. The flowers are bilaterally symmetrical, axillary, pink, 0·8–1·5cm long, with a broad standard and wing which are both shorter than the keel. The fruit is a pod, larger than the calyx, with 1–4 seeds.

Habitat grassy places. **Distribution** throughout the region. **Active ingredients** essential oil, saponin, glycoside, tannin, flavone, ononide. **Effect** mildly diuretic, purgative. **Parts used** usually the roots; more rarely the fresh or dried shoots. The roots are dug up, washed, split and cut, and gradually dried in a warm room. The shoots must be dried in a properly ventilated place in shade. **Application M:** as an infusion (2 teaspoons per cup water) 2–3 times daily against dropsy and inflammation of the bladder and kidneys; also against rheumatism, arthritis and chronic skin disorders.

Genista tinctoria

Sarothamnus scoparius

Ononis spinosa

Ⓜ *Melilotus officinalis* (L.) Pall. Papilionaceae

Common Melilot (July–Sept.) A trailing to erect herb with branched stems, 40 –90cm (up to 120cm) tall. The leaves are trefoil with stipules joined to the stem. The leaflets are oblong-elliptic, 1·5–3cm long, the margins toothed with veins terminating in the teeth. The flowers are arranged in lax racemes, up to 6mm long, yellowish, bilaterally symmetrical; the standard is as long as the wings and both are longer than the keel. The fruit is a pod, up to 6mm long, glabrous, wrinkled, ovoid and somewhat compressed, at first green, later brown.   ▪

Habitat pastures, fields, roadsides, waste places. **Distribution** throughout Europe; naturalized in S. England. **Active ingredients** coumarin glycosides (mainly melilotin), flavones, essential oil, tannin, mucilage. **Effect** mild expectorant, emollient, mildly sedative, astringent, anti-inflammatory; relieves spasms. **Parts used** dried leaves and shoots gathered when in full bloom and slowly dried in shade (the aromatic odour of the fresh plant disappears in drying). **Application M:** for domestic purposes an infusion (2 teaspoons per cup) 2–3 times a day is taken against sleeplessness, thrombosis, nervous tension, flatulence, varicose veins, intestinal disorders; externally in a decoction (3 teaspoons to 3 cups of cold water, boiled for 2 minutes and left for 30 minutes) either added to bathwater or as a compress for suppurating or slow-healing bruises, cuts and eruptions of the skin.

Ⓔ *Trifolium pratense* L. Papilionaceae

Red Clover (May–Sept.) A perennial with stems 12–60cm (up to 70cm) tall, erect or rising at the tips. The leaves are ternate; the petioles are 5–25cm long; the leaflets are 1–5cm long, obovate or elliptic, usually obtuse, green, often with a whitish area in the lower half; stipules triangular with a fine point. The flowers are arranged in dense, terminal, globose, heads, up to 3·2cm wide, purplish pink-purple or sometimes off-white, sessile. The calyx has 5 unequal teeth, the tube is ribbed, hairy within. The corolla is longer than the calyx, up to 2cm long, persistent. The fruit is a pod, up to 2·3mm long, thickened at the apex.

Habitat meadows, pastures and other grassy places. **Distribution** throughout the region. **Parts used** the flowers and young leaves. **Application E:** an infusion of the dried flowers makes a fine tea-substitute: use 1–2 teaspoons per cup of water, sweeten with honey and serve with a slice of fresh lemon. The young leaves, gathered before flowering, can be added to salads, sauces, and soups; on their own they can be used as a vegetable and prepared like spinach.

Ⓔ *Trifolium repens* L. Papilionaceae

White Clover, Dutch Clover A perennial with trailing stems, rooting at the nodes, usually glabrous, up to 60cm long. The leaves are similar to those of *T. pratense*, but smaller and with shorter petioles. The flowers are scented, arranged in dense axillary globular heads up to 25mm wide, white or pinkish to (rarely) purple. The calyx has 5 narrowly triangular teeth; the tube is twice as long as the teeth, whitish with green venation, bell-shaped. The corolla is up to 1·4cm long, soon becoming brown and deflexed; the standard is up to 1cm long, folded over the fruit. The fruit is a pod, linear, flattened, up to 5·5mm long, up to 6-seeded.

Habitat as for *T. pratense* but especially on clay soils. **Distribution** throughout the region. **Parts used and application E:** as for *T. pratense*. As is the case with most wild vegetable plants it should be used in moderation. This species can easily be identified by its creeping stems which root at the nodes and by its axillary flower heads.

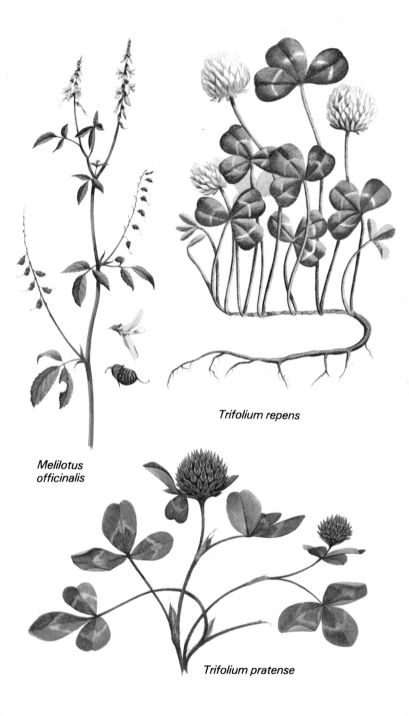

Melilotus officinalis

Trifolium repens

Trifolium pratense

(M) **_Anthyllis vulneraria_** L. Papilionaceae
Kidney-vetch, Ladies' Fingers (May – Aug./Sept.) A perennial herb with pubescent stems, erect or ascending, sometimes only at the tip, 10–60cm tall. The leaves are pinnate, the basal ones often with a terminal leaflet, 3–15cm long, the terminal leaflet usually the longest. The flowers are 1–1·5cm long, yellow, yellow-red, or red, arranged in very condensed, paired, 2·5–4cm wide cymes. The calyx is inflated, narrowed at the mouth, more or less densely woolly. The petals are long, claw-shaped, exceeding the calyx, the keel curved inwards. The fruit is a pod, semicircular, compressed, glabrous, with a criss-cross pattern on the surface, 1-seeded.

Habitat dry situations, stony rocks, shingle, usually in shallow calcareous soil. **Distribution** throughout the region. **Active ingredients** flavonoids, tannins, saponin, mucilage. **Effect** astringent, mildly purgative. **Parts used** the entire flowering plant, dried or fresh; dry in fresh air without artificial heat. **Application M:** as the specific epithet implies this drug is an ancient remedy for eruptions of the skin, slow-healing wounds, minor burns, cuts and bruises. A decoction (1–1½ tablespoons per 500ml of water, boil for 1–2 minutes, keep for 5–15 minutes, strain) can be either added to bathwater or applied as a compress to the affected area (sometimes the bruised fresh herb is applied). A mild infusion (1–2 teaspoons per cup of water) is taken 2–3 times a day against constipation or drunk as a spring tonic. The dried flower heads on their own can be used as a substitute for real tea.

☠ **_Coronilla varia_** L. Papilionaceae
(M) **Crown Vetch** (April–Aug.) A straggling perennial with stems 20–80cm (up to 120cm) long. The leaves are pinnate with a terminal leaflet, the lower with 7–12 pairs of leaflets; leaflets up to 2cm long and 1·2cm wide, oblong to elliptical, with a narrow scarious margin; stipules are present, free, small, membranous. The flowers number 5–20, bilaterally symmetrical, arranged in axillary heads (peduncle exceeding the leaves). The calyx has almost equal small teeth and a bell-shaped tube. The corolla is up to 1·5cm long, exceeding the short calyx, white, purple or pink. The fruit is a pod, up to 8cm long, slender, 4-angled, breaking up into 1-seeded parts.

Habitat dry grassy places, railway embankments, roadsides, etc. **Distribution** C. and S. Europe; introduced into Great Britain. **Active ingredients** the glycoside coronillin. **Effect** stimulates heart function. **Parts used** the dried or fresh plant. **Application C:** the glycoside contained in this drug is one of the most poisonous substances in any native plant. It should therefore _in no circumstances_ be used in the home.

☠ **_Colutea arborescens_** L. Papilionaceae
(M) **Bladder Senna** (May–June) A deciduous much-branched shrub, 1·6m high with the young shoots usually pubescent. The leaves are pinnate with a terminal leaflet; there are up to 6 pairs of leaflets, up to 3cm long and 2cm wide, broad-elliptical to ovate, silky-hairy beneath. The flowers number 3–8, bilaterally symmetrical, arranged in erect axillary racemes. The calyx is bell-shaped, somewhat 2-lipped. The corolla is up to 2cm long, yellow, with red markings on the standard. The fruit is a showy inflated pod, closed at the apex, up to 7·5cm long and 3cm wide, greenish. The seeds are up to 4mm long.

Habitat open woods, roadsides, railway banks, waste areas. **Distribution** cultivated and naturalized in Europe north of the Alps; naturalized in parts of England, especially the south. **Active ingredients** bitter principles, tannin, essential oil, vitamin C, organic acids. **Effect** emetic, diuretic and mildly purgative. **Parts used** the dried leaves and seeds. **Application M:** on account of its unreliability this drug is rarely used. **Note** _the seeds are poisonous._

Coronilla varia

Anthyllis vulneraria

Colutea arborescens

Ⓜ *Filipendula ulmaria* (L.) Maxim. Rosaceae
Ⓔ **Meadowsweet** (June–Aug.) A perennial herb with usually erect, 50–120cm stems, branched mainly above. The basal leaves are up to 65cm long, on long petioles, with 2–5 pairs of large leaflets up to 8cm long, ovate, with double-toothed margins, usually tomentose beneath but sometimes pubescent or glabrous, interspersed with small ones up to 1·5cm long; the stem leaves are smaller and with fewer leaflets. The flowers are small, arranged in dense, many-flowered, cymose panicles. The sepals usually number 5, pubescent, reflexed. The petals number 5 or 6, up to 5·5mm long, creamy-white or whitish-green, obovate, claw-shaped. The stamens are numerous. The carpels number 6–10, twisted together in fruit, 1·5–2mm long.

Habitat wet ground. Distribution throughout the region. Active ingredients gaultherin, spiraeine, essential oil, salicylic acid and derivatives, citric acid, tannin. Effect diuretic, astringent, antirheumatic; alleviates fever and spasms, stimulates sweating. Parts used the dried flowers; more rarely the leaves and young shoots; the fresh root only for homoeopathic preparations. Application M: as an infusion (1–2 teaspoons per cup water) 2–3 times a day against colds, influenza, headache; also added to other preparations for rheumatic pain, dropsy, arthritis, inflammation of the bladder and kidney disorders; it can, on account of its rapid diuretic effect, also be used as a spring tonic. E: fresh flowers can be added to home-made wines.

Ⓜ *Rubus fruticosus* Rosaceae
Ⓔ **Blackberry, Bramble** (Under the name *R. fruticosus* goes an aggregate of various species, individually difficult to identify, but which for the purposes of this book can be treated as one) A deciduous shrub, suckering by adventitious buds from the roots. The stems are erect to prostrate, armed with prickles of various kinds (absent in the first year). The leaves are pinnate, the leaflets number 5–7, white tomentose beneath. The flowers appear only on second year stems, arranged in terminal and axillary cymes with 5 sepals and 5 petals. The fruit is fleshy, consisting of numerous 1-seeded segments, at first red later shining black.

Habitat woodland, hedges, heath and scrub. Distribution throughout the region. Active ingredients tannin, vitamin C., flavone, organic acids (leaves), citric and malic acids, mucilage, pectin, sugar (fruits). Effect mildly astringent and diuretic. Parts used the leaves. Application M: as an infusion against diarrhoea and stomach disorders; used in several proprietary medicines. E: the leaves (dried very slowly to allow them to ferment) make an excellent tea which many people prefer to real tea. The fruits can be used as for those of *R. idaeus* and make excellent jam and syrup; they are difficult to pick but usually plentiful.

Ⓜ *Rubus idaeus* L. Rosaceae
Ⓔ **Raspberry** (June–Sept: leaves) A deciduous shrub, suckering by buds from the roots. The stems are up to 150cm tall, erect, round in cross-section, pruinose, armed with numerous straight prickles. The leaves are pinnate, the leaflets up to 7cm (the terminal one the longest), 4–12cm long, ovate to ovate-lanceolate from a rounded or almost heart-shaped base, with a dense whitish indumentum beneath, the margins irregularly toothed. The flowers are up to 1·1cm in diameter, regular, 1–10, arranged in dense terminal and axillary cymes. The sepals number 5, with long acuminate tips. The petals number 5–8, white, erect, about as long as the sepals. The fruit is fleshy, consisting of numerous 1-seeded segments, pubescent, red or sometimes opaque yellow.

Habitat hilly districts, woods, scrub and heath. Distribution throughout the region; frequently cultivated. Active ingredients tannins, organic acids, Vitamin C (leaves), citric acid, malic acid, sugar, aromatic compounds, pectin (fruits). Effect astringent, anti-inflammatory. Parts used the dried leaves, dried slowly in thin layers in a well-ventilated place without artificial heat. Best kept loosely in linen bags. Application M: the medicinal effect is minimal but the dried leaves make an ideal herbal tea. A syrup prepared from the fruits is given (diluted) in the home against feverish conditions. E: the fruits are mainly used for making a fine syrup and an excellent jam.

Filipendula ulmaria

Rubus fruticosus

Rubus idaeus

Ⓜ *Potentilla anserina* L. Rosaceae

Silverweed (May–Aug.) A perennial herb with a (usually) branched stock, covered with silky hairs all over, producing 20–60cm (up to 80cm) rooting stolons. The basal leaves are arranged in a rosette, up to 26cm long, pinnate; the 6–12 pairs of leaflets are up to 6·5cm long, usually silvery-hairy on both surfaces, with finely toothed margins. The flowers are regular, solitary, axillary, long-pedicelled, yellow. The sepals number 5, ovate, above an epicalyx of 5 segments. The petals number 5, obovate, up to 1·1cm long. The fruit is a group of achenes.

Habitat roadsides, waste areas, damp areas, dunes, etc. **Distribution** throughout the region. **Active ingredients** tormentol, tannin, bitter principles, flavone. **Effect** astringent, anti-inflammatory; relieves spasms. **Parts used** the entire plant without roots, fresh or dried. Gather on a dry day and dry in a well-ventilated room away from light; the herb should not lose colour in the process. **Application M:** only as an infusion: 1 teaspoon per cup water, allow to stand for 5–10 minutes, strain; use against painful menstruation, bladder and kidney complaints, and violent diarrhoea. Added to the bathwater or used in a compress (2–3 tablespoons per 500ml of water), it is externally applied to wounds and piles. Used in several proprietary medicines.

Ⓜ *Potentilla erecta* (L.) Räusch Rosaceae

Common Tormentil (June–Sept./Oct.) A perennial herb with flowering stems arising from a rather stout woody stock, 55cm tall, ascending at the tip or almost erect, not rooting at the nodes, covered with appressed silky hairs. The leaves (at least the lower ones) are ternate; the basal leaves are long-petiolate; the stem leaves are sessile; the leaflets are up to 1·1cm long, obovate to wedge-shaped with coarse teeth along the margins. Flowers are long-pedicelled, 0·8–1.1cm in diameter, numerous, in terminal cymes. The sepals and epicalyx segments usually number 4. The petals number 4 (rarely more), yellow, much longer than the sepals, obovate to almost circular. The fruit is a group of achenes.

Habitat grassland, bogs, woods, mountains and heaths, in acid soil. **Distribution** throughout the region. **Active ingredients** tormentil tannin acid, tormentil red, a glycoside, traces of essential oil. **Effect** strongly astringent. **Parts used** the dried rhizome; dig up, cut into small pieces, wash, and dry in sun or moderate heat. **Application M:** as a decoction (4–5 teaspoons per 500ml of water, boil for 4–8 minutes, strain) 2–3 times a day against diarrhoea and intestinal inflammation; more effective is the powdered drug (a pinch taken with a glass of red wine or black tea 4–5 times daily). The powder can also be added to toothpaste or water for a mouthwash against mouth infections. Added to the bathwater or in form of a compress the decoction can be applied to minor burns, grazes and sunburn. **Note** *excessive use may lead to vomiting.*

Ⓜ *Potentilla reptans* L. Rosaceae

Creeping Cinquefoil (June–Aug.) A perennial with a stout stock; the stems are 25–100cm long, usually prostrate, rooting at the nodes and producing new plants, pubescent to almost glabrous. The basal leaves form a persistent rosette, long-petiolate, palmately divided into 5 (rarely more) leaflets, scattered hairy or nearly glabrous; the stem leaves are similar but with shorter petioles. The flowers are always solitary, long-pedicelled, 1·8–2·6cm in diameter, yellow. The sepals number 5, above 5 epicalyx-segments. The petals number 5, obovate, about twice the length of the sepals. The fruit is a group of dry achenes.

Habitat grassland, waste areas and hedge banks, roadsides, along rivers, in dry sunny locations. **Distribution** throughout the region. **Active ingredients** tannins, flavones. **Effect** astringent; relieves spasms. **Parts used** the flowering plant (without roots), fresh or dried; collect on a dry day and dry in sunlight or a warm room (do not allow to discolour). **Application M:** externally as a decoction (3–4 tablespoons per 500ml of water, boil for 3–5 minutes) for bathing cuts, piles or inflammation of the vagina; internally as an infusion (2 teaspoons per cup of water) against intestinal spasms, painful menstruation and as a mouthwash against inflammations of the mouth and throat.

Potentilla erecta

Potentilla anserina

Potentilla reptans

Ⓜ *Fragaria vesca* L. Rosaceae
Ⓔ **Wild Strawberry** (May–June) A perennial herb with a thick, woody stock and long, arching stolons rooting at the nodes. The leaves are trefoils, all in a basal rosette; the petiole is long, hairy; the leaflets are up to 6·5cm long, ovate to obovate or diamond-shaped, with scattered hairs, margins toothed. The flowering stems are erect, up to 30cm tall, slightly exceeding the leaves. The flowers are regular, up to 1·8cm in diameter. The sepals usually point backwards in fruit. The petals number 5, white, ovate, acuminate. The fruit is bright red with numerous projecting seeds.

Habitat woods, grassland and scrub. Distribution throughout the region. Active ingredients tannin, essential oil, flavone, vitamin C. Effect diuretic, astringent. Parts used the dried young leaves; collect on a dry day and dry in shade. Application M: although an infusion of 2 teaspoons per cup water is given 3–4 times a day against various ailments (arthritis, gall stones, disorders of the liver, stomach upsets, etc.) it is mainly used as a healthy and tasty tea-substitute (best spiced with lemon rind, cinnamon or vanilla and sweetened with honey). Note leaves of the cultivated strawberry cannot be recommended for the same use. E: the fruits are superior in taste, although not in size, to the garden strawberry. They are best eaten fresh or used for making jam, syrup, fruit cups or wine.

Ⓜ *Geum urbanum* L. Rosaceae
Wood Avens, Herb Bennet (March–April/May: roots; May–Oct: herb) A peren-nial herb, with a short, thick rhizome and erect, branched, pubescent, 15–65cm, stem. The basal leaves are pinnate, with 2–5 pairs of unequal leaflets, the terminal one longest, up to 10cm long, almost circular and deeply lobed. The stem leaves are longer: the lower leaves pinnate to ternate, the upper simple; all leaves are crenate or toothed. The flowers are up to 1·6cm in diameter, with a regular epicalyx on large pedicels. The sepals number 5, green, triangular-lanceolate. The segments of the epicalyx are oblong-linear. The petals number 5, yellow, up to 9mm long, spreading, about as long as the sepals. The fruit consists of a sessile group of glabrous achenes, jointed near the apex, the lower section hooked and persistent.

Habitat woods, hedge banks, walls and as a weed in parks, etc., usually in moist soil. Distribution throughout the region. Active ingredients essential oil, eugenol, bitter principle, tannin, the glycoside gein, resin, flavone, leucoanthocyanins. Effect antisep-tic, astringent, anti-inflammatory, digestant, anti-diarrhoeal. Parts used mainly the dried roots, but also the flowering herb; dry in shade or in a warm room. Application M: internally as an infusion (1 – 1 ½ teaspoons per cup water, stand for about 10 minutes, strain), 3 times a day against diarrhoea, intestinal disorders, stomach upsets and disorders of the liver. It can also be used as a mouthwash against gingivitis and other inflammations of the mouth and throat; a stronger infusion can be added to the bathwater for open cuts and haemorrhoids.

Ⓜ *Geum rivale* L. Rosaceae
Water Avens A perennial herb related to *G. urbanum* but with flowers nodding not erect; petals not spreading, almost erect, 1 – 1·5cm long, claw-shaped and with the apex notched, mat orange-pink or reddish. The fruit is a group of achenes, jointed above the hairy middle, the lower part glabrous, persistent and hooked.

Habitat damp places. Distribution throughout Europe; in the British Isles rare except in Wales and the north. Active ingredients similar to those of *G. urbanum*. Effect astringent, antidiarrhoeal, stomachic. Parts used the dried rootstock or the fresh flowering herb. Application M: similar in effect to *G. urbanum* but generally weaker and therefore obsolete as a drug. However it is widely used as a stomach tonic in the form of an infusion of 2 teaspoons per cup of water drunk like tea several times a day.

Fragaria vesca

Geum rivale

Geum urbanum

Ⓜ *Dryas octopetala* L. Rosaceae

Mountain Avens (June–July) A small creeping shrub with prostrate or ascending stems up to 50cm long (usually much shorter). The leaves are simple, numerous, petiolate; the blade is 0·4–2·5cm (up to 4cm) long, ovate-oblong or oblong from a rounded or truncate base, dark green and glabrous on the upper surface, densely white-tomentose on the lower surface, the margins crenate to toothed. The flowers are regular, solitary, axillary, up to 4cm in diameter. The sepals number 7–10, green. The petals usually number 8 (sometimes up to 16), white, oblong, up to 1·8cm long. The fruit consists of a dense group of achenes, each bearing the persistent feathery style.

Habitat amongst rocks and in crevices in mountains. Distribution in Britain confined to northern uplands, in Europe to the Alps. Active ingredients tannins, silicic acid, mineral salts. Effect astringent, digestant. Parts used the entire plant just before or at flowering time. Application M: as a stomach tonic in the form of a herbal tea (infusion); it is also used for gargling as a remedy for gingivitis and other disorders of the mouth and throat.

Ⓜ *Agrimonia eupatoria* L. Rosaceae

Common Agrimony (May–June) A perennial with erect stems, 25–60cm tall, usually simple, green or tinged with red, densely leafy in the lower part. The basal leaves are pinnate, with 3–6 pairs of leaflets interspersed with smaller ones; the longest leaflet is up to 6·5cm long, all deeply toothed and usually densely hairy; the upper stem leaves are smaller, with fewer pairs of leaflets. The flowers are up to 8mm in diameter, numerous, regular, arranged in terminal spike-like racemes. The sepals number 5, green. The petals number 5, golden-yellow, obovate, obtuse. The fruit consists of 1 or 2 achenes enclosed within the conical receptacle which is covered with hooked spines.

Habitat hedge banks, waysides, margins of woods, etc. Distribution throughout the region. Active ingredients tannins, essential oil, bitter principles, nicotinic acid, vitamins. Effect astringent; stimulates bile flow; also antispasmodic, antidiarrhoeal, anti-inflammatory. Parts used the dried plant without roots; collect shortly before or at beginning of flowering, dry away from light in moderate temperature (not over 35°C); *do not* use thick stems or fruiting herb. Application M: as an infusion (1 teaspoon per cup water, stand for 15 minutes) unsweetened against gastro-enteritis, gall and liver disorders, also kidney and bladder ailments.

Ⓜ *Alchemilla vulgaris* Rosaceae

Lady's Mantle (May/July–Aug./Sept.) (An aggregate of many species with the same medicinal properties). A perennial with a thick woody stock. The stems are ascending, sometimes only at the tips, 5–50cm tall, with few, small, shortly petiolate leaves. The basal leaves are usually numerous, circular or kidney-shaped, 1–15cm in diameter, up to half their length palmately lobed; the margins are toothed and hairy; the petiole is usually long. The flowers are greenish-yellow, small, up to 4mm in diameter, regular, arranged in compound terminal cymes. There is an epicalyx with 5 sepals but no petals. The fruit (when developed) is a single achene.

Habitat moist meadows, woods, pastures. Distribution throughout the region. Active ingredients tannins, bitter principles, traces of essential oil, salicic acid. Effect mildly astringent, diuretic, anti-inflammatory; relieves spasms, stimulates menstrual flow. Parts used the dried leaves and flowering shoots; dry in shade or sun. Application M: an infusion (2 teaspoons per cup water) is taken 2–3 times a day against complaints of the menopause and menstrual pain; and a stronger infusion, boiled for a short time, against diarrhoea; it is also used as a mouthwash and externally for bathing suppurating and slow-healing sores, cuts or grazes.

Dryas octopetala

Alchemilla vulgaris

Agrimonia eupatoria

Ⓜ *Sanguisorba officinalis* L. Rosaceae

Ⓔ **Great Burnet** (flowering June–Sept.) A perennial herb with stems rising from a stout, woody stock, glabrous, 18–80cm (up to 110cm) tall, erect, branched. The basal leaves and lower stem leaves are pinnate, with 3–7 pairs of leaflets; leaflets 0·5–5cm long, increasing in size upwards, ovate to oblong-ovate from a usually heart-shaped base, margins crenate to toothed, glaucous beneath, green tinged red above. The flowers are regular, hermaphrodite, arranged in dense terminal heads, with 2–3 bracteoles below each flower. The sepals number 4, dull crimson. There are no petals. The stamens number 4. The fruit is an achene, enclosed by the hardened receptacle.

    Habitat grassland. **Distribution** throughout the region. **Active ingredients** tannin, sanguisorbine (a glycoside), saponin, traces of essential oil. **Effect** astringent, anti-diarrhoeal. **Parts used** the dried leaves and young shoots before flowering; dry in sun or shade. **Application M:** as an infusion (2 teaspoons per cup water) 2–3 times a day against diarrhoea and intestinal disorders and internal haemorrhages. The freshly pressed juice is recommended against tuberculosis. **E:** the young leaves and shoots gathered in spring (before the plants are in flower) can be eaten on their own or mixed with others in salads, added to soups or as a vegetable.

Ⓔ *Sanguisorba minor* Scop. *(Poterium sanguisorba)* Rosaceae

Salad Burnet (flowering May–Aug.) Distinguishable from the Great Burnet by the numerous stamens (as opposed to 4) and polygamous flowers.

    Habitat grassland, usually on calcareous soils. **Distribution** throughout the region. **Application E:** the leaves and young shoots of this plant (gathered before flowering) are used as indicated for the preceding species; they are much tastier and more often used for culinary purposes. In past centuries this herb was used as a spice for beer, wine and brandy.

Ⓜ *Rosa canina* L. Rosaceae

Ⓔ **Dog Rose** (Aug./Sept.–Oct./Dec.) A deciduous shrub, up to 3m tall. The stems are erect or arching, green or brownish, armed with stout curved and hooked prickles. The leaves are pinnate, with 2–3 pairs of leaflets; the petiole and midrib often have slender prickles; the leaflets are up to 4cm long, ovate, obovate or elliptic, usually glabrous, with toothed margins. The flowers are usually solitary, rarely 4 or more together, regular; the pedicels are up to 2cm long. The sepals number 5, usually turned back and falling in fruit. The petals number 5, spreading, 1·9–2·6cm long, pink or white. The styles are glabrous or hairy. The fruit is a many-seeded pseudocarp, 1·2–2·2cm long, globose to ellipsoid, smooth and shining, scarlet.

    Habitat hedges, woods, scrub, roadsides, banks, etc. **Distribution** throughout the region. **Active ingredients** vitamin C, carbohydrates, tannins, pectin, carotene, traces of essential oil, fruit acids, fatty oil (seeds). **Effect** mildly laxative, weakly diuretic, mildly astringent. **Parts used** the dried fruits with or without seeds, or seeds; collect the fruits (hips) when ripe, halve and dry in the open or in moderate warmth (40–45°C); store in open jars or linen bags. **Application M:** as a decoction (2–2½ teaspoons finely cut fruit per cup water, boiled for 10 minutes to achieve optimum vitamin C content) several times a day against constipation, colds, gall disorders and disorders of the kidneys, and bladder; also as a spring tonic and against general exhaustion. **E:** before the fruits are used for culinary purposes the seeds and with them the short brittle hairs (used as itching powder by schoolboys) must be removed. The fruit can be used for making jam, syrup, soups, a superb wine and liqueur.

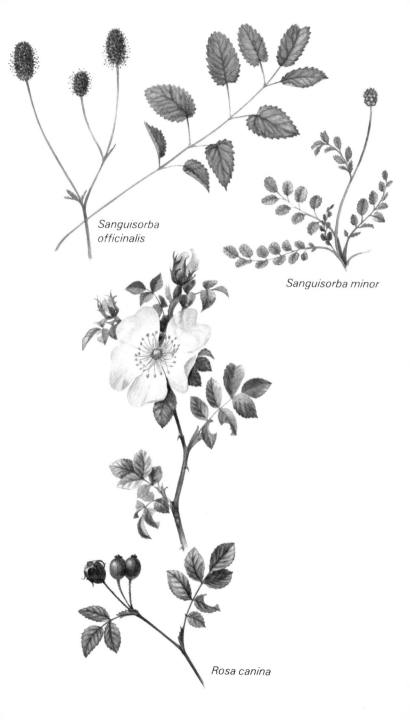

Sanguisorba officinalis

Sanguisorba minor

Rosa canina

Ⓜ️ *Prunus padus* L. Rosaceae

Bird Cherry A deciduous tree, 3–12m (up to 15m) tall, with a peeling, unpleasant smelling bark and ascending branches. The leaves are 4–10cm long, obovate or elliptic from a rounded or heart-shaped base, acuminate, glabrous, but with tufts of hairs in the axils of the main nerves beneath; the petiole is up to 2cm long. The flowers are numerous; arranged in drooping racemes, regular, hermaphrodite. The sepals number 5, short, with glandular margins. The petals number 5, white, 0·5–1cm long, toothed. The fruit is 5–8mm in diameter, globose, shining, black.

Habitat moist open woods, along rivers, often cultivated as an ornamental tree. Distribution throughout the region. Active ingredients prunolaurasin, tannin, gum, resin. Effect diuretic, sedative; mild pain-killer; alleviates fever. Parts used the bark, dried or fresh, cut when tree is in flower and dried in shade. Application M: an infusion (1 teaspoon per cup water just brought to boil) is given 2–3 times a day against colds and feverish conditions, obstinate cough, headache, rheumatic pain and arthritis, and eruptions of the skin.

Ⓜ️ *Prunus spinosa* L. Rosaceae

Blackthorn, Sloe (April–May: flowers; Oct.–Nov: fruits) A much-branched deciduous shrub, often forming dense thickets, up to 4m tall, with rigid branches, the twigs with short lateral spiny shoots. The leaves are simple, up to 4cm long, oblong-ovate to oblanceolate from a wedge-shaped base, with crenate to toothed margins; the petiole is up to 1cm long. The flowers appear before the leaves, regular, hermaphrodite, usually solitary, numerous. The sepals number 5, green. The petals number 5, white, up to 8mm long, oblong-obovate. The fruit is globose, 0·9–1·5cm wide, dark blue or bluish-black, distinctly pruinose, with greenish strongly astringent flesh and with a globose stone.

Habitat woods, hedges, scrub. Distribution throughout the region. Active ingredients carbohydrates, traces of cyanogenic and flavone glycosides (flowers); tannin, organic acids, pectin, sugar, gum (fruit flesh). Effect diuretic, mildly antidiarrhoeal. Parts used the fresh or dried flowers; the fruits, dried in a warm place. Application M: an infusion of fresh or dried flowers (1 teaspoon per cup) is given 2–3 times a day against diarrhoea (especially for children), bladder and kidney disorders, weakness of the stomach, and catarrh. An unsweetened compôte made from fresh fruits is given 1 teaspoon a time against the same ailments. E: the dried fruits can be added to herbal teas; the fresh or dried fruits used in the preparation of liqueurs.

Ⓜ️ *Crataegus laevigata* (Poiret) DC. *(C. oxyacanthoides)* Rosaceae

Ⓔ **Midland Hawthorn** (April–May: flowers; July–Oct: fruits) A deciduous, thorny, much-branched shrub or small tree, up to 10m tall. The leaves on short shoots simple, 1·5–5·5cm long, obovate, broader than long, 3–5 lobed, the lobes short, broad, obtuse, toothed; the leaves on long shoots more deeply lobed and with leaf-like stipules. The flowers are regular, up to 1·8cm in diameter, arranged in 5–10 flowered corymbs. The sepals are up to 8mm long, white. The anthers are pink or purplish. The styles usually number 2. The fruit is 0·9–1·2cm in diameter, with 2 stones, red.

Habitat woods, scrub, hedges, parks. Distribution throughout Europe; in the British Isles rare in the north. Active ingredients various flavonoids, trimethylamine, ursolic and aleanolic acids, purine-derivatives, tannin, essential oils, fruit acids, etc. Effect cardiac sedative; dilates the vessels, reduces blood pressure. Parts used the dried flowers; the fresh or dried fruits. Application M: an infusion (2 teaspoons per cup water, kept for 15 minutes) taken 2–4 times a day is recommended against high blood pressure; it is only effective when used for several weeks. The same is given against weak circulation and the ailments mentioned above. A compôte made from fresh fruits is given against diarrhoea and nervous conditions connected with the menopause. E: the fruits, which are neither bitter nor poisonous, can be used for jam or other preserves, but they are not particularly tasty.

Prunus padus

Prunus spinosa

Crataegus monogyna

Crataegus laevigata

Ⓜ *Crataegus monogyna* Jacq. Rosaceae

Ⓔ **Hawthorn** (May–June: flowers; July–Oct: fruits) A deciduous shrub or small tree, similar to *C. oxyacanthoides* but the leaves on short shoots are longer than broad; the lobes are triangular, from halfway between margin to midrib. There is usually 1 style. The fruit almost always has 1 stone.

Habitat woods, scrub, hedges, often planted. **Distribution** common throughout the region. **Active ingredients, effect and application M:** as for *C. oxyacanthoides*.

Ⓜ *Sorbus aucuparia* L. Rosaceae

Ⓔ **Rowan, Mountain Ash** (May–June: flowers; July–Sept: fruits) A deciduous tree with a slender crown, up to 20m tall, with ascending branches and a smooth greyish bark. The leaves are pinnate, up to 27cm long; the leaflets are in up to 9 pairs, all of the same size and shape, up to 6·5cm long, oblong from a slightly asymmetric base, dark green on the upper, bluish-green on the lower surface, the margins toothed. The flowers are regular, 0·8–1cm in diameter, arranged in compound pubescent corymbs. The sepals are triangular, usually obtuse. The petals number 5, white, about 3·5mm long, ovate. The anthers are cream-coloured. The fruit is almost globose, up to 9mm in diameter, scarlet.

Habitat hedgerows, woods, mountains, along roads, often cultivated, sometimes found on walls and old buildings. **Distribution** throughout the region. **Active ingredients** malic acid, parasorbic acid, sorbitol, vitamin C, sugar, tannin. **Effect** mildly diuretic, mildly purgative; stimulates menstrual discharge. **Parts used** the dried flower; the fruits, dried or fresh. **Application M:** either an infusion (flowers and or dried fruit: 2 teaspoonsfuls per cup water, allow to stand for 10 minutes) or the juice of freshly pressed fruits or a compôte prepared from them is given against menstrual pain, constipation, rheumatic pain and as an aid in the treatment of kidney disorders; the dried flowers are also used for herbal teas. **E:** contrary to common belief the fruits of this tree are not poisonous. They are however rather bitter and should be kept for 8–12 hours in a weak solution of vinegar or boiled for a moment and the water poured away, before use. They can then be used for jams, syrups, wine and soups.

Ⓜ *Sorbus aria* (L.) Crantz Rosaceae

Ⓔ **Whitebeam** A deciduous tree with a wide and dense crown, up to 25m tall, rarely growing as a large shrub. Related to *S. aucuparia* but distinguishable by its simple leaves, which are 4–12cm long, ovate to elliptic or sometimes obovate, with lobed margins and a densely white tometose lower surface.

Habitat woods and scrub, often planted and naturalized. **Distribution** throughout the region. **Active ingredients, effect, parts used and application:** as for *S. aucuparia*.

Ⓜ *Malus sylvestris* Mill. Rosaceae

Ⓔ **Crab Apple** (Oct./Nov.) A deciduous tree with a dense crown, or large shrub, up to 11m tall; the bark greyish-brown, fissured and scaly. The twigs have many short shoots. The leaves are entire, 25–45cm long, ovate to broad-elliptic from a broadly wedge-shaped or rounded base, margins crenate to toothed; the petioles are up to 2cm long. The flowers are regular, 3–4cm in diameter, arranged in umbel-like corymbs. The sepals number 5, green, tomentose on the inner surface. The petals number 5, white and often tinged with pink, obovate, 1·5–3cm long. The anthers are yellow. The fruit is fleshy, almost globose, over 2cm in diameter, yellowish-green and often tinged red.

Habitat woods, scrub, hedges. **Distribution** throughout the region. **Active ingredients** malic and citric acid, pectin, tannin, sugar. **Effect** antidiarrhoeal, astringent. **Parts used** the ripe fruits, best collected after the first frost. **Application M:** an infusion of finely cut dried flesh (2 teaspoons per cup water) or the pressed juice or pulp of the fresh fruit (1–2 teaspoons) is given against diarrhoea. **E:** in the kitchen Crab Apples can be used for jellies and other preserves, fresh or preserved juice or cider. Because of their acidity they are best mixed with other fruits.

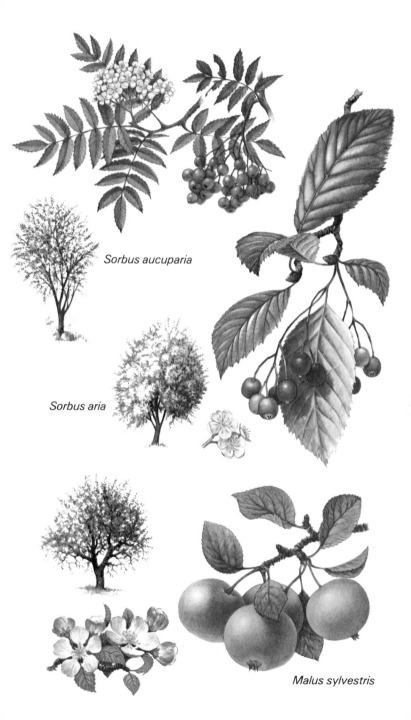

Sorbus aucuparia

Sorbus aria

Malus sylvestris

(M) **Cydonia oblonga** Mill. Rosaceae
(E) **Quince** (Sept.– Oct.)   A deciduous shrub or tree, up to 6m tall, the shoots hairy when young, later glabrous. The leaves are entire, 4–10cm long, ovate to oblong, hairy on the lower surface. The flowers are solitary, regular, up to 4·5cm in diameter, on short tomentose pedicels. The sepals number 5, green, with toothed margins, persistent. There are 5 petals, longer than the sepals, usually pink, sometimes white. The stamens are numerous. The fruit is up to 3·5cm (up to 12cm in cultivation) in diameter, globose or more often pear-shaped, scented, at first green, yellow when mature, slightly tomentose.

Habitat as an escape from cultivation in woods and hedges; often used as a stock for grafting pears in horticulture. **Distribution** widely cultivated throughout the region. **Active ingredients** plenty of mucilage, tannin, vitamin C, fatty oil, pectin, amygdalin. **Effect** mildly but reliably laxative, astringent, anti-inflammatory. **Parts used** mainly the seeds but also the dried flesh (remove seeds, rinse and dry in warm place at 40–45°C.; cut pulp into thin slices and dry in open air). **Application M:** the dried pulp is chewed to treat diarrhoea. The slime contained in the outer seedcoat (put whole seeds in cold water, allow to stand for 3–5 hours, strain through a very fine sieve or a piece of linen) is given internally against cough, constipation or enteritis or other intestinal disorders; externally it is applied to minor burns, added to lukewarm water to make a mouthwash or gargle against inflammation of the mouth or throat. **E:** the fresh pulp of quince makes excellent jellies and preserves. **Note** *the seeds are poisonous and should never be eaten!*

(skull) **Sedum acre** L. Crassulaceae
(M) **Wall-pepper** (June-July)   A small evergreen herb. The stems are numerous, 2–12cm long, trailing and ascending with erect shoots, much branched, matted. The leaves are alternate, entire, succulent, up to 6mm long, overlapping, more distant on some flowering stems, sessile, triangular in cross-section, with a short basal extension. The flowers are regular, hermaphrodite, 1–1·2cm in diameter, arranged in a branched inflorescence. The sepals number 5, lanceolate, spreading, yellow. The fruit consists of a group of follicles.

Habitat walls, roofs, rocks, shingle, dumps, in grassland and waste places on dry soil. **Distribution** throughout the region. **Active ingredients** rutin, alkaloids, mucilage, organic acids, tannin. **Effect** astringent; causes redness and blistering. **Parts used** fresh or dried leaves and flowering shoots: dry in a warm place. **Application M:** in homoeopathy a tincture based on fresh plants is prepared as a remedy against piles and anal irritations. In folk medicine the bruised fresh plant is applied to wounds and minor burns; it is also supposed to soften corns and calluses. Its internal use is not advisable: the plant is slightly *poisonous*, and causes headache, dizziness and nausea.

(E) **Sedum reflexum** L. Crassulaceae
(June-Aug.)   A relatively robust evergreen herb, forming loose mats. The stems are trailing to ascending with erect shoots, 10–35cm long; the sterile shoots are leafy almost throughout without persistent dead leaves. The leaves are sessile, succulent, bent backwards on flowering stems, more or less round in cross-section, up to 2·2cm long, spur-like, extended at the base. The flowers are 1·1–1·6cm in diameter, regular, hermaphrodite, arranged in dense umbel-like cymes. The sepals are green. The petals number 6–8, linear-lanceolate, acute, spreading, bright or pale yellow. The fruit is a group of follicles.

Habitat walls, rocks, shingle, warm grassy places on sandy soil. **Distribution** throughout the region; often cultivated in Britain. **Parts used** the fresh young non-flowering shoots. **Application E:** the slightly astringent sour taste of this plant makes it a useful addition to salads. It can also be added to soups and used as a vegetable.

Cydonia oblonga

Sedum acre

Sedum reflexum

Ⓜ️ *Sempervivum tectorum* L. Crassulaceae

Ⓔ **Houseleek, Welcome home husband, however drunk you be** (April–Sept.) A robust stoloniferous succulent herb. The leaves are crowded in perennial basal rosettes up to 15cm in diameter, 2–6·5cm long, obovate-lanceolate, with the apex pointed, green, but tinged intense red on the upper surface, glabrous. The flowering stems are 20–65cm tall, robust, covered with glandular hair all over. The flowers are regular, hermaphrodite, up to 3cm in diameter, arranged in a panicle. The petals number 8–18, lanceolate, reddish, fused from the base for a short distance. The fruit is a group of follicles.

Habitat roofs, old walls, chimneys, rocks. **Distribution** cultivated and often natural-ized throughout the region. **Active ingredients** malic acid, tannin, mucilage. **Effect** astringent; heals wounds. **Parts used** the leaves, fresh or (rarely) dried. **Application M:** in folk medicine the juice is applied to herpetic eruptions of the skin, suppurating wounds, mastitis and minor burns; mixed with lard or vaseline it is applied to inflamed eyelids or to the hands. **E:** in some parts of Europe the young leaves and shoots are eaten as salads.

Ⓜ️ *Parnassia palustris* L. Parnassiaceae

Grass of Parnassus (July–Sept.) A perennial herb with stems arising from a short erect stock, 8–32cm tall, glabrous; the flowering stem has a single deeply heart-shaped leaf below. The basal leaves are numerous, 1–5·5cm long, ovate from a heart-shaped base, the apex acute, the margins entire. The flowers are solitary, terminal, regular, hermaphrodite; inside the petals are 5 staminodes bearing nectaries with yellow glands on the upper surface. The petals number 5, broadly elliptic or oblong, up to 1·2cm long, white, with distinct veins. The fertile stamens number 5. The fruit is a capsule, splitting lengthways.

Habitat moors, marshes and scree. **Distribution** all over Europe; sporadic in the British Isles. **Active ingredients** tannins. **Effect** sedative, astringent. **Parts used** the entire dried flowering plant. **Application M:** in folk medicine an infusion (1 teaspoon per cup water) is given 2–3 times daily against diarrhoea, nervous conditions (restless-ness) and nervous heartbeat.

Ⓜ️ *Ribes nigrum* L. Grossulariaceae

Ⓔ **Blackcurrant** (April–June: leaves; July: berries) A deciduous shrub up to 2·20m high. The leaves are alternate, petiolate, 2·5–10·5cm long and slightly broader, ovate-elliptic from a heart-shaped base, 3–5 lobed, with brown glands on the lower surface. The flowers number 5–10, arranged in drooping racemes, hermaphrodite, regular, 6–8·5mm in diameter, with a bell-shaped pubescent receptacle and a glandu-lar ovary. The sepals are oblong, the apex recurved. The petals are shorter than the sepals, ovate, white. The fruit is a globose berry with a persistent calyx, up to 1·5cm in diameter, black.

Habitat hedges and woods. **Distribution** throughout the region, often cultivated. **Active ingredients** Vitamin C, tannin, enzymes, traces of essential oil (leaves); plenty of vitamin C, fruit acids, sugar, rutin, tannin and pectin. **Effect** diuretic; promotes sweating (leaves); stimulates secretion; anti-inflammatory (berries). **Parts used** the dried leaves, the fresh or dried berries. **Application M:** an infusion of dried leaves (1–2 teaspoons per cup water, allow to stand for 8–12 minutes) 2–3 times a day is taken internally against dropsy, rheumatic pain and whooping cough and can also be used in a compress for slow-healing cuts and abscesses. The freshly pressed juice of the berries (1 small cup 2–3 times a day) is given against diarrhoea and infections of the intestines and the stomach. An infusion prepared from dried berries is used for gargling against infections of mouth and throat. **E:** the berries make excellent jam and can be used in various ways in baking and cooking.

Ⓔ *Ribes rubrum* L. Grossulariaceae

Red Currant A deciduous shrub similar to the preceeding species but the leaves and ovary are without glands: not strong smelling when rubbed: berries red or rarely white or yellowish-white.

Sempervivum tectorum

Ribes nigrum

Parnassia palustris

Habitat hedges, woods. **Distribution** native or introduced throughout the region. **Parts used** the fruits. **Application E:** this plant has no medicinal application but the fruits are edible and best used for making preserves or a jelly either on their own or mixed with other fruit. They are also excellent for home wine-making.

Ⓜ *Drosera rotundifolia* L. Droseraceae

Sundew (July–Aug.) A delicate insectivorous perennial herb, stoloniferous. The leaves are arranged in a basal rosette, long-petiolate, spreading, almost circular, 0·6–1·1cm in diameter, fringed with tentacle-like glandular hairs, green, tinged with red. The flower scape is 5–27cm tall, usually simple, slender, erect but sometimes floating. The flowers are regular, hermaphrodite, 3–5mm wide, on short pedicels, white, arranged in few-flowered cymes. The sepals number 5, fused at the base. The petals number 5, exceeding the sepals, up to 6·5mm long. The fruit is a many-seeded capsule, slightly exceeding the sepals; the seeds are minute, winged.

Habitat heath, moors, bogs, usually with *Sphagnum*. **Distribution** throughout the region. **Active ingredients** droserone, flavonoids, tannin, traces of essential oils, organic acids. **Effect** expectorant, diuretic; relieves spasms. **Parts used** the entire flowering herb without roots, dried or fresh. **Application M:** mainly used in the treatment of bronchitis, persistent coughs, whooping cough and asthma. Generally used as a tincture (in combination with *Pimpinella*) but also as an infusion (1 teaspoonful of diced herb per cup water, allow to stand for 12 minutes) 2–3 times a day. Causes a harmless discolouring of the urine.

Ⓜ *Lythrum salicaria* L. Lythraceae

Purple Loosestrife (June–Aug.) A perennial with a somewhat pubescent stem 50–120cm (up to 150cm) tall, erect, simple or sometimes branched, with 4 longitudinal raised lines. The leaves are opposite, the uppermost sometimes alternate, the lowermost in whorls, sessile, 3·5–8cm long, lanceolate to ovate from a usually heart-shaped base, acute. The flowers are regular, hermaphrodite, 1–1·6cm in diameter, arranged in whorls in the axils of bracts along a spike-like, dense inflorescence, up to 35cm long. The calyx is pubescent, with a 4–7mm tube and 4–6 teeth. The petals number 4–6, up to 1·1cm long, ovate, purple. The stamens number 12. The fruit is a capsule, contained within the calyx, narrowly ovoid, 3–5mm in diameter.

Habitat river banks, moist places. **Distribution** throughout the region. **Active ingredients** the glycoside salicarin, tannin, pectin, mucilage, resin, traces of essential oil. **Effect** astringent; allays bleeding. **Parts used** the flowering herb, dried or fresh; dry in shade or in a warm well-ventilated room. **Application M:** the bruised fresh herb is applied to slow-healing cuts, grazes and bruises. An infusion (1 teaspoon per cup water, allow to stand for 5–8 minutes) is taken 2–3 times a day against internal bleeding, diarrhoea and dysentery.

☠ *Daphne mezereum* L. Thymelaeaceae
Ⓜ

Mezereon (March–April) A deciduous shrub, 40–110cm (up to 200cm) tall, sparingly branched; the bark is greyish-brown; the young twigs are hairy. The leaves are alternate, 2·5–11cm long, oblanceolate, herbaceous, light green, glabrous. The flowers are regular, hermaphrodite, 0·8–1·2cm in diameter, very fragrant, appearing before the leaves, purple or rarely white, arranged in clusters of 2–4 in the axils of the leaves of the previous season. The sepals number 4. Petals are absent. The stamens number 8. The fruit is a drupe, 0·8–1·2cm in diameter, scarlet.

Habitat calcareous soil in woods. **Distribution** irregular throughout the region. **Active ingredients** a coumarin glycoside, mezerein, resin, fatty oil. **Effect** counteracts leukaemia, causes redness. **Parts used** the dried or fresh bark. **Application C:** this drug is *very poisonous* and must only be used under strict medical supervision. It is used in allopathic preparations against various skin disorders and ulcers. Homoeopathic preparations are given for diseases of the skin, the respiratory tract, bladder ailments and against digestive disorders.

Lythrum salicaria

Drosera rotundifolia

Daphne mezereum

Ⓜ *Hippohae rhamnoides* L. Elaeagnaceae

Ⓔ **Sea Buckthorn** (Sept.– Oct.) A tall, much-branched shrub, 0·8–3m high (rarely as a tree up to 10m). The leaves are alternate, 1–9cm long, linear-lanceolate, almost sessile, covered with minute scales all over, later green on the upper surface. The flowers appear before the leaves on the previous year's growth, about 3mm in diameter, dioecious, green; the male flowers have a short receptacle and 2 large sepals and 4 stamens, arranged in short deciduous spikes; the female flowers are arranged in short axillary racemes, with elongated receptacles and 2 tiny sepals. The fruit is a dry drupe surrounded by part of the fleshy receptacle, almost globose, 5–8mm diameter, bright orange.

Habitat sea cliffs and dunes; occasionally by rivers. **Distribution** along the North Sea, Atlantic and Baltic coasts; along rivers and alpine streams. **Active ingredients** high quantities of Vitamin C (also B and E), carotenes, fruit acids, flavones, fatty oil. **Effect** mainly tonic. **Application M:** the freshly pressed juice can be taken against the common cold, febrile conditions, tiredness, exhaustion etc. Use only stainless steel or enamelled tools and ceramic or glass containers; avoid heat and access to air and excessive light. The juice is widely used in the production of vitamin-rich medicaments and cosmetic preparations such as face-creams and toothpaste. **E:** the fresh juice can be preserved with honey (3–4 cups of juice parboiled with 1 cup of honey) and used as an addition to fruit preserves, as a sweetener for herbal teas or as a basis for liqueurs. Preserved juice of *Hippophae* is commercially available in most health food stores.

Ⓔ *Chamaenerion (Epilobium) angustifolium* (L.) Scop. Onagraceae

Rosebay Willow-herb, Fireweed (April– May: shoots; April–June: leaves) A perennial herb with extensively spreading horizontal roots. The stems are erect, up to 130cm tall, leafy, almost round in cross-section. The leaves are alternate, 4–16cm long, usually ascending, narrowly oblong-lanceolate to oblong-elliptical, tapering towards both ends, entire or somewhat toothed, blue-green beneath. The flowers are bilaterally symmetrical, positioned horizontally, 2–3cm in diameter, arranged in a many-flowered, dense, spike-like raceme. The sepals number 4, erect, up to 1·3cm long, dark purple. The petals number 4, the upper 2 broader than the lower, claw-shaped, rose-purple. The stamens and style are protruding and bending downwards; capsule with 4 valves, seeds numerous.

Habitat edges of and clearings in woods, waste places (even in towns), scree slopes, rubbish tips, etc. **Distribution** throughout the region. **Parts used** young shoots and leaves. **Application E:** the young shoots as well as the underground stock are used as a vegetable; the shoots can be treated like asparagus. The leaves can be eaten as salad or as a vegetable. The leaves, dried in the sun, can be used in herbal tea mixtures.

Ⓔ *Oenothera biennis* L. Onagraceae

Evening Primrose An annual herb with a large fleshy rootstock. The stems are 40–90cm (up to 115cm) tall, rather stout, leafy, pubescent. The basal leaves are petiolate, narrowly oblanceolate, hairy, the stem leaves are almost sessile, lanceolate to ovate-lanceolate with finely toothed margins, the veins are green at first, later turning reddish. The flowers are large and showy, arranged in a terminal leafy spike with 4 green sepals inserted on a 1·8–4·5cm flower tube. The petals number 4, up to 3cm long, heart-shaped, broader than long, yellow. The fruit is 3–3·5cm long, cylindrical, pubescent, and opens lengthwise by 4 valves.

Habitat waste places, roadsides, railway and canal banks, dunes. **Distribution** naturalized throughout the region. **Parts used** the fleshy rootstock, to be dug up in the autumn of the first or in the spring of the second year (only when the basal leaves are still appressed to the ground). **Application E:** wash and scrape thoroughly, boil in salted water till soft and use as a vegetable. **Note** *do not eat the leaves or any part of this plant except the root.*

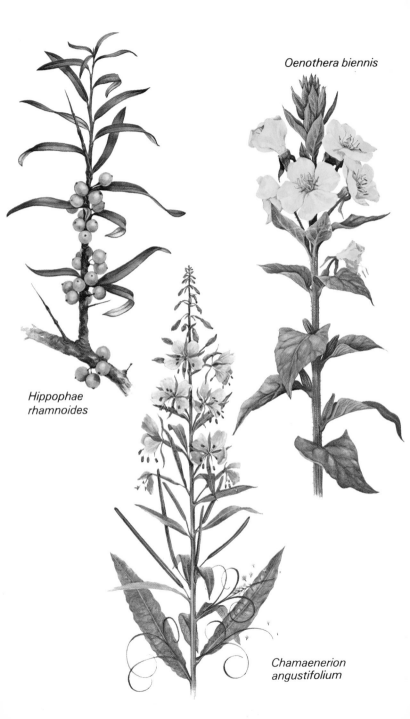

Oenothera biennis

Hippophae rhamnoides

Chamaenerion angustifolium

Ⓜ️ *Viscum album* L. Loranthaceae

Mistletoe (Jan.–Dec.) A woody evergreen plant, parasitic on trees. The stem is 20–110cm tall, stout, green, much-branched. The leaves are 4–8·5cm long, very shortly petiolate, narrow-obovate, often somewhat curved, obtuse, thickly leathery. The flowers are almost sessile, unisexual, arranged in dense cymes. The calyx is rather small or absent. The petals number 4 and are similar to the sepals. The stamens number 4, sessile, opening by pores. The fruit is a white viscous berry.

Habitat among the branches of several deciduous trees (mainly apple) but sometimes on conifers. **Distribution** throughout the region. **Active ingredients** viscotoxin, arginine, choline, acetylcholine, starch, sugar, a fatty oil. **Effect** tonic, tumour-inhibiting, diuretic; relieves spasms and blood pressure. **Parts used** the entire herb (without berries) best collected in winter and dried below 45°C; store in the dark. **Application M:** mainly given for high blood-pressure and arteriosclerosis. As boiling affects its active ingredients the drug is best used powdered (1 pinch 2–3 times a day) or as a cold infusion (2 teaspoons per cup of cold water, allow to stand overnight) taken in the morning before breakfast or twice daily before meals.

Ⓔ *Cornus mas* L. Cornaceae

Cornelian Cherry A small deciduous tree or shrub, up to 8m tall, with greenish-yellow twigs. The leaves are 4–10cm long, ovate to elliptical, with 3–5 pairs of veins, dull green beneath, acute or acuminate, entire. The flowers are arranged in axillary umbels; the bracts are yellowish-green, 0·6–1cm long, deciduous; hermaphrodite, regular, in 4 parts, appearing in early spring long before the leaves. The sepals are very small or absent. The petals are yellow, 2–2·5mm long. The stamens number 4, alternating with the petals. The fruit is a fleshy drupe with a single stone, 1·3–1·6cm long, elliptic in outline, red.

Habitat hedges, edges of woods, parks. **Distribution** throughout the region, often planted. **Parts used** the mature fruit, best collected when just about to fall off otherwise the full aroma is not developed. **Application E:** the ripe fruit can be eaten raw or as a preserve. The juice is a fine basis for jam, as it is not rich in pectin it is best mixed with other fruits. Can also be used for wine, sauce, or a refreshing non-alcoholic drink.

Ⓜ️ *Hedera helix* L. Araliaceae

Ivy (April–July) A woody climbing plant, often creeping and covering large areas on the ground, or climbing up to over 25m. The stems are stout, up to 2·5cm in diameter, forming numerous roots. The leaves are simple, dark green and glossy, of 2 kinds: those on flowering shoots entire, ovate to diamond-shaped; the others palmately 3–5 lobed, up to 10cm long, the lobes triangular. The flowers are regular, arranged in terminal umbels, these often in large panicles. The calyx has 5 small teeth. The petals number 5, free, yellowish-green, up to 4·5mm long. The stamens number 5. The fruit is berry-like, globose, 2–3 seeded, black, 7–8mm in diameter.

Habitation on the ground in woods or hedges, or climbing in trees, over rocks, walls, etc. **Distribution** common throughout the region. **Active ingredients** saponins and the glycoside hederin, pectin, organic acids, fatty substances. **Effect** slightly sedative, expectorant; stimulates secretion. **Parts used** young and dried leaves; dry in shade. **Application M:** a hot infusion (½ teaspoon per cup water, allow to stand for 12 minutes) is taken internally 2–3 times a day against gout, rheumatic pain, cough and whooping cough, and applied externally as a warm compress to burns and suppurating cuts. **Note** *the berries are poisonous.*

Viscum album

Cornus mas

Hedera helix

Ⓜ *Sanicula europaea* L. Umbelliferae

Sanicle (May–Sept.) A perennial herb with a short fibrous stout stock, 18–40cm (up to 60cm) tall. The basal leaves are up to 6cm long, palmately 3–6 lobed; the lobes are wedge-shaped with toothed margins; the petiole 5–25cm long (the leaves can be mistaken for *Ranunculus* when the plant is not in flower). The inflorescence is composed of umbels arranged in a cyme (false umbel), these usually of 3 rays. The bracts and bracteoles are entire. The flowers are white or pink; the outer male, the inner hermaphrodite. The fruit is about 3mm long.

Habitat woods on calcareous or loamy soil. **Distribution** throughout the region. **Active ingredients** tannin, bitter principle, saponin, traces of essential oil, mineral salts. **Effect** anti-inflammatory, expectorant, mildly astringent; relieves flatulence. **Parts used** the dried flowering herb; more rarely the rootstock (collect in autumn, cut into small pieces, dry in shade). Application **M:** an infusion (2 teaspoons per cup water) is given 3–4 times a day for flatulence, infections of the bronchial tract, and cough; it is also used as a mouthwash for inflamed gums or ulcers, for ailments of the throat, or for bathing cuts and grazes; also as a compress. For stomach disorders the infusion is prepared from the rootstock.

Ⓜ Ⓔ *Anthriscus cerefolium* (L.) Hoffm. Umbelliferae

Chervil (May–June) An annual plant with stems 50–70cm tall, erect, branched, hollow, pubescent above the nodes. The leaves are 3-pinnate, the segments pinnatifid, pubescent on the lower surface. The umbels are compound, 2·5–5·5cm in diameter, on short pubescent peduncles; bracts are absent; the bracteoles are linear, fringed with hairs. The flowers are 1·8–2·2mm in diameter, very shortly pedicelled, white. The fruit is 0·9–1cm long, oblong-ovoid, smooth, with a long slender beak; styles erect.

Habitat hedge banks, roadsides, waste places. **Distribution** introduced throughout the region. **Active ingredients** apiin, bitter principle, essential oil. **Effect** mildly diuretic; purifies the blood; stimulating the metabolism, promotes sweating. **Parts used** the fresh herb just before flowering. Application **M:** the pressed juice is given (1 tablespoon twice a day) for dropsy, arthritis and chronic skin ailments, or as a spring tonic. It can also be used as an infusion (1 tablespoon per cup water, allow to stand for 12 minutes). The bruised fresh leaves and stems are applied to slow-healing wounds. **E:** as a condiment this herb is a main ingredient of *fines herbes*. Whether used in warm savoury dishes or in salads it should only be added shortly before serving.

Ⓔ *Myrrhis odorata* (L.) Scop. Umbelliferae

Sweet Cicely A strongly aromatic perennial herb with stout stems, 10–60cm (up to 125cm) tall, erect, hollow, grooved. The leaves have prominent sheaths, are 2–3 times pinnate, 10–30cm long, pale green beneath; the segments are oblong-ovate, pinnately cut into toothed lobes. The umbels are compound, up to 5·5cm in diameter, terminal; the rays number 4–20; bracts are absent; some partial umbels have male flowers only (with shorter peduncles); others have hermaphrodite flowers. The flowers are 2·5 –4mm in diameter; the petals are unequal, white. The fruit is 1·5–2·5cm long, sharply ridged; the styles are diverging, slender.

Habitat woods, hedgerows, grassy places, often found near human habitations. **Distribution** throughout the region, especially in mountain areas. **Parts used** the whole plant. Application **E:** the roots of this plant, if not too old, can be boiled and mixed with other vegetables or added to salads. Fruits and leaves have an aniseed flavour; they can be eaten on their own or added to salads. The chopped fresh herb can be added as a natural sweetener to dishes or preserves based on sour-tasting fruits (apples, raspberries, *Berberis* fruits, etc.).

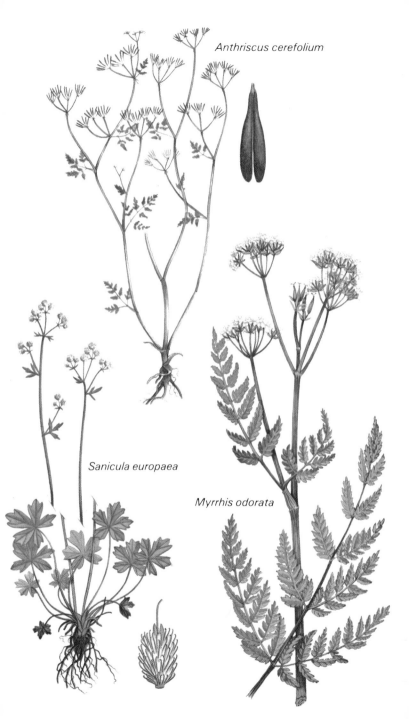

Anthriscus cerefolium

Sanicula europaea

Myrrhis odorata

Ⓜ **_Coriandrum sativum_** L. Umbelliferae

Ⓔ **Coriander** An annual 15–70cm tall, foetid when fresh. The stems are solid, rigid. The lower leaves are usually 1–2 pinnate; the segments are ovate from a wedge-shaped base, pinnatisect or irregularly toothed; the upper leaves have linear lobes. The umbels are 1–3cm in diameter, the rays number 3–5 (up to 19); the bracts are absent or 1; the bracteoles number 3, linear. The petals are white or pink, unequal, the longest up to 3mm long; the fruit is ovoid or globose, the pericarps not separating, hard, reddish-brown.

Habitat waste places, arable land, mostly escaped from cultivation. **Distribution** rarely naturalized north of the Alps. **Active ingredients** essential oil, coriandrol, fatty oil, tannin, sugar. **Effect** stimulates the stomach; relieves spasms and flatulence. **Parts used** the mature fruits. **Application M:** for domestic purposes an infusion (1 teaspoon per cup water; for babies and small children ¼–½ a teaspoon per cup) is given twice a day before meals for flatulence, diarrhoea and abdominal colic. The seeds, used as a spice for salads or even chewed, stimulate stomach secretions and are beneficial in case of lack of appetite. The oil contained in the fruit is used in the production of fine perfumes, *eau de Cologne* and soap. **E:** as a condiment coriander fruit is widely used in Europe for spicing sausages and bread.

Ⓜ **_Apium graveolens_** L. Umbelliferae

Ⓔ **Wild Celery** (June–Aug.) A strong-smelling biennial herb with stems 30–60cm (up to 100cm) tall, solid, grooved. The lower leaves are pinnate; the segments are triangular to diamond-shaped, 5–50cm long, lobed, crenate or toothed; upper leaves ternate. The umbels are axillary, terminal, often positioned opposite the leaves, shortly pedunculate or sessile; the rays number 4–12, unequal; bracteoles are absent. The flowers are minute, 0·5mm in diameter, whitish or greenish-white. The fruit is broad-ovoid, 1·5–2mm in diameter.

Habitat along rivers, ditches, and in similar damp localities. **Distribution** throughout the region; in Britain usually near the sea. **Active ingredients** the flavone glycoside apiin, essential oil, falcarinon and carveol. **Effect** slightly diuretic, supposedly aphrodisiac. **Parts used** the herb at flowering time. **Application M:** in homoeopathy this drug is used in preparations for kidney complaints and rheumatic pain. A juice pressed from leaves and roots is commercially available, 1 tablespoon given 3 times a day, as a kidney stimulant. **Note** *an overdose of the main ingredient (apiin) may lead to miscarriage.* **E:** the leaves of this plant can be added to soups, but are too strong tasting to appeal to most people.

Ⓜ **_Petroselinum crispum_** (Mill.) A.W. Hill Umbelliferae

Ⓔ **Parsley** (June–Aug: flowers) A biennial herb with a stout tap-root. The stems are 20–75cm tall, solid, striate, with ascending straight branches. The lower leaves are 3-pinnate, triangular, glossy; the segments are 1–2·2cm long, wedge-shaped, lobed (crisped only in cultivated plants); the upper leaves ternate. The umbels are compound, 2–5·5cm in diameter, flat-topped; the rays number 8–20; the bracts number 1–3, entire or 3-lobed, sheath-like at the base; the bracteoles number 5–8, linear-oblong to ovate or with a rigid point. The petals are notched, yellowish. The fruit is 2·5–3mm long, broad-ovoid.

Habitat waste places, on rocks and walls. **Distribution** native of S. Europe; introduced in Britain. **Active ingredients** essential oil with apiol and myristicin; Vitamin C (leaves). **Effect** strongly diuretic, expectorant; supposedly aphrodisiac; stimulates menstrual flow; relieves flatulence. **Parts used** the tap-root, fresh or dried; also the fresh herb and the mature fruit. **Application M:** for domestic use an infusion (1–1½ teaspoons root or leaves per cup, allow to stand for 5–10 minutes) is taken 2–3 times a day for flatulence, dropsy and menstrual complaints. **E:** the value of parsley is too well known to need description. The fresh herb is one of our best sources of vitamin C.

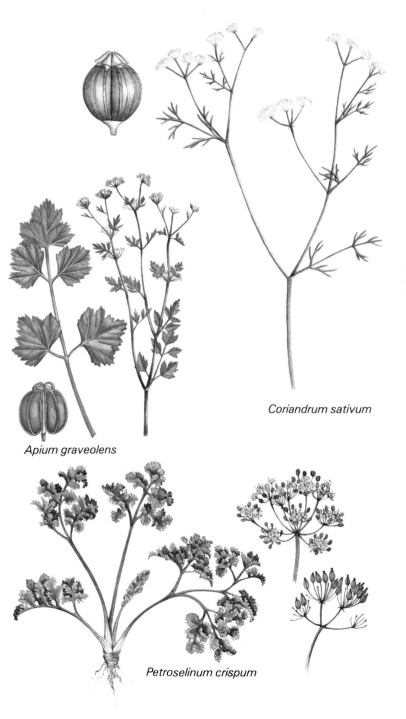

Coriandrum sativum

Apium graveolens

Petroselinum crispum

☠ *Cicuta virosa* L. Umbelliferae
Ⓜ **Cowbane**   A perennial herb with an ovoid or shortly cylindrical, compartmented rootstock. The stems are stout, up to 120cm tall, rigid, hollow. The leaves are 10–35cm long, triangular, 2-pinnate; segments are 2–11cm long, linear-lanceolate, deeply and acutely toothed, asymmetrical at the base. The umbels are compound, terminal and lateral, positioned opposite the leaves, 7–14cm in diameter, flat-topped; the rays number 10–20, not quite equal; the umbels are 30–50 flowered; bracts are absent; the bracteoles number 6–8. The flowers are 3mm in diameter. The fruit is broader than long, up to 2mm long.

Habitat ditches, marshes and similar moist localities. **Distribution** very local in most parts of the British Isles; N. and E. Europe. **Active ingredients** cicutoxin, cicutol. **Effect** convulsive. **Parts used and application C:** although used in the past for homoeopathic preparations for epilepsy, meningitis and other ailments affecting the brain this plant *is highly toxic* (even small quantities of the rootstock can cause death) and is never used for medicinal purposes. It is illustrated here since it can be mistaken for other species (e.g. parsnip). The most important differences are: the aquatic habitat (waterlogged or at least moist for most of the year); nearly all the other species concerned dwell in dry habitats; and the rootstock is either hollow or septate (in longitudinal section it appears divided into chambers or has yellow horizontal lines).

Ⓜ *Carum carvi* L. Umbelliferae
Ⓔ **Caraway** (July–Aug.)   A biennial or perennial herb with a spindle-like tap-root. The stems are 25–80cm tall, striate, hollow, leafy. The leaves are 2-pinnate, triangular to linear-oblong; the segments are 0·3–2·5cm long, pinnatifid with the lobes linear-lanceolate to linear. The umbels are compound, 2–4cm in diameter, irregular; the rays number 5–16, very unequal, 0·5–3cm long; the bracts and bracteoles are absent or number 1. The flowers are 2–3mm in diameter, the outer larger than the central ones; the petals are white, deeply notched. The fruit is oblong, 3–4mm long, with shallow ridges, strong smelling when rubbed.

Habitat arable land, waste places. **Distribution** rarely naturalized in the British Isles; widely introduced in N. and C. Europe. **Active ingredients** essential oil with carvone, limonene; resin, coumarins, fatty oil, tannin. **Effect** disinfectant, digestive, mildly expectorant, relieves spasms and flatulence. **Parts used** the mature fruits; cut the whole umbels before they are fully mature, keep in the sun or a warm place; remove the seeds when blackish-brown. **Application M:** the ideal remedy for lack of appetite, slow digestion, flatulence and abdominal colic. Either chew a pinch of dried seeds 2–3 times a day or take an infusion (1–1 ½ teaspoons crushed seed per cup water). The drug is contained in several proprietary medicines for the same complaints. Oleum Carvi (obtainable from the chemist) can also be used effectively, especially for children. **E:** the use of caraway seeds as a spice goes back to the dawn of history. Today it is widely used in Europe for flavouring bread, cakes, biscuits, cheese etc., and as a spice in cooking meat dishes, sauerkraut and sausages of various kinds; it is also used as a base for the famous Kümmel-liqueur. Young leaves of the plant are much less spicy than the seeds and make a fine addition to salads and soups. The fleshy rootstock can be eaten as a vegetable (prepare like parsnips).

Cicuta virosa

Carum carvi

Ⓜ *Pimpinella major* (L.) Huds. Umbelliferae

Greater Burnet Saxifrage (March–April or Sept.–Oct.) A perennial herb with a stout rootstock. The stems are glabrous, 40–120cm tall, hollow, angled or strongly ridged, brittle, branched above. The leaves are usually pinnate; the segments number 2–9, ovate or oblong, 2–10cm long, toothed, the uppermost stem leaves ternate. The umbels are terminal, compound, flat-topped, 2·5–6cm in diameter; the rays number 10–25, slender; bracts and bracteoles are absent. The flowers are 3mm in diameter, the petals white or pinkish. The fruit is 2·5–5mm long, ovoid, with prominent white ridges.

Habitat hedge banks, edges of woods and similar grassy places. **Distribution** throughout Europe except for the extreme north; Britain except for Wales. **Active ingredients** essential oil, saponin, tannin, pimpinellin, bitter principle, coumarin derivatives, resin. **Effect** expectorant, anti-inflammatory; possibly mildly diuretic, mildly astringent. **Parts used** the rootstock, fresh or dried; clean, cut into small pieces or shred, dry in a warm place. **Application M:** the drug is mainly used for soothing coughs or the effects of bronchitis and laryngitis (an infusion of 2 teaspoons per cup, allow to stand for 15 minutes, drink hot, 2–3 times daily). It can also be used as a mouthwash or for gargling (tonsilitis, ulcers, infected gums, etc.).

Ⓜ *Pimpinella saxifraga* L. Umbelliferae

Burnet Saxifrage A perennial closely related to *P. major* but can be recognized by its downy stem with angles or ridges.
Effect and application as for *P. major*.

Ⓜ *Aegopodium podagraria* L. Umbelliferae

Ⓔ **Ground Elder, Goutweed** (May–July) A glabrous perennial herb, with long slender rhizomes. The stems are sometimes over 100cm tall, hollow, grooved. The leaves are 1–2 ternate, 8–22cm long, triangular; the segments are up to 8cm long, ovate from an often asymmetrical base, sessile to shortly petiolate, the margins irregularly toothed. The umbels are compound, hemispherical, 2–6·25cm in diameter; the rays number 10–21, smooth, up to 4cm long. Most of the flowers are hermaphrodite, without sepals, about 1mm in diameter, the petals white, the outer ones largest. The fruit is 3–4mm long, ovate, laterally compressed.

Habitat grassy places, road and waysides, waste places near human habitation; a persistent weed in gardens. **Distribution** throughout the British Isles and the rest of Europe. **Active ingredients** essential oils, caffeic acid. **Effect** anti-inflammatory, mildly diuretic. **Parts used** the flowering herb, fresh or dried. **Application M:** the use of this plant for medical purposes goes back to medieval times. In homoeopathy the essence is used for arthritis and rheumatic pain. For domestic use an infusion (1–1½ tablespoons per cup water, allow to stand for 5 minutes) is taken 3–4 times a day for the same ailments as well as for disorders of the intestines and bladder. A slightly stronger infusion is applied externally as a compress or bath for insect stings, burns, other wounds and piles; the bruised leaves can be used for the same purpose. **E:** young leaves and shoots before flowering can be used for salads, soups or as a vegetable.

Pimpinella major

Pimpinella saxifraga

Aegopodium podagraria

☠ *Oenanthe aquatica* (L.) Poir. Umbelliferae
Ⓜ **Fine-leaved Water Dropwort**   A stout aquatic annual or biennial herb with fibrous roots, stoloniferous. The stems are stout, 30–150cm tall, hollow, striate. The basal leaves are 3–4 pinnate, finely segmented, with thread-like lobes when submerged; aerial leaves 2–3 pinnate, pinnatifid, with lanceolate to ovate segments which are pinnatifid. The petioles are sheathing at the base. The umbels are compound, 2–5cm in diameter, terminal; the rays number 4–16, rough to the touch; bracts are absent; the bracteoles number 4–8, linear-lanceolate; the partial umbels rounded. The flowers are white, 2mm in diameter, the sepals distinctive; the petals are not quite equal. The fruits are 3·5–4·5mm long, ovoid.

    Habitat stagnant or slow-flowing water; also in semi-dry fen ditches. **Distribution** most of England, E. Wales, S.E. Scotland and C. Ireland; throughout the rest of Europe. **Active ingredients** phellandrene, phellandral, falcarinon and related compounds. **Effect** expectorant, diuretic; stimulates sweating, relieves flatulence. **Parts used** the mature fruits. **Application C:** on account of its toxicity this drug is not recommended for domestic purposes (although in the past it was used for bronchitis, cough, pneumonia, and digestive disorders). In homoeopathy it is still used for the same complaints. **Note** the majority of native Umbelliferae are not poisonous, or only slightly so. Exceptions are this plant, *Conium* and *Cicuta*; except for *Conium* they inhabit predominantly aquatic localities.

Ⓜ *Foeniculum vulgare* Mill. Umbelliferae
Ⓔ **Fennel** (March–April: rhizome; Sept.–Oct: fruit)   A bluish-green glabrous biennial or perennial herb, the stems with a characteristic smell, 60–180cm (up to 250cm) tall, solid, striate, with a small hollow when old. The leaves are 3–4 pinnate, triangular; the segments up to 5cm long, thread-like, not all in the same plane; the petioles are sheathing at the base. The umbels are compound, terminal, 4–8·5cm in diameter; the rays number 10–40, smooth; bracts and bracteoles are absent. The flowers are 1–2mm in diameter, all hermaphrodite, yellow; sepals are absent; outer petals not radiating. The fruit is 4–6mm long, ovate-oblong in outline; the styles are recurved or divergent.

    Habitat waste ground, roadsides, on cliffs near the sea. **Distribution** coasts of England and Wales and parts of Ireland. Native to the Mediterranean region and elsewhere in Europe. **Active ingredients** essential oil with anethole and fenchone, fatty oil, albumin, sugar, coumarin-derivatives, starch. **Effect** diuretic, expectorant; relieves spasms and flatulence, promotes secretions. **Parts used** mainly the mature fruits; more rarely the dried older rhizome. **Application M:** this time-honoured drug is contained in numerous proprietary medicines (mainly cough mixtures). In the home it is used as an infusion (1–2 teaspoons crushed fruits per cup water, allow to stand for 10–15 minutes) 2–3 times a day for bronchitis, cough, flatulence, lack of appetite, and to stimulate lactation (a somewhat weaker infusion can be given unsweetened to bottle-fed babies). In powdered form it is used for constipation. A stronger infusion (2–4 teaspoons per cup water) is used externally as a compress for the relief of conjunctivitis or inflammation of the eyelids; also effective as a gargle and mouthwash. **E:** young fennel leaves add an agreeable flavour to vegetable dishes but especially to fish. The typically swollen bases of the petioles in cultivated forms make an excellent salad and can also be served as a vegetable. Fennel is also used for the production of fennel honey and liqueurs as well as for scenting soap.

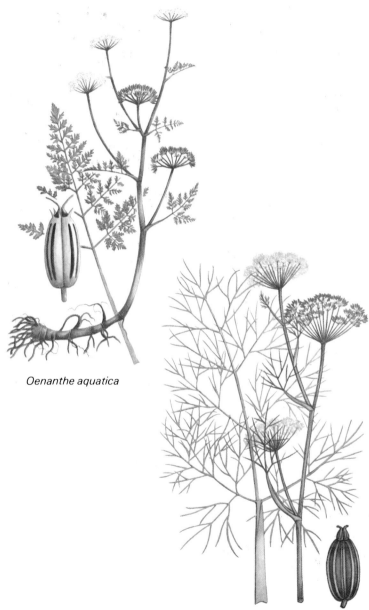

Oenanthe aquatica

Foeniculum vulgare

Ⓜ **Anethum graveolens** L. Umbelliferae

Ⓔ **Dill** Often confused with *Feoniculum* but easily distinguishable by its annual habit, the hollow stem and the strongly compressed fruit. The stems are only up to 70cm tall, bluish-green, smelling strongly when crushed. The leaves are 3–4 pinnate. The umbels are compound; the rays number 7–30, up to 9cm long; bracts and bracteoles are absent. The flowers are usually all hermaphrodite, yellow; sepals are absent; the outer petals not radiating. The fruit is 4·5–6mm long, elliptical, strongly compressed, dark brown with paler wings.

Habitat waste ground and on rubbish tips; mainly cultivated. **Distribution** widely cultivated in Europe. **Active ingredients** essential oil with carvone, fatty oil, protein, tannin, mucilage, resin. **Effect** relieves spasms and flatulence. **Parts used** the mature fruits. **Application M:** an infusion (2 teaspoon crushed seeds per cup water), taken as hot as possible before meals for flatulence, abdominal colic, dyspepsia, insomnia (after the evening meal) and to stimulate lactation. **E:** dill seeds, whole or crushed, are a fine condiment for salads and conserves; the chopped young foliage is much less aromatic than the seeds and adds a distinctive flavour to soups and fish sauces.

Ⓔ **Meum athamanticum** Jacq. Umbelliferae

Spignel, Meu, Baldmoney (June–Aug.) A strongly aromatic perennial with stems 15–60cm tall, hollow, with a dense tuft of persistent fibrous brownish remains of old petioles at the base. The leaves are mostly basal, 3–4 pinnate, ovate or broadly lanceolate, the divisions capillary, almost whorled. The umbels are compound, 2·5–6·5mm in diameter; the rays number 6–15, unequal, rough; the terminal umbel with hermaphrodite and some male flowers; the lateral umbels with mainly male flowers. The flowers are white or tinged reddish; sepals are absent; the outer petals not radiating. The fruit is 6–7mm long, ovoid, hardly compressed.

Habitat mountain grassland. **Distribution** scattered throughout the region. **Parts used** the fresh or dried herb gathered shortly before or at flowering time; also the rootstock, dried or fresh. **Application E:** as a condiment it adds a subtle sweetish-aromatic flavour to soups, stews and vegetable dishes; the crushed fresh herb can be rubbed on to pork or lamb before cooking.

Ⓜ **Angelica archangelica** L. Umbelliferae

Ⓔ **Garden Angelica** (Sept.–Oct.) A very robust herb with hollow, striate stems up to 200cm tall, green. The leaves are large, 2–3 pinnate, the primary pinnae shortly stalked; the lobes are sessile and usually decurrent, up to 16cm long, lobed or deeply toothed; the petioles of the lowest leaves are long, with an inflated base. The umbels are compound, large; the rays number 35–42, not quite equal, up to 8·5cm long; bracts are usually absent, the bracteoles are many, linear. The flowers are all hermaphrodite, light green. The sepals is small. The outer petals are not radiating. The fruit is ovate-oblong or broadly elliptic, dorsally compressed, 5·5–6mm long, with winged lateral ridges.

Habitat waste places, river banks, ditches; often cultivated. **Distribution** British Isles; N. and E. Europe. **Active ingredients** essential oil with mainly phellandrene, angelica acid, bitter principle, coumarin-derivatives, fatty oil. **Effect** diuretic, expectorant, relieves flatulence, causes redness. **Parts used** mainly the rootstock; cut or shred and dry in a warm place; more rarely the fresh leaves. **Application M:** as a decoction (1 teaspoon per cup water; heat to simmering then leave to stand for 10–15 minutes) 1–3 times a day for flatulence, dyspepsia or lack of appetite. A tincture is applied externally for rheumatic pain and neuralgia. **E:** the plant is widely used as an important ingredient in herbal liqueurs (Ettaler Klosterlikör; Chartreuse, etc.) as well as in snuff mixtures and perfumes. In the home young leaves and shoots can be added to soups and vegetable dishes.

Anethum graveolens

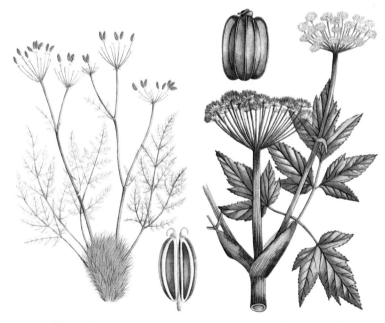

Meum athamanticum

Angelica archangelica

Ⓜ *Angelica sylvestris* L. Umbelliferae

Wild Angelica (March–April or Sept.–Oct.) A perennial closely related to *A. archangelica* but the flowers are white or pinkish, the stems usually purplish, the fruit only 4–5mm long.

Habitat along streams and ditches, in fens, woods and in damp grassy places. **Distribution** common throughout the region. **Active ingredients** essential oil, coumarin derivatives. **Effect** mainly expectorant; mild stomach stimulant. **Parts used** as for *A. archangelica*. **Application M:** much less important than *A. archangelica* but occasionally used as a decoction for bronchial catarrh, cough and dyspepsia.

Ⓜ *Levisticum officinale* Koch Umbelliferae

Ⓔ **Lovage** (April or Sept.–Oct.) A robust, strongly aromatic, glabrous perennial herb with stems up to 220cm, hollow, striate, with persistent scale-like remains of petioles at the base. The leaves are 2–3 pinnate, large; the lobes are diamond-shaped from a wedge-shaped base, the lower half entire, the upper deeply acutely lobed or coarsely sessile. The umbels are compound, dense, large; the rays number 12–20, stout; the bracts are numerous, bent back; the bracteoles are numerous, not bent back. The flowers are yellowish. The sepals are very small; the outer petals are not radiating. The fruit is 5–7mm long, broad-elliptic, dorsally compressed, smooth, with all the 10 ribs narrowly winged.

Habitat arable land, waste places, frequently cultivated. **Distribution** naturalized locally in the British Isles and most of the rest of Europe. **Active ingredients** essential oil, coumarin-derivatives, isovaleric acid, angelica acid, resin, starch. **Effect** diuretic, mildly expectorant; relieves flatulence, stimulates menstrual flow and stomach function. **Parts used** the rhizome, usually dried. **Application M:** a decoction (1–1½ teaspoons shredded or pulverized per cup water, allow just to simmer and then stand for 12 minutes) can be taken for cystitis, lack of appetite, flatulence, dropsy and indigestion; the steam can be inhaled for bronchitis. The drug is more effectively used in a mixture with *Betula, Juniperus,* and *Ononis*; it is contained in a few pharmaceutical herbal teas. **E:** as a condiment the young leaves are valued for flavouring soups and meat dishes; fresh leaves are rubbed on to meat. The food industry uses it extensively for meat and vegetable extracts. It is also used in herbal liquors (bitters); and in perfumes.

Ⓜ *Peucedanum officinale* L. Umbelliferae

Hog's Fennel, Sulphur Weed A perennial herb with a stout, woody stock, crowned by numerous persistent fibrous remains of petioles. The stem is 60–150cm (up to 200cm) tall, solid, striate. The lower leaves are up to 6 times ternately divided, the primary divisions long-stalked; the lobes are up to 11cm long, linear, the upper stem leaves are smaller and less divided. The umbels are compound, up to 16cm in diameter, the rays number 15–45, unequal; bracts are usually absent. The bracteoles are present, linear. The flowers are 2mm in diameter, all hermaphrodite, yellow; the sepals are distinct; the outer petals are not radiating. The fruit is 6–7·5mm long, elliptical to obovate; the lateral ridges winged.

Habitat banks near the sea; cliffs. **Distribution** S. and C. Europe; S.E. England. **Active ingredients** peucedanin (a coumarin-derivative), essential oil, bitter principle, gum, starch. **Effect** diuretic; stimulates sweating. **Parts used** the rootstock (as for *Levisticum officinale*). **Application M:** this drug is only used in homoeopathic preparations for bronchial catarrh, cough, intermittent fever and to stimulate menstrual discharge. In the home it can be used against the same ailments as an infusion (2 teaspoons per cup water; allow to stand for 5–8 minutes) taken 2–3 times a day.

Angelica sylvestris

Peucedanum officinale

Levisticum officinale

Ⓜ **Peucedanum ostruthium** (L.) Koch Umbelliferae

Masterwort (March–April or Sept.–Oct.) Closely related to *P. officinale* but the stems are 25–100cm tall, hollow; leaves only 1–2 ternate; segments lanceolate to ovate from an asymmetrical base, lobed and coarsely toothed; bracteoles are bristly; flowers white or pinkish; fruit only 3·5–5mm long.

Habitat river banks, along ditches, moist grassy places. **Distribution** mountains of C. Europe; naturalized in England. **Active ingredients** essential oil, bitter principle, tannin, resin, fatty oil, hesperidin. **Effect** digestant, expectorant, slightly gastric sedative, mildly diuretic. **Parts used** the rhizome; collect, remove roots, cut or shred and dry in warm place. **Application** as a decoction (1–2 teaspoons per cup water, allow to simmer for a short time, then leave to stand for 10 minutes) 2–4 times a day mainly for flatulence, indigestion or lack of appetite, but also for bronchial catarrh. The drug is contained in a few proprietary medicines. For homoeopathic preparations the fresh rhizome is used. It is also used in a number of commercial herbal liquors drunk either as aperitifs or for the above complaints.

Ⓔ **Pastinaca sativa** L. Umbelliferae

Wild Parsnip (May–July: leaves and shoots; Sept.–Oct: seeds) A strong smelling biennial herb with stems 25–150cm (up to 180cm) tall, hollow or solid, furrowed and angular, the leaves pinnate; the pinnae are in 3–11 pairs, 2–10cm long, ovate to oblong-ovate, usually entire, rarely pinnatifid, toothed, finely hairy on both surfaces; the petioles of the lower leaves are swollen near the base, those of the upper leaves are swollen throughout. The umbels are compound, up to 10cm in diameter; the rays number 5–17; the bracts and bracteoles are absent or falling early. The flowers are yellow, without sepals, the outer petals not radiating. The fruit is almost circular, dorsally compressed, 5–7mm long, the lateral ridges narrowly winged.

Habitat road and waysides, waste places and grassy localities. **Distribution** scattered throughout Britain; most of the rest of Europe. **Parts used** the root, collected in late autumn or in winter (preferably after the first frost); the young leaves and shoots before flowering; the mature seeds. **Application E:** the leaves and shoots are either added to soups or used, mixed with others, as a vegetable. Older leaves and roots should be blanched with boiling salted water before using to remove their sharp flavour; the roots can be used like carrots. The fruits make a fine condiment (similar in taste to dill). **Note** do not mistake this plant for *Conium.*

Ⓜ **Heracleum sphondylium** L. Umbelliferae
Ⓔ

Hogweed, Cow Parsnip, Keck (June–Aug./Sept.) A stiffly hairy biennial herb with stems 50–220cm (up to 300cm) tall, hollow, ridged. The leaves are usually pinnate, large, up to 65cm long, of variable shape; the lobes are up to 18cm long, coarsely toothed; the petioles are conspicuously inflated and sheathing, often tinged with purple, hairy. The umbels are compound, dense, up to 15cm in diameter, terminal and axillary; the rays number 10–20; the bracts are few; the bracteoles are linear when present. The flowers are white, greenish-white or pink; the sepals are minute; the petals are usually rather unequal, the larger notched. The fruit is 0·7–1cm long, obovate to almost circular, dorsally compressed with the lateral ridges broadly winged.

Habitat grassy places, hedges, roadsides, open woods. **Distribution** throughout the region. **Active ingredients** essential oil with n-octylacetate, pimpinellin, iso-pimpinellin and related compounds. **Effect** mildly expectorant; supposedly relieves blood pressure. **Parts used** the herb shortly before or at flowering time. **Application M:** the drug is used in a few proprietary medicines for laryngitis and bronchitis. In some people the plant causes an allergic dermatitis. **E:** young leaves, shoots and peduncles before flowering can be eaten. Wash thoroughly and boil in salted water. Use as a vegetable or add to soups. **Note** not to be mistaken for the Giant Hogweed (*H. mantegazzianum*) which grows up to 5m tall, has enormous umbels with 50–150 rays and contains a resin which may cause painful skin-irritations.

Peucedanum ostruthium

Pastinaca sativa

Heracleum sphondylium

Ⓜ️ ***Daucus carota*** L. Umbelliferae

Wild Carrot A biennial herb with stems 25–100cm tall, solid, striate or ridged, with spreading or backward-pointing hairs. The leaves are 2–3 pinnate, the segments up to 3cm long, lanceolate to ovate, pinnatifid or coarsely toothed, usually hairy. The umbels are compound, dense, more or less flat-topped and depressed towards the centre, up to 7·5cm in diameter; the rays are numerous; the bracts are pinnatisect; the bracteoles number 7–10, entire. The flowers are white but the central one is usually dark purple, the outer petals radiating. The fruit is 2–3·5mm long, ovoid, armed with rows of flattened, hooked spines.

Habitat arable land and grassy places. **Distribution** throughout the region. **Active ingredients** essential oil, pectins, abundant in provitamin A, also vitamins B1 and C, lecithin. **Effect** diuretic, general tonic; treats diarrhoea and worms. **Parts used** the rootstock, mainly fresh but also dried and powdered. **Application M:** the finely grated fresh root (or its juice) is given for nervous and/or physical exhaustion (only effective when used regularly over a period of time), dropsy and internal inflammations. Freshly grated carrots are given to small children for worms. The dry powder is given to babies and small children for diarrhoea. **Note** the subspecies *sativus* is the cultivated carrot.

☠️ ***Aethusa cynapium*** L. Umbelliferae

Fool's Parsley (July–Aug.) A glabrous herb with 5–90cm (up to 120cm) tall, hollow, finely striate stems. The leaves are 2–3 pinnate, triangular to lanceolate; the segments are up to 1·7cm long, pinnatifid, lanceolate to ovate, with rough margins; the petioles are short with a sheathing base. The umbels are compound, 2–6cm in diameter; the terminal rays number 4–20, up to 3cm long, finely toothed. Bracts are usually absent; the bracteoles number 3–4, bent back, linear. The flowers are white, 2mm in diameter, without sepals and with unequal petals. The fruit is 2·5–3mm long, broad-ovoid, slightly dorsally compressed.

Habitat waste places, arable land. **Distribution** common throughout the British Isles and most of the rest of Europe. **Active ingredients** coniine, aethitsine and aethusanol. **Effect** *this plant is fatally poisonous and must not be mistaken for Parsley or Chervil.*

☠️ ***Conium maculatum*** L. Umbelliferae

Ⓜ️

Hemlock A glabrous, foetid, biennial herb with stems up to 200cm tall, hollow, striate, furrowed above, purple-spotted in the lower parts. The basal leaves are 2–4 pinnate, triangular; the segments are up to 2·2cm long, oblong, pinnatifid or deeply toothed; the petioles are long, shortly sheathing at the base. The umbels are compound, 2–6cm in diameter; the rays number 10–20, not quite equal, rough. The bracts number 5–6, bent back; the bracteoles 3–6, often joined at the base. The flowers are white, 2mm in diameter; sepals are absent; the outer petals not radiating. The fruit is 2·5–5mm long, ovoid, slightly compressed.

Habitat damp localities, rubbish tips, roadsides, open woods, usually near water. **Distribution** throughout the region. **Active ingredients** coniine, conhydrin and related alkaloids. **Effect** violently emetic, convulsive; causes paralysis of the central and peripheral nervous systems. **Parts used** the flowering herb. **Application C:** on account of its extreme toxicity this drug *cannot be used for domestic purposes,* and even in medicine it is only used in a few proprietary medicines (e.g. ointments for neuralgia and certain rheumatic complaints). Even small quantities lead to a painful death (it was probably the plant with which Socrates was put to death). It can be distinguished from other species described here by its nauseating smell (cat's urine) and the presence of purplish spots on the stem and leaf petioles.

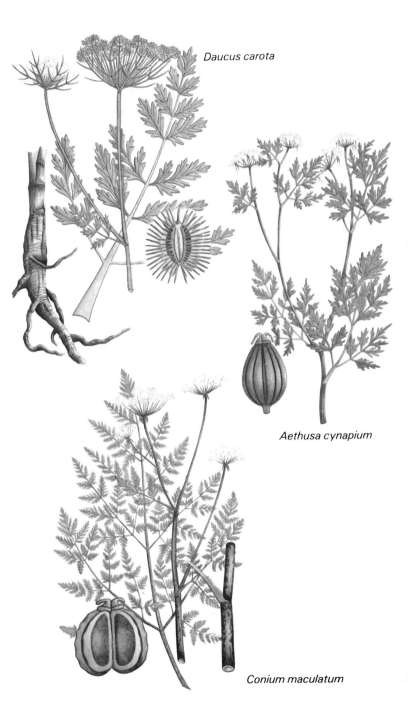

Daucus carota

Aethusa cynapium

Conium maculatum

Ⓜ *Eryngium campestre* L. Umbelliferae

Field Eryngo (July – Aug.) A perennial with stems 25 – 60cm tall, much-branched, rather rigid, solid. The basal leaves are up to 22cm long, pale green to bluish-green, triangular-ovate, deeply pinnatifid; the lobes are decurrent on the midrib, toothed to spiny, the margins thickened; the petiole is as long as the blade. The flowers are arranged in dense, pedunculate, ovoid heads, 1 – 1·6cm wide. The bracts number 5 – 8, about 2 – 3 times as long as the heads. The flowers are 2 – 3mm in diameter, white; the sepals are longer than the petals. The fruit is about 5mm long, slightly compressed, densely clad with white, acute scales.

Habitat dry open grassy places, mostly in coastal areas. **Distribution** only in a few localities in England and Wales. **Active ingredients** essential oil, saponins, sugar. **Effect** expectorant; relieves spasms; mildly diuretic (the herb). **Parts used** the rootstock and the fresh flowering herb. **Application** a decoction (1 – 1½ teaspoons per cup water, allow to simmer for a ½ minute and stand for 5 – 10 minutes) is taken 2 – 3 times a day for dropsy, bladder stones or infections of the urinary tract, skin disorders, whooping cough, for abdominal colic and to promote menstrual discharge.

Ⓜ *Bryonia cretica* L. ssp.*dioica* (Jacq.) Tutin

Red Bryony (Sept. – Oct.) A climbing perennial with a substantial tuberous vertical stock. The stems are wiry, very long, brittle, branched, covered with stiffly swollen-based hairs; climbing with coiled tendrils. The leaves are petiolate, palmately 5-lobed, heart-shaped at the base. The flowers are dioecious, arranged in axillary cymes; pedunculate in the male, sessile in the female plants. The calyx is shortly bell-shaped with 5 teeth. The corolla has 5 lobes, whitish-yellow. The stigma is hairy. The stamens number 3. The fruit is a smooth, globular berry, 5 – 8mm in diameter, red, with up to 6 yellowish seeds.

Habitat hedges, copses, scrub, along fences, etc. **Distribution** most of Europe except Scandinavia. **Active ingredients** bryoresin, glycosides, essential oil, bryocinin. **Effect** anti-rheumatic, strongly purgative, anti-inflammatory. **Parts used** the rootstock; cut or dice and dry in warm place or in the sun. **Application C:** virtually obsolete but sometimes used in homoeopathic preparations. A decoction is occasionally used *under medical supervision* against severe constipation, arthritis and to promote menstrual discharge.

Ⓜ *Aristolochia clematitis* L. Aristolochiaceae

Birthwort A perennial with a long creeping rhizome. The stems are 20 – 85cm tall, erect, simple, usually numerous. The leaves are 5 – 17cm long, broadly ovate from a heart-shaped base; the petiole is half as long as the blade. The flowers have short pedicels, bilaterally symmetrical with a long, lightly curled, cylindrical, basally swollen tube, 2 – 3cm long, yellow; the limb is oblong to ovate, entire, as long as the tube. The fruit is a pear-shaped capsule, up to 2·5cm long.

Habitat waste ground, gardens, orchards, old vineyards; frequently cultivated for medicinal purposes. **Distribution** England; E. Europe. **Active ingredients** aristolochic acid (2 forms), essential oil, tannin, bitter principle, sugar. **Effect** mainly anti-inflammatory; also relieves spasms, promotes sweating and menstrual flow. **Parts used** the flowering herb with or without rhizome. **Application M:** this ancient drug is contained in numerous proprietary medicines as well as in homoeopathic preparations. In the home the drug can *only be used externally* against slow-healing cuts, eczema and infected finger and toe nails (1 – 2 teaspoons of drug to ½ litre water, boil for a short time, allow to stand for 30 minutes; apply as a warm compress 2 – 3 times daily). *Internal use of this infusion causes damage to kidneys and leads to uterine bleeding.*

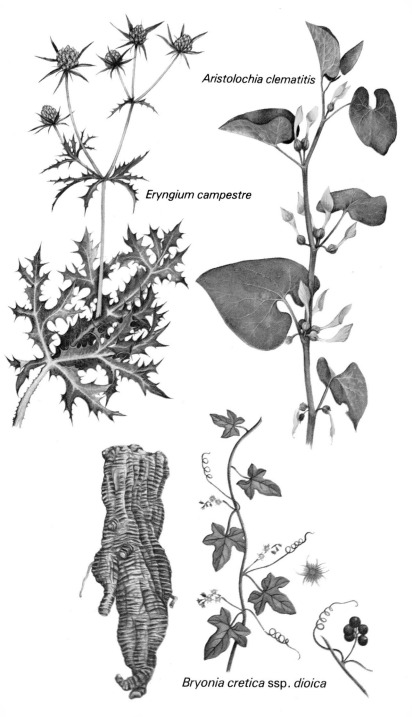

Aristolochia clematitis

Eryngium campestre

Bryonia cretica ssp. *dioica*

☠ *Asarum europaeum* L. Aristolochiaceae

Ⓜ **Asarabacca** An evergreen herb with a creeping rhizome. The stems are rather short, up to 10cm tall. The leaves are 2–10cm long, broader than long, kidney-shaped from a deeply heart-shaped base, obtuse, dark green, long-petiolate. The flowers are regular, solitary, terminal. The perianth is in 1 whorl, persistent in fruit, 1·1–1·5cm in diameter, brownish, pubescent on the outside; the lobes are triangular. The stamens number 12, in 2 whorls. The fruit is an irregularly opening, globose capsule.

Habitat woods. **Distribution** rare in England; from Belgium and parts of Germany to Finland and Spain. **Active ingredients** essential oil (with or without asarone), resins, mucilage, flavonoids. **Effect** purgative, diuretic, emetic, stimulating secretion in the respiratory tract. **Parts used** entire plant when in flower; dry in a warm place. **Application C:** because of harmful side effects the plant is rarely used. In the home a weak infusion (½ teaspoon per cup water, leave for 15 minutes) twice daily is used against laryngitis, liver complaints, asthma, bronchitis and dropsy (*only to be taken in moderation*); the powdered drug is used in snuff.

Ⓜ *Euphorbia peplis* L. Euphorbiaceae

Purple Spurge (July–Sept.) An annual herb with 1–7cm long prostrate stems, bluish-green, often tinged with red. The leaves are up to 1·1cm long, shortly petiolate, oblong, obtuse and often broadly notched with a large basal auricle, the stipules are split into fine segments. The bracts are similar to the leaves. The flowers are arranged in a cup-shaped involucre (cyathium) with conspicuous, almost circular glands. The involucre is 1–2mm wide, peduncled. The fruit is a glabrous, 3-valved capsule, 3–5mm in diameter.

Habitat beaches, mainly on shingle. **Distribution** Atlantic coast from France southwards; S.W. England. **Active ingredients** euphorbone, saponin, resin, tannin, organic acids, traces of essential oil. **Effect** purgative, expectorant, diuretic. **Parts used** the flowering herb. **Application** this drug is completely obsolete in both allopathy and homoeopathy. It has been used in the past in folk medicine in the Mediterranean area and in France as a remedy for arthritis, bronchitis, asthma and dropsy. The white sap of this species has been applied to warts; its effect is doubtful, and its application is not recommended because this acrid substance causes blisters and inflammation of the skin.

Ⓜ *Mercurialis perennis* L. Euphorbiaceae

Dog's Mercury (March–April) A hairy perennial herb, usually dioecious, with a long creeping rhizome. The stems are juicy, erect, 12–40cm tall, simple. The leaves are opposite, with small stipules, up to 8cm long, elliptic-ovate or elliptic-lanceolate; the petiole is short. The flowers have a lobed calyx and 8–15 stamens, 4–5mm in diameter: the female flowers number 1–3, in axillary inflorescences up to 7mm long; the male flowers grow in clusters arranged in spikes. The fruit opens by 2 valves, 6–8mm wide, stiffly hairy.

Habitat woods, rocks in mountains (mostly in beech-woods). **Distribution** throughout the region. **Active ingredients** saponin, bitter principle, essential oil. **Effect** purgative, diuretic; stimulating metabolic processes. **Parts used** the fresh or dried flowering herb (dry in shade). **Application M:** a homoeopathic preparation (essence) from the fresh herb is given for rheumatism, dropsy, diarrhoea and disorders of gall bladder and liver. In the home an infusion (1 teaspoon dried herb per cup water, allow to stand for 5 minutes) is taken 2–3 times a day after meals against the same conditions and stomach or intestinal disorders.

Ⓜ *Mercurialis annua* L. Euphorbiaceae

Annual Mercury Similar and closely related to *M. perennis* but annual, becoming glabrous and having branched stems.

Habitat waste places; weed on arable land and in gardens. **Distribution** widespread throughout the region. **Active ingredients, effect and application M:** as for *M. perennis.* **Note** the leaves of these species must never be used for culinary purposes.

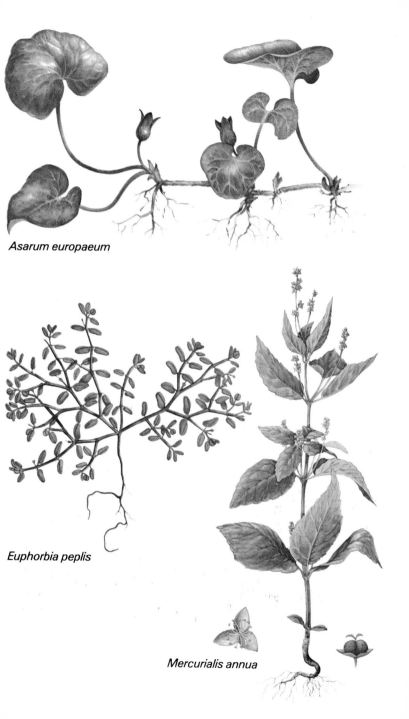

Asarum europaeum

Euphorbia peplis

Mercurialis annua

Ⓜ **Ruta graveolens** L. Rutaceae

Rue (June–July/Aug.) A perennial with few-branched stems, often woody at the base, glabrous, up to 45cm tall, usually erect. The leaves are alternate, up to 15cm long, 2–3 pinnatisect, gland-dotted, the lower ones petiolate, the upper ones usually sessile; the terminal segment is lanceolate to obovate, up to 9mm wide. The flowers are glandular, arranged in a lax cyme with leaf-like bracts. The sepals number 4, lanceolate, acute. The petals number 4, yellow, oblong-ovate, toothed, wavy. The stamens number 8. The fruit is a 4–5 lobed capsule, splitting, glabrous.

Habitat cultivated ground, vineyards, along walls and in similar localities. **Distribution** naturalized from cultivation in S. Europe; cultivated in the British Isles mainly for ornamental purposes. **Active ingredients** rutin (a flavonoid glycoside), essential oil with methyl ketones, coumarin derivatives. **Effect** mildly sedative, diuretic; stimulates sweating, relieves spasms. **Parts used** the leaves or the entire herb before flowering. **Application M:** in homoeopathy an essence is used for phlebitis, varicose veins, rheumatic pain and arthritis. An infusion (2 teaspoons per cup water, allow to stand for 12 minutes) is given 2–3 times a day for the same complaints but also for delayed menstruation or to induce perspiration. Bruised fresh leaves can be applied to slow-healing cuts, bruises and burns.

Ⓜ **Dictamnus albus** L. Rutaceae

A bushy perennial herb, 30–80cm high; the stems are branched, usually woody below, slightly hairy, glandular; the axis of the inflorescence, and the bracts and pedicels are covered with stalked glands. The leaves are alternate, pinnate, dotted with translucent glands, with 3–6 pairs of lanceolate to ovate leaflets. The flowers are showy, arranged in terminal racemes. The sepals number 5, lanceolate. The petals number 5, white, bluish or pink with purplish markings, 2–2·5cm long, elliptic-lanceolate. The stamens number 10. The filaments curve upwards, partly glandular. The fruit is a 5-lobed capsule.

Habitat grassland, open woodland, rocky hills, vineyards, old walls or gravel pits. **Distribution** C. and S. Europe; cultivated in Britain. **Active ingredients** dictamnin (an alkaloid) essential oil, saponin, bitter principle. **Effect** diuretic; relieves spasms. **Parts used** the dried rootstock. **Application M:** in homoeopathy an essence prepared from fresh leaves is given for female complaints and constipation. An infusion (1 teaspoon of shredded root per cup) is taken 1–2 times a day for certain complaints. **Caution** *on account of the toxicity of dictamnin excessive use of this drug should be avoided.*

Ⓜ **Polygonum aviculare** L. Polygonaceae

Knotgrass (July–Oct.) An annual plant with branched stems, relatively robust, 5–120cm (up to 200cm) long, spreading or erect. The roots are fibrous. The leaves are alternate, 2–5cm long, lanceolate to ovate-lanceolate, almost acute; the leaves of the main stem are much longer than those of the flowering branches. The stipules are fused into a tubular 4–5·5mm long, silvery organ (the ochrea). The flowers number 1–6, axillary. The perianth segments number 5, united at the base, with white or pink edges. The stamens number 5–8. The fruit is 2–4mm long, dull brown, dotted, usually enclosed within the persistent perianth.

Habitat waste places, roadsides, railway embankments, coast. **Distribution** common throughout the region. **Active ingredients** silicic acid, tannin, saponin, mucilage, traces of essential oil. **Effect** astringent, diuretic, mildly expectorant. **Parts used** the flowering herb, dried in thin layers in a warm well-ventilated place. **Application M:** an infusion (1½–2 teaspoonsful per cup water, allow to stand for 5–10 minutes) is taken 2–3 times a day for pyelitis, arthritis, rheumatic pain, diarrhoea and (doubtful) diseases of the lungs. In homoeopathy an essence prepared from the fresh herb is given for the same complaints. It is also used in various herbal tea mixtures.

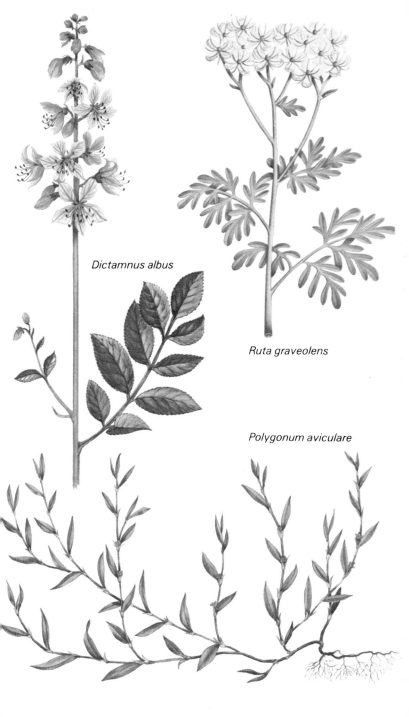

Dictamnus albus

Ruta graveolens

Polygonum aviculare

Ⓜ *Polygonum hydropiper* L. Polygonaceae

Water-pepper (June– Oct.) Related to *P. aviculare*, but it is acridly burning to the taste. The roots are fibrous, the stems 25–75cm tall, usually erect, branched. The leaves are 3–10cm long, lanceolate, almost sessile, fringed with hairs. The flowers are arranged in many-flowered, nodding spikes which are leafy and interrupted in the lower part. The perianth segments are greenish, covered with many yellow glands, almost free to the base. The fruit is 2·7–3·2mm long, mat, dark brown to black.

Habitat shallow water (ponds, ditches, waterlogged grassland) and other damp localities. **Distribution** throughout the region. **Active ingredients** tannin, traces of essential oil, mucilage, a glycoside. **Effect** astringent, anti-inflammatory, diuretic, stimulates menstrual flow, arrests bleeding. **Parts used** the entire fresh herb. **Application M:** a homoeopathic preparation (essence) is given for piles, menstrual pain or other menstrual complaints. In the home the powdered drug (3–5 pinches a day) or an infusion (2–3 teaspoons per cup water, allow to simmer and stand for 12–15 minutes) is used 2–3 times a day for the same complaints, as well as for dropsy. Bruised fresh leaves are applied to bleeding or slow-healing cuts or grazes.

Ⓜ *Polygonum persicaria* L. Polygonaceae

Red Shank, Willow-weed (July–Oct.) This species can be distinguished from *P. hydropiper* by its stout inflorescence which is not nodding, and its perianth-segments, which are not glandular. The leaves are up to 10cm long, lanceolate, fringed with hairs, sometimes woolly beneath and often with black marks.

Habitat waste places, cultivated land, near ponds and ditches. **Distribution** throughout the region. **Active ingredients** essential oil, persicarin, tannin. **Effect** astringent, anti-inflammatory, antidiarrhoeal. **Parts used** the flowering herb. **Application M:** this plant is used in neither allopathy nor homoeopathy but is known to play a part in French folk medicine.

Ⓜ Ⓔ *Polygonum bistorta* L. Polygonaceae

Snakeroot, Easter-ledges (June–Aug: herb; Sept.–Oct: rhizome) Related to the two preceding species *P. persicaria* and *P. hydropiper* but of perennial habit, with unbranched stems and a rather stout, contorted rhizome. The leaves are of two kinds: basal leaves 5–15cm long, broad-ovate from an almost heart-shaped or truncate base, the petioles winged in the upper part; upper leaves triangular, with sheathing petioles. The flowers are arranged in a terminal, erect, dense spike, up to 1·5cm wide. The perianth segments are usually pink, rarely white.

Habitat grassy places (meadows, pastures, roadsides, railway embankments, etc.). **Distribution** throughout the British Isles, rare in S.E. counties and in Ireland; N. and C. Europe except Scandinavia. **Active ingredients** tannin, gallic acid, starch, albumin. **Effect** astringent, anti-inflammatory; arrests bleeding. **Parts used** the dried flowering herb, or the dried rhizome (cut into small pieces, dry in the sun or a moderate temperature). **Application M:** an infusion (2–3 teaspoons herb or 1½–2 teaspoons rhizome per cup water, allow to stand for 15 minutes) can be taken 2–3 times a day for internal bleeding and diarrhoea or as a mouthwash for throat and gum infections. The drug is more effective in powdered form (take 3–5 pinches), especially for diarrhoea. **E:** young shoots and leaves of this plant can be eaten like spinach and may even taste better. In the Lake District they are eaten as 'Easter-ledge puddings'.

Polygonum hydropiper

Polygonum persicaria

Polygonum bistorta

Ⓜ **Rumex acetosa** L. Polygonaceae

Ⓔ **Sorrel** (April–May) A perennial with usually erect, glabrous, 20–70cm stems. The leaves are alternate, 3–10·5cm long, oblong-lanceolate from a base with lobes pointing downwards, obtuse or somewhat acute; the upper leaves are almost sessile and usually clasping the stem. The flowers are arranged in whorls, in a large, usually leafless inflorescence up to 40cm long. The perianth segments number 6 in 2 whorls, the outer ones bent back and pressed against the pedicel after flowering, the inner ones 3–4mm long, ovate or circular to heart-shaped. The fruit is up to 2·6mm long, glossy.

Habitat grassy places and clearings in woods. **Distribution** throughout the region. **Active ingredients** oxalic acid, quercetin-3-d-galactosid, vitamin C. **Effect** anti-inflammatory; stimulates secretion. **Parts used** the young fresh leaves and shoots and the fresh rootstocks (collected in summer). **Application M:** in allopathic medicine this drug is almost obsolete and only used in a few preparations for sinusitis, sino-bronchitis and similar conditions. Homoeopathic preparations (essences) are given for spasms and skin ailments. In the home bruised fresh leaves are applied to bruises, cuts, skin eruptions, and burns. **E:** on account of their vitamin content the tips of young shoots, young leaves and buds (best gathered in March/April) are used for salads or added to soups and vegetable dishes. However, it should be used only sparingly and infrequently.

Ⓜ **Rumex alpinus** L. Polygonaceae

Monk's Rhubarb (April or Sept.–Oct.) A perennial herb 30–75cm tall, growing with a thick, long-creeping much-branched rhizome. The leaves are large, 15–50cm long and almost as broad, broadly ovate to circular from a heart-shaped base, with wavy margins. The flowers are arranged in joined whorls in a little-branched inflorescence, borne on up to 1cm long pedicels, bent back in fruit. The perianth segments number 6, in 2 whorls; the inner one enlarged in fruit, up to 6mm long, ovate from a truncate base, not warty. The fruit is 2·5–3mm long. **Note** this plant is easily mistaken for *R. obtusifolius* (Broad-leaved Dock) which is, however, not rhizomatous.

Habitat along streams and roads, and near human habitations in hilly areas. **Distribution** mountain areas of C. and S. Europe; introduced in N. Britain. **Active ingredients** tannin, a glycoside, anthraquinone derivatives, resin. **Effect** purgative. **Parts used** the dried rhizome (clean, cut lengthwise and dry in sun or warm place). **Application M:** mainly against constipation. Best taken powdered (2–4 pinches 1–3 times daily), less effective as an infusion (½–1 teaspoon per cup of water, allow to stand for 10–15 minutes) 2–4 times a day.

Ⓜ **Parietaria erecta** Mert. et Koch Urticaceae

Pellitory of the Wall (July–Oct.) A perennial with a slender stem, 30–80cm long, round in cross-section, much-branched, spreading or ascending at the tips, softly hairy. The leaves are alternate, entire, 0·5–7cm long, lanceolate to ovate, obtuse to acuminate, glossy and somewhat brittle; the petiole is long but shorter than the blade. The flowers are rather small, usually unisexual, greenish, arranged in terminal (ternate) and axillary (male) dense cymes. The perianth of female flowers is tubular with 4 teeth; that of male flowers in 4 parts surrounded by an involucre of 1 bract and 2 bracteoles. The fruit is enclosed by the perianth.

Habitat on and along old walls, hedge banks, fences. **Distribution** scattered throughout the region. **Active ingredients** tannins, bitter principle, mineral salts (saltpetre). **Effect** mildly diuretic, stimulating healing of wounds. **Parts used** the entire fresh or dried flowering herb. **Application M:** this drug is used together with *Betula, Juniperus, Herniaria, Ononis* and others in a few proprietary medicines for infections of the urinary tract. In the home an infusion (1 teaspoon per cup water, allow to stand for 5 minutes) is given internally 4–5 times a day for complaints of the bladder and kidneys and externally for bathing burns, skin-infections, and slow-healing wounds, or as a compress.

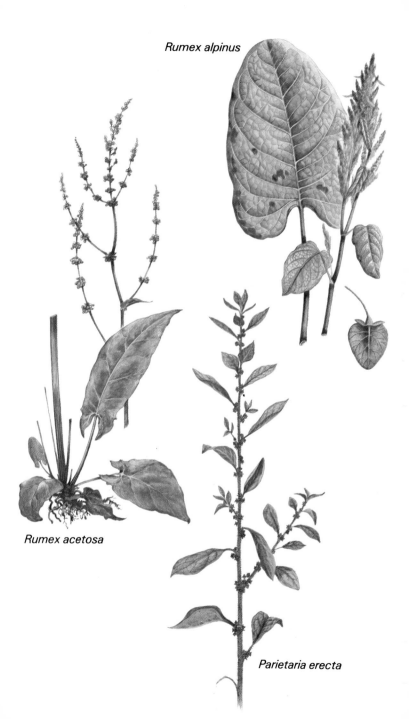

Rumex alpinus

Rumex acetosa

Parietaria erecta

Ⓜ️ ***Urtica dioica*** L. Urticaceae

Ⓔ **Stinging Nettle** (June–July) A perennial herb covered with brittle stinging hairs all over. The stem is 25–150cm long, creeping, rooting at the nodes and sending up erect shoots. The leaves are opposite, 3·5–8·5cm long, ovate from a usually heart-shaped base, margins toothed, apex acuminate, long-petiolate, the blade of the lower ones shorter than the petiole. The flowers are green, rather small, unisexual, arranged in axillary, dense or loose inflorescenses up to 10cm long. The perianth is in 4 parts; the female flowers have unequal segments. The fruit an achene, 1–1·25mm long, enclosed by the large perianth segment.

Habitat waste places, often close to human habitations, hedge banks, woods, along fences and similar grassy places; usually in nitrate-rich soil. **Distribution** throughout the temperate regions of the world. **Active ingredients** tannin, Vitamin C, silicic acid, formic acid, acetic acid, iron, glucoquinine, histamine, abundant chlorophyll. **Effect** mainly mildly diuretic, but also anti-rheumatic, tonic, blood stimulant. **Parts used** the fresh or dried herb at flowering time; cut and dry in the sun or moderate heat (under 45°C); store away from light. **Application M:** in homoeopathy an essence is prepared from the fresh herb for eczema and other skin ailments. In the home a decoction (1½–2 teaspoons per cup, simmer briefly, allow to stand for 10–15 minutes) is given 2–3 times a day for cystitis and rheumatic pain (taken over a period of at least 6 weeks). The effectiveness of this drug as a hair tonic is claimed but not proven. The freshly pressed juice (1–2 tablespoons 2–3 times a day) is given for anaemia, nervous and physical exhaustion and as a spring tonic. **E:** young shoots (cut in March–April before flowering) are a valuable source of vitamin C and can be added to salads or blanched and eaten fresh mixed with cottage cheese. They can also be eaten as a vegetable treated like spinach.

Ⓜ️ ***Urtica urens*** L. Urticaceae

Small Nettle (April; July–Oct.) An annual closely related to *U. dioica* but can be distinguished by its annual habit, smaller size, (up to 65cm tall), smaller leaves (up to 4cm long) and the fact that the lower leaves are shorter than the petioles.

Habitat, distribution, effect and application as for *U. dioica*.

Ⓜ️ ***Humulus lupulus*** L. Cannabiaceae

Ⓔ **Hop** (July–Sept.) A climbing perennial, the stems twisting clockwise, 2·5–6·5m long, rough with bent back hairs. The leaves are petiolate, opposite, 5–15cm long, broadly ovate from a usually heart-shaped base, usually deeply 3–5 lobed, rarely entire, margins toothed, lobes acuminate. The flowers are pendulous, dioecious; the male flowers are 4–5mm in diameter, in much-branched inflorecences; the female flowers are arranged in cone-like spikes with broad, membranous, glandular, persistent overlapping bracts; the 'cone' is up to 2·2cm long in flower, 5·3cm in fruit. The fruit is an achene.

Habitat hedges, thickets, along fences. **Distribution** Britain, often as an escape from cultivation; throughout the rest of Europe. **Active ingredients** essential oil, resin, tannins, lupulin. **Effect** mildly sedative, stomachic, anti-aphrodisiac. **Parts used** the female inflorescences and (more effective) the glands, which are extracted by shaking and sieving the dried 'cones'. **Application M:** best used either powdered (2–4 pinches) or as an infusion (2–3 teaspoons per cup, allow to stand for 8–12 minutes) taken in the evening for insomnia, before meals for nervous stomach upsets, 3–4 times a day for nervous heart conditions and excessive sexual urge. An alternative preparation can be made by soaking the 'cones' in cold water for 3–4 hours, simmering briefly, then standing for 10 minutes. The drug loses its effectiveness in storage. In folk medicine cushions are filled with dried hops to overcome insomnia. **E:** the hop is most important in the preparation of good beer. The immature leaves and the tips of young shoots are a fine addition to salads and soups. Lateral shoots which are cut out in cultivation can all be used as a vegetable: boil first in salted water and pour water away.

Urtica dioica

Humulus lupulus

Ⓜ **Ulmus procera** Salisb. **(U. campestris)** Ulmaceae
English Elm A large suckering tree up to 40m tall with stout branches and a fissured bark; the twigs are usually pubescent. The leaves are alternate, simple, 3·5–9cm long, ovate or almost circular from an asymmetrical rounded or somewhat wedge-shaped base, rough on the upper side, pubescent with tufts on the lower surface. The flowers appear before the leaves, with a bell-shaped 4–5 lobed perianth; the anthers are reddish. The fruit is a samara, winged all round, compressed, circular, shortly pedicelled.

Habitat roadsides, hedges, margins of woods. **Distribution** all over England but less common in the north; frequently cultivated in W. and S. Europe. **Active ingredients** tannin, bitter principle, mucilage, resin. **Effect** astringent, anti-inflammatory, mildly diuretic. **Parts used** the dried young inner bark from 3–4 year old branches. **Application M:** in homoeopathy an essence prepared from fresh bark is given for eczema. For domestic purposes an infusion (1 tablespoon shredded bark per cup water) is taken 3 times a day for diarrhoea, arthritis, rheumatic pain, eczema or for inducing perspiration. A slightly stronger infusion can be used for bathing inflamed wounds, piles or as a mouthwash and gargle for inflammation of mouth and throat. The bark of the related native Wych Elm *U. glabra* can equally be used.

Ⓜ **Morus nigra** L. Moraceae
Ⓔ **Black Mulberry** (Aug.–Sept: fruits) A large dense shrub or tree up to 15m with rather stout branches and a dark brown scaly bark. The leaves are alternate, 5–20cm long, broadly ovate from a heart-shaped base, entire or somewhat lobed, pubescent beneath, the margins toothed, long-petiolate. The flowers are unisexual, greenish, and arranged in dense spikes. The perianth of the male flowers is in 4 parts with 4 stamens; the female flower has 4 almost free segments, becoming fleshy in fruit. The fruit is a dense syncarp composed of druplets which are surrounded by the fleshy perianth; the syncarp is dark purple, up to 2·6cm long.

Habitat usually cultivated in gardens or parks, occasionally as an escape in woodland or hedges. **Distribution** widely cultivated in most of Europe. **Active ingredients** in the fruit sugar, pectin, colouring substances; in the leaves adenine, asparic acid, silicic acid, phytosterine. **Effect** mildly purgative (fruits), astringent, reducing blood sugar (leaves). **Parts used** the mature fruit and the dried leaves; collect from early to mid summer, dry in the sun or in a warm place. **Application M:** the mature fruits are turned into a syrup which acts as a mild laxative (agreeable to small children) or is used to improve both flavour and colour of other liquid medicines. In homoeopathy the leaves are used in the treatment of diabetes. **E:** the fruits have a fine sweetish-sour aromatic taste and can be eaten raw. Unfortunately they deteriorate quickly and cannot be kept. Mixed with other fruits they can be used for jams or as a filling for tarts and cakes.

Ⓜ **Betula pendula** Roth **B. verrucosa** Betulaceae
Ⓔ **Silver Birch** (April–June) A deciduous tree over 25m tall, with a silver-white, peeling bark, blackish and fissured towards base of the trunk, and more or less pendulous branches. The buds have several scales, not sticky. The leaves are alternate, simple, 2–5·5cm long, ovate to triangular from a broadly wedge-shaped or truncate base, acuminate, glabrous; the margins double-toothed; the petiole is up to 2cm long. The flowers are monoecious with the sexes in different inflorescences. The male flowers are arranged in 3–6cm drooping catkins; the female flowers in erect cylindrical or ovoid catkins up to 3·5cm long. The stamens number 2, bifid below the anther. The fruit is a flattened winged nutlet with persistent styles.

Habitat woods, heathland. **Distribution** throughout Britain and most of Europe. **Active ingredients** tannins, saponins, bitter principle, glycosides, traces of essential oil, flavonoids. **Effect** promotes slight sweating; possibly mildly diuretic. **Parts used** fresh or dried young leaves; dry in shade or in a warm place; the sap (collected when rising in spring). Birch tar, produced from the fresh wood, is used in unctions for eczema and other skin ailments. **Application M:** as an infusion (2–3 teaspoons per cup water, allow to stand for 10–12 minutes) 2–4 times a day for cystitis or other inflammations of the urinary tract, dropsy, rheumatic pain and arthritis; it is also used as a spring tonic.

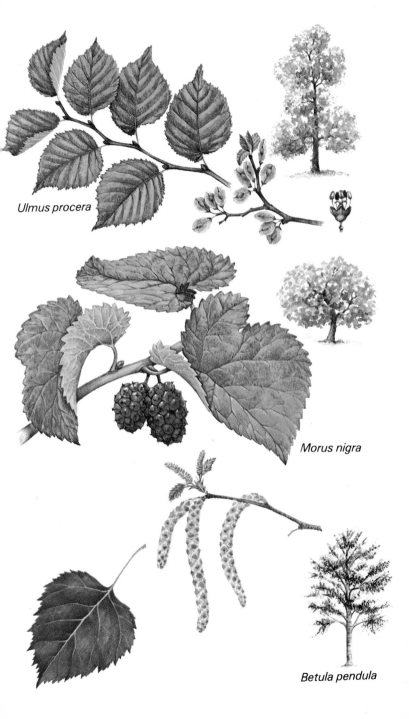

Ulmus procera

Morus nigra

Betula pendula

The sap is used for the preparation of hair tonics; it is also taken as spring tonic. **E:** the fresh sap is an excellent basis for a home-made wine, but excessive tapping of trees is liable to cause severe damage. **Note** the related Birch *Betula pubescens* has similar properties. It can be distinguished from the Silver Birch by the smooth bark and acute or nearly acute leaves with irregularly toothed margins.

Ⓜ️ *Alnus glutinosa* L. Gaertn. Betulaceae

Alder (April) A large deciduous tree, 20–40m tall, with a darkish-brown, fissured bark and glabrous twigs. The buds are purplish, stalked, somewhat sticky. The leaves are alternate, petiolate, 2·5–9·5cm long, almost circular or broad-ovate from a wedge-shaped base, obtuse, broadly notched or rounded, with 4–7 pairs of veins, bright green, with tufts of hairs beneath, sticky when young. The flowers appear before the leaves, arranged in cone-like catkins. The male catkins are arranged in groups of 3–6, up to 6cm long; the stamens number 4. The female catkins are 0·8–1cm in flower, and 0·8–2·8cm long in fruit, usually ovoid, with 5-lobed, thick woody scales. The fruit is winged.

Habitat wet ground in woods, near lakes and along streams. **Distribution** common throughout the region. **Active ingredients** tannins, resins, fatty oil, emodin, alnusen, alnusenon. **Effect** mainly astringent. **Parts used** the dried bark of young twigs, or inner bark of 2–3 year old branches; the dried buds (dry in sun or in a warm place). **Application M:** in both allopathy and homoeopathy a decoction (2–3 teaspoons per cup water, simmer for 3–4 minutes) is used as a gargle for tonsillitis or other throat infections or as a mouthwash for inflamed gums and mouth ulcers. An infusion (1–2 teaspoons per cup water) is given 2–3 times a day internally for rheumatic pain. In the past powdered bark has been mixed with other substances to make toothpaste and sticks of bark have been chewed for cleaning teeth. In the leather industry the bark is used as a tanning or colouring agent.

Ⓜ️ *Fagus sylvatica* L. Fagaceae

Ⓔ **Beech** (Sept.–Oct: fruits) A large deciduous tree, over 35m tall, with a smooth grey bark. The buds are spindle-shaped, pointed. The leaves are alternate, petiolate, 3·5–9cm long, ovate-elliptic from a rounded or wedge-shaped base, acute, with margins wavy and fringed with hairs, finely hairy beneath, with 5–9 pairs of veins. The male flowers are arranged in tassel-like heads, long-peduncled; the perianth is bell-shaped; the stamens number up to 16. The female flowers are in pairs, surrounded by a scaly cupola below. The fruit is composed of 1–2 brown, shiny nuts enclosed by the scaly green cupola.

Habitat mainly woods, often planted in parks and along roads. **Distribution** most of the British Isles but native only to S. E. and S. England and most of the rest of Europe. **Active ingredients** fatty oil, oxalic acid, a poisonous triterpene, saponin. **Effect** antiseptic (see below). **Parts used** the nuts; the fresh wood. **Application M:** the fresh wood is used in the pharmaceutical industry for the production of tar (creosote) which is used in medicinal soaps and unctions for infections of the skin. **E:** the nuts yield an excellent cooking and salad oil (peel or bruise, and press); the residue should not be eaten because it is *poisonous*.

Ⓜ️ *Castanea sativa* Mill. *C. vesca* Fagaceae

Ⓔ **Sweet Chestnut** A large deciduous tree, up to 30m tall, typically with a spirally-curved fissured bark. The leaves are alternate, large, up to 27cm long, oblong-lanceolate from a wedge-shaped or nearly heart-shaped base, acute or acuminate, with spine-tipped teeth, glabrous on the upper surface, pubescent on the lower surface, shortly petiolate. The flowers of both sexes are arranged in more or less erect, 10–21cm catkins; the female flowers are few, at the base; the male flowers are numerous, above. The stamens number 10–20, with yellowish-white anthers. The fruit is up to 3·5cm in diameter, shining brown, 1–3 enclosed by a prickly, 2–4 valved cupule.

Habitat parks, along roads. **Distribution** naturalized in Austria, S.W. Germany, France and S.E. England. **Active ingredients** Quercetin, tannin, resin. **Effect** expectorant. **Parts used** the dried leaves; dry in shade or in a warm room. **Application M:** in both allopathic and homoeopathic medicine this drug is obsolete. For domestic purposes it

Alnus glutinosa

Fagus sylvatica

Castanea sativa

is still recommended as an infusion (1½–2 teaspoons per cup water, allow to stand for 10–15 minutes), 2–3 times a day for persistent cough and whooping cough. **E:** the mature fruits are a valuable source of carbohydrate. They may be eaten as a purée (excellent with game or for stuffings) or roasted.

Ⓜ *Quercus robur* L. Fagaceae

Ⓔ **Common Oak**   A massive deciduous tree, with a fissured brown-grey bark and brown-grey glabrous twigs. The leaves are alternate, 4–11 cm long, shortly petiolate to almost sessile, obovate-oblong, from a rounded or heart-shaped base, usually glabrous, pinnately lobed. The flowers of each sex are in a different inflorescence. The male ones are in pendulous 2–4·2 cm catkins; the perianths are 4–7 lobed; the stamens number 6–8 (up to 12); the female flowers number 1–5, arranged in a spike. The fruit (acorn) is solitary, up to 4 cm long, oblong, surrounded at the base by a cupule which is covered with small overlapping scales.

Habitat woods, parks, hedgerows, often planted. **Distribution** most parts of the British Isles and all over the rest of Europe. **Active ingredients** abundant tannin, bitter principle. **Effect** strongly astringent, anti-inflammatory. **Parts used** the dried bark of 5–12 year old branches. **Application M:** a decoction (boil 2 tablespoons of shredded bark in ½ litre of water for 12–15 minutes) is used for bathing eczema, skin eruptions, sweaty feet, and piles, or is applied as a compress to inflamed eyes; also as a gargle or mouthwash for throat and mouth infections, or as a vaginal douche for genital inflammations and discharge. Internally this drug is mainly used in some proprietary medicines for diarrhoea, flatulence and dyspepsia. In homoeopathy an essence is made from fresh bark for disorders of the spleen and gall bladder; it is also reputed to put alcoholics off their drink. **E:** mature acorns are used as coffee-substitute. Peel, roast and grind to powder; use on its own or mixed with real coffee.

Ⓜ *Quercus petraea* (Matt) Liebl. Fagaceae

Ⓔ **Durmast Oak, Sessile Oak**   Related to *Q. robur* but the leaves are always distinctly petiolate, the petiole over 1 cm long, covered with stellate hairs along either side of the midrib beneath, the leaves without small basal lobes.

Habitat mainly woods. **Distribution, active ingredients, effect, and application** as for *Q. robur.*

Ⓜ *Corylus avellana* L. Corylaceae

Ⓔ **Cobnut, Hazelnut** (May–July)   A large shrub (rarely grown as a small tree), with a smooth reddish-brown peeling bark. The twigs are densely covered with reddish glandular hairs. The leaves are alternate, simple, petiolate, 0·4–1·1 cm long, almost circular from a heart-shaped base, with a rigid point, shallowly lobed or double-toothed, pubescent to glabrous. The flowers of each sex are in different inflorescences: the male flowers in 1–4 pendulous catkins up to 6·5 cm long with 4 stamens; the female flowers few, arranged in erect short spikes up to 6 mm long, with red styles. The fruit is a nut, globose or ovoid, up to 2 cm wide, surrounded by a lobed green involucre.

Habitat scrub, hedges, woods. **Distribution** common throughout the region. **Active ingredients** essential oil, myricitroside, palmitic acid. **Effect** stimulating circulation and bile production. **Parts used** the dried or fresh leaves; very rarely the bark as a substitute for *Hamamelis*. **Application** in allopathy the drug is only used as a constituent in a few patent medicines for liver and gall disorders. In the home an infusion (2 teaspoons per cup water) is taken 3–4 times a day for diarrhoea. **E:** the nut is very tasty and rich in fatty oil and vitamins. It yields a valuable salad and cooking oil which is also widely used in perfumery and oil painting.

Quercus robur   *Quercus petraea*

Corylus avellana

Ⓜ *Populus nigra* L. Salicaceae

Black Poplar (April–May) A large suckering deciduous tree, rarely over 30m tall with an almost black, fissured bark, the trunk and older branches with large swollen bosses. The leaves are alternate, 4–10cm long, triangular-ovate from a wedge-shaped or truncate base, crenate to toothed, the petiole is up to 6cm long, without apical glands. The flowers have a cup-like disk, appearing before the leaves, all arranged in pendulous catkins; the male catkins are 2·5–6cm long, the stamens number 8–20; the female catkins are 5–7·5cm long, up to 15·5cm in fruit; the seeds have long silky hairs.

Habitat moist ground in woods and along streams. **Distribution** throughout most of the British Isles but perhaps only native in E. England; naturalized over most of the rest of Europe. **Active ingredients** the glycosides populin and salicin, essential oil, tannin. **Effect** anti-inflammatory, diuretic, anti-irritant, antirheumatic; alleviates fever. **Parts used** mainly the fresh or dried leaf buds; collect in spring, dry in sun or moderate heat. **Application M:** the drug used in a few proprietary medicines for piles, chilblains, skin infections, suppurating cuts, and rheumatic conditions. In the home an infusion (2–3 teaspoons per cup water, allow to stand for 8 minutes) can be taken 2–3 times a day (as hot as possible to induce perspiration) for bronchitis, pneumonia, arthritis and rheumatism. A decoction (3 tablespoons per 500ml water, boil for 5–8 minutes) is applied externally for piles.

Ⓜ *Populus tremula* L. Salicaceae

Aspen Related to *P. nigra* but with smooth bark, obtuse, almost circular leaves and catkin scales fringed with hairs.

Habitat woods. **Distribution** throughout the region. **Active ingredients** tremulacin, salicyltremuloidin, salicin. **Effect** mildly diuretic; reducing puric acid in the blood. **Parts used** the bark; the fresh or dried leaves. **Application M:** this drug is only used in a few proprietary medicines for chronic prostate and bladder disorders.

Ⓜ *Salix alba* L. Salicaceae

White Willow (April–May) A deciduous tree, up to 26m tall, with ascending branches and a deeply fissured grey bark. The leaves are alternate, shortly petiolate, up to 11cm long, lanceolate from a wedge-shaped base, with silky whitish appressed hairs on both sides. The flowers appear with the leaves, arranged in dense cylindrical catkins; the male ones are up to 5cm long with 2 stamens, anthers yellow; the female ones are up to 4cm; 6·5cm in fruit. The fruit is a capsule.

Habitat marshes, moist grassland, and woods, commonly along streams and rivers. **Distribution** throughout the British Isles (frequently planted) and all over the rest of Europe. **Active ingredients** the glycoside salicin, tannin, resin. **Effect** anti-rheumatic, anti-neuralgic, astringent; alleviates fever. **Parts used** the dried bark from 3–6 year old branches (dry in the sun or warm place). **Application M:** since the main active ingredient (salicin, used in aspirin) can now be produced synthetically this drug is obsolete. In the home a decoction (1–1½ teaspoons per cup water, boil ½–1 minute, allow to stand for 12–15 minutes) is taken 2–3 times a day for the common cold and other feverish conditions, neuralgia, headache, arthritis, rheumatic pain and cystitis. Externally the decoction is applied to slow-healing cuts, ulcers and burns. In homoeopathy an essence is prepared from fresh bark for the same ailments. **Note** the Crack Willow *S. fragilis* and the Purple Willow *S. purpurea* are used for medicinal purposes in the same way.

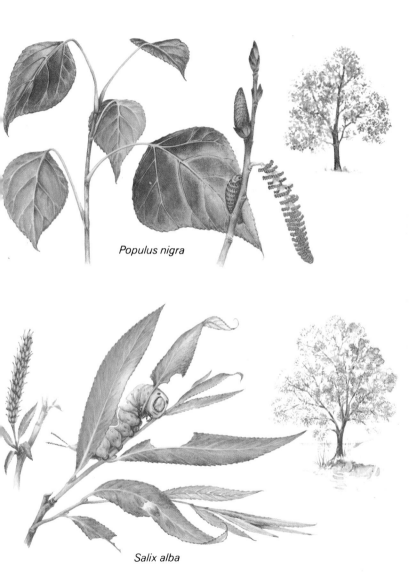

Populus nigra

Salix alba

Ⓜ *Ledum palustre* L. Ericaceae

Labrador Tea (June–Aug.) An evergreen shrub, 40–110cm tall, with red-brown tomentose twigs. The leaves are alternate, entire, shortly petiolate, up to 3·7cm long, linear to linear-oblong, dark green on the upper surface, red-brown tomentose on the lower surface, margins rolled inwards. The flowers are 1·2–1·6cm in diameter, arranged in umbel-like terminal racemes. The calyx has 5 short lobes. The petals number 5, free, elliptic, cream-coloured. The stamens usually number 10; the anthers open by pores. The fruit is an oblong capsule, 4–5mm long.

Habitat bogs and moors. **Distribution** rare in the British Isles; scattered in N. and C. Europe. **Active ingredients** essential oil with ledum-camphor, arbutin, flavone-glycoside, tannin, pectin, citric acid. **Effect** mildly expectorant, relieves spasms; stimulates sweating and menstrual flow. **Parts used** the dried flowering herb or the young shoots. **Application M:** in allopathic preparations for bronchitis, catarrh, pneumonia, pleurisy. In homoeopathy a tincture is made from young shoots for the same disorders as well as for asthma, whooping cough, menstrual pain and certain skin ailments. The use of this herb for domestic purposes is not advisable.

Ⓜ *Rhododendron ferrugineum* L. Ericaceae

An evergreen shrub, 30–80cm (up to 120cm) tall, with erect branches; the young twigs are covered with rust-brown scurfy scales. The leaves are alternate, shortly petiolate, 2–4cm long, elliptic-oblong, entire, shiny green on the upper surface, densely covered with rust-brown scales on the lower surface, the margins rolled back. The flowers are arranged in short 5–10 flowered terminal racemes. The calyx is 1–1·5mm long, 5-lobed. The corolla is 1·3–1·6cm long, bell-shaped to funnel-shaped, pink-red, deeply 5-lobed, scaly on the outside. The stamens number 10. The fruit is a many-seeded 7-sided capsule.

Habitat scrub and open woods in mountain areas; acid soils. **Distribution** the Alps and Pyrenees. **Active ingredients** essential oil, arbutin, andromedotoxin, tannin. **Effect** diuretic, anti-rheumatic, stimulates sweating. **Parts used** the dried leaves. **Application M:** used in a few proprietary medicines for certain forms of arthritis and rheumatic pain, but since it may cause diarrhoea and vomiting it should *only be used under medical supervision.* **Note** the widely naturalized *Rhododendron ponticum* is used in the preparation of medicine for malfunction of the heart and circulation but it cannot be used for domestic purposes.

Ⓜ *Arctostaphylos uva-ursi* (L.) Spreng. Ericaceae

Bearberry (June–Aug.) An evergreen prostrate shrub, rooting with the branches, mat-forming. The leaves are alternate, entire, 1·2–2·2cm long, obovate to obovate-elliptic from a wedge-shaped base, dark green on the upper surface, pale green and distinctly nerved on the lower surface. The flowers are arranged in short, dense, 5–12 flowered racemes with pedicels up to 5mm long. The calyx is 5-lobed. The corolla is more or less globular, 4·5–6·5mm in diameter, white suffused pink. The fruit is a drupe, globose, 7–8·5mm in diameter, shining red, rather dry.

Habitat on or between rocks, banks on moors, mountain forests, heaths. **Distribution** throughout most of Europe and common in N. Britain. **Active ingredients** tannin (abundant), arbutin, methylarbutin, essential oil, organic acids. **Effects** diuretic (possibly), antiseptic (to the urinary tract). **Parts used** the dried or fresh leaves, best dried in the sun. **Application M:** the drug is in several proprietary medicines for disorders of the urinary tract. A decoction (2 teaspoons per cup water; put into cold water and boil for 15 minutes), is sometimes taken twice a day for cystitis and pyelitis. *This remedy should only be applied under medical supervision and over short periods,* otherwise it may cause vomiting, nausea or even poisoning.

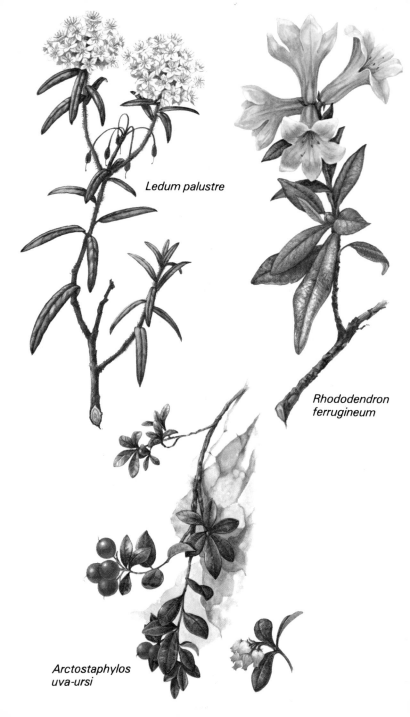

Ledum palustre

Rhododendron ferrugineum

Arctostaphylos uva-ursi

Ⓜ *Calluna vulgaris* (L.) Hull Ericaceae

Ling, Heather (July–Sept.) A small evergreen shrub, 20–65cm high, with numerous stems rooting at the nodes and ascending at the tips. The leaves are opposite, rather small, up to 2·2mm long, linear, with 2 short basal extensions, not petiolate, the margins are rolled inwards; the leaves are on short shoots densely arranged in 4 rows. The flowers are solitary, axillary, with a calyx-like involucre, arranged in a loose terminal raceme-like inflorescence. The calyx is deeply 4-lobed, light purple, 3·5–4·5mm long. The corolla is smaller than the calyx, bell-shaped. The stamens number 8; the anthers open by pores. The fruit is a few-seeded capsule, globular, 2–2·5mm in diameter, splitting lengthwise.

Habitat heaths, moors, bogs, open woods; always on acid soil. **Distribution** throughout the region. **Active ingredients** a glycoside, tannin, organic acids, resin. **Effect** diuretic, mildly sedative; promotes sweating and glandular secretion. **Parts used** the flowering dried branches or dried flowers only. **Application M:** in homoeopathy an essence is prepared from the fresh branches for arthritis, rheumatism and insomnia. In the home an infusion (2–3 teaspoons per cup water, allow to stand for 10 minutes) is given 3–4 times a day for cough, colds, diarrhoea, disorders of the bladder and kidneys, rheumatic pain and nervous exhaustion.

Ⓜ *Vaccinium myrtillus* L. Ericaceae

Ⓔ **Bilberry, Huckleberry, Whortleberry** (June–July: leaves) A deciduous shrub, 20–60cm high, with a creeping rhizome, numerous branched erect stems, and green angular twigs. The leaves are alternate, shortly petiolate, 0·8–3·5cm long, ovate, acute, finely toothed, light green, with distinct criss-cross venation. The flowers are 1–2, axillary. The corolla is pitcher-shaped, up to 6mm in diameter, greenish-pink, with very short, turned-back lobes. The anthers are awned, opening by pores. The fruit is a berry, 6–8mm in diameter, globose, black, pruinose.

Habitat heaths, moors, woods; on acid soil. **Distribution** throughout the region. **Active ingredients** tannin, mytillin, pectin, arbutin, Vitamins B and C. **Effect** astringent, diuretic; reducing level of blood sugar (leaves only). **Parts used** mainly the mature dried or fresh fruits; more rarely the dried leaves; both are best dried in shade. **Application M:** 2 tablespoons of dried berries are taken once a day for enteritis; the same amount can be taken fresh for constipation. As a decoction (3 tablespoons dried berries to 500ml water, boil for 8–10 minutes) take 1 cup 3 times daily against diarrhoea or use as a hot mouthwash for gingivitis or a gargle for inflammation of the throat. A decoction based on leaves is sometimes used but can lead to harmful side-effects (hydroquinone poisoning) when used excessively or for long periods. **E:** the fresh fruits are sweet and very tasty. The freshly pressed juice is refreshing and a valuable source of vitamins B and C. The berries can be used in the home for soups, pies, preserves, jams, wine, etc.

Ⓜ *Vaccinium vitis-idaea* L. Ericaceae

Ⓔ **Cowberry, Red Whortleberry** (Sept: leaves) Similar to *V. myrtillus* but having evergreen, persistent, glossy, leathery leaves and flowers arranged in short drooping racemes; corolla bell-shaped, white tinged with pink; fruit is larger, 0·8–1·1cm in diameter, red and acid.

Habitat moors and woods, on acid soils. **Distribution** N. Europe, mountains of C. Europe; N. and W. Britain. **Active ingredients** arbutin, tannin, vitamin C, a flavone-glycoside. **Effect** similar to *Arctostaphylos*. **Parts used** the dried leaves (collect in the autumn; dry at room temperature) and the mature berries. **Application M:** as a decoction (1–2 teaspoons per cup, boil for 12–20 minutes) twice a day for arthritis, rheumatic conditions, diabetes and diarrhoea. Because of its arbutin content this otherwise harmless tea should not be drunk regularly. The raw mature berries, fresh or dried, are eaten unsweetened as a remedy for diarrhoea. **E:** the fruits are used extensively for culinary purposes.

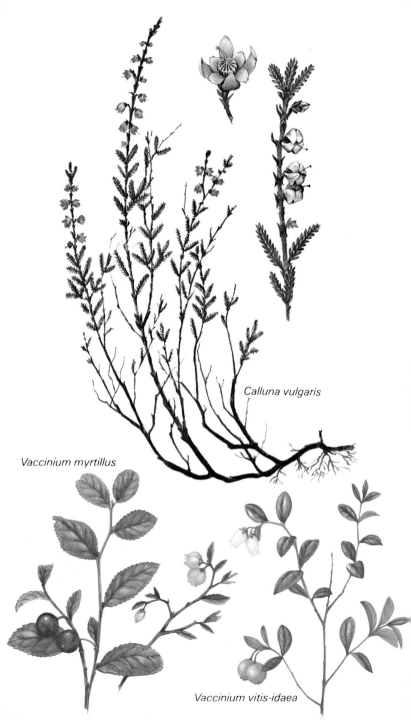

Calluna vulgaris

Vaccinium myrtillus

Vaccinium vitis-idaea

Ⓜ *Pyrola rotundifolia* L. Pyrolaceae

Larger Wintergreen (July–Sept.) An evergreen plant with a creeping branching rhizome. The stem is 15–25cm (up to 35cm) tall. The basal leaves are crowded into a rosette, 1·8–5·5cm long, circular to ovate, crenulate, dark green, glossy; the petiole is usually longer than the blade; the stem leaves are reduced to oblong-lanceolate scales. The flowers are 0·8–1·2cm in diameter, bell-shaped, arranged in a lax terminal raceme. The calyx has 2–4·5mm acuminate lobes. The petals are pure white. The anthers open by pores at the end of short tubes. The fruit is a capsule and opens by valves.

Habitat fens, bogs, amongst damp rocks and in shady woods. **Distribution** throughout the region but scattered in England and Scotland. **Active ingredients** arbutin, homoarbutin, gallic acid, sugar. **Effect** diuretic, disinfectant. **Parts used** the fresh or dried leaves. Application as for *Chimaphila umbellata*.

Ⓜ *Chimaphila umbellata* (L.) W. Barton Pyrolaceae

Spotted Wintergreen (June–Aug.) An evergreen dwarf shrub, 10–30cm tall, with a creeping whitish rhizome. The leaves are usually alternate, 3·5–7cm long, oblanceolate to linear, toothed, leathery; the petiole is up to 5mm long. The flowers are 0·7–1·2cm in diameter, nodding, arranged in terminal umbel-like corymbs. The calyx has 5 ovate, obtuse 1·5–2·5mm lobes. The petals number 5, ovate-circular, pinkish. The anthers have short tubes and open by pores. The fruit is a capsule, splitting lengthwise.

Habitat dry, mainly coniferous, woods. **Distribution** N. and C. Europe; not Britain. **Active ingredients** arbutin, ericolin, chimaphilin (glycosides), urson, tannin. **Effect** diuretic and disinfectant. **Parts used** the fresh or dried leaves of the flowering herb. **Application M:** an infusion (1 teaspoon per cup, allow to stand for 5 minutes) is taken 3–4 times a day for dropsy, cystitis and less effectively for rheumatic pain and diabetes; the bruised fresh leaves are applied to wounds in folk medicine. In homoeopathy an essence is prescribed for inflammations of the urinary system. The plant is also used by the food and cosmetic industries for its delicate scent and flavour.

Ⓜ *Primula veris* L. Primulaceae

Cowslip, Paigle (March-May or Oct: rhizome; March-May: flowers) A more or less densely pubescent perennial herb with a short stout rhizome. The leaves are 5–21cm long, ovate-oblong from a contracted base, obtuse, crenulate or toothed; the petiole is long and winged. The flowers are nodding, regular, 0·9–1·6cm in diameter, arranged umbel-like on a distinct scape up to 30cm long. The calyx is up to 1·6cm long, 5-toothed. The corolla is deep yellow or buff with orange markings at the base of the lobes; the tube is up to 1·6cm long; the mouth has folds; the lobes number 5, notched. The fruit is a dehiscent capsule, ovoid, 0·8–1·1cm in diameter, contained within the calyx.

Habitat grassy places; mainly on calcareous soil. **Distribution** throughout the region. **Active ingredients** saponins, traces of essential oils, volemite. **Effect** expectorant, diuretic. **Parts used** mainly the dried rhizome; dig up, wash, cut and dry in sun or at room temperature; also the dried flowers (calyx or corolla only): dry in shade, store in the dark. **Application M:** the drug is used in various proprietary medicines for bronchitis, coughs, chills, influenza and other febrile conditions. In homoeopathy an essence from the entire fresh herb is made for kidney complaints and catarrh. In the home a sweetened infusion (1½–2 teaspoons of shredded rhizome or 2–3 teaspoons of flowers or a mixture of both per cup, bring just to the boil and allow to stand for 8–12 minutes) can be taken 2–3 times a day for bronchitis, headache and cough. **Note** the rhizome and roots (not the flowers) of Oxlip *P. elatior* are similarly effective.

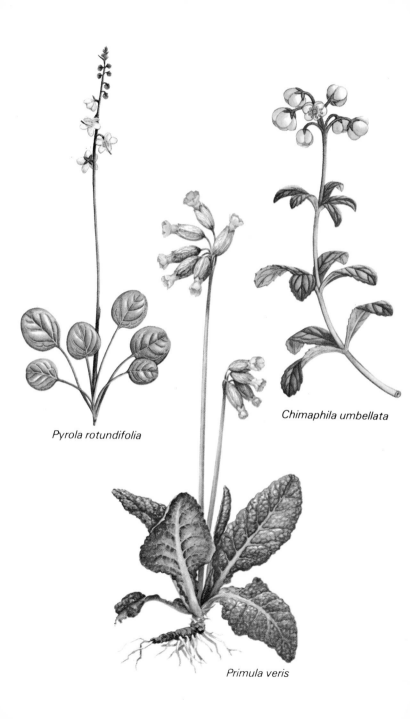

Pyrola rotundifolia

Chimaphila umbellata

Primula veris

Ⓜ *Lysimachia nummularia* L. Primulaceae

Creeping Jenny (June–July) A creeping perennial herb with branching shoots up to 70cm long. The leaves are entire, opposite, shortly petiolate, circular to broadly ovate from a rounded or truncate base, obtuse, dotted with glands. The flowers are regular 1·6–2·7cm in diameter, solitary, axillary; the pedicels are shorter than the leaves, stout. The calyx has 5 ovate acuminate teeth. The corolla is yellow, almost bell-shaped, with gland-dotted and finely fringed lobes. The stamens are not protruding. The fruit is a 5-valved, almost globose capsule.

Habitat moist soil in grassy places. **Distribution** scattered throughout the British Isles (rare in the north) and the rest of Europe. **Active ingredients** tannins, saponin, silicic acid. **Effect** mildly astringent, diuretic. **Parts used** the fresh or dried herb without the roots. **Application M:** the bruised fresh herb is applied externally to slow-healing cuts, for muscular pain and rheumatic conditions of the joints. An infusion (1–1½ teaspoons per cup water, allow to stand for 5–10 minutes) is taken 3–4 times a day for diarrhoea and internal haemorrhages.

Ⓜ *Anagallis arvensis* L. Primulaceae

Scarlet Pimpernel, Shepherd's Weather-glass (June–Oct.) A small annual or perennial herb with trailing or ascending, 5–45cm (up to 65cm), 4-angled stems. The leaves are opposite, 10–35cm long, sessile, ovate to lanceolate, acute, with tiny black glands on the lower surface. The flowers are regular, axillary, solitary. There are 5 calyx teeth, narrowly lanceolate, pointed. The corolla is 1–1·4cm in diameter, 5-lobed, wheel-like, lobes entire, crenulate or finely toothed. The stamens number 5, inserted at the base of the corolla tube. The fruit is a globose, 4–5·5mm wide, transversely dehiscent capsule.

Habitat cultivated land, waste places, roadsides, dunes. **Distribution** throughout the region. **Active ingredients** saponins, essential oil. **Effect** diuretic; stimulates bile flow. **Parts used** the entire dried or fresh flowering herb. **Application M:** although this drug was frequently used in the past it is now completely obsolete in allopathic medicine. In homoeopathy an essence prepared from fresh material is given for itching skin eruptions (internally) or for the removal of warts (externally). In the home an infusion (½ teaspoon per cup water, allow to stand for 5–10 minutes) is taken sip by sip over the whole day for dropsy, skin infections and disorders of the liver and gall bladder.

Ⓜ *Fraxinus excelsior* L. Oleaceae

Ash (May–June: leaves) A deciduous tree, 15–25m tall with grey bark, smooth but becoming fissured with age. The buds are black. The leaves are opposite, usually pinnate, 12–30cm long; the leaflets number 7–13, lanceolate to ovate, pointed, toothed, 4–7cm long. The flowers are polygamous, regular, arranged in axillary panicles, appearing before the leaves, without perianth, purplish. The stamens number 2. The fruit is a samara, winged at the apex, 2·5–3·2cm long, light brown.

Habitat woods, hedges, scrub; usually on calcareous soil. **Distribution** throughout the region. **Active ingredients** tannin, essential oil, the glycoside fraxin, mannite, mucilage, Vitamin C. **Effect** mildly diuretic, mildly purgative. **Parts used** the dried leaves, without the petiole and rachis; the bark, peeled off in spring and dried carefully in a warm place. **Application M:** an infusion (1 teaspoon per cup water, allow to stand for 5 minutes) can be taken 3–4 times a day for constipation, dropsy, arthritis, rheumatic pain, cystitis. A decoction (1 teaspoon of bark per cup water, just bring to the boil, allow to stand for 8 minutes) is taken internally for feverish conditions and externally in compresses applied to suppurating cuts and sores. The drug is also used in some proprietary medicines for intractable constipation and in the treatment of rheumatic conditions.

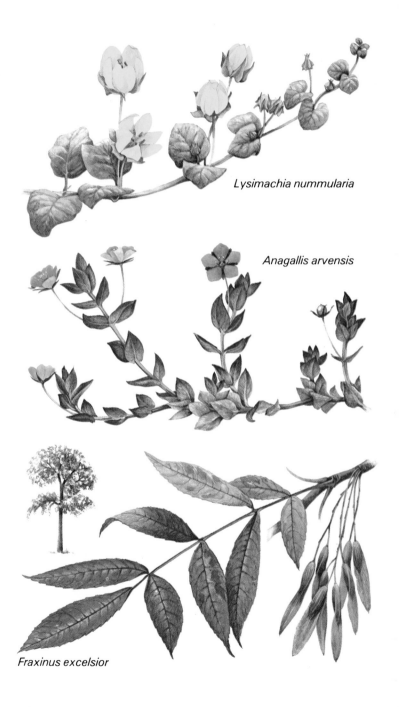

Lysimachia nummularia

Anagallis arvensis

Fraxinus excelsior

Ⓜ *Vinca minor* L. Apocynaceae

Lesser Periwinkle A small shrub with ascending stems, rooting, 25–65cm long, and giving rise to erect flowering shoots. The leaves are opposite, shortly petiolate, 2–4cm long, lanceolate-elliptic, glabrous. The flowers are regular, hermaphrodite, solitary, axillary, up to 3·2cm in diameter. The calyx has 5 lanceolate lobes. The corolla is bluish-purple, mauve or white, with a conical tube and 5 asymmetrical lobes. The stamens number 5. The styles are united to form a column. The fruit consists of divergent follicles (rarely maturing in Britain).

   Habitat woods, copses, hedge banks, parks. **Distribution** throughout the region. **Active ingredients** the alkaloids vincamine, isovincamine and vincamidine, bitter principle vincine, tannin, pectin, carotine. **Effect** diuretic; stimulates the vessels. **Parts used** the dried flowering herb. **Application M:** this drug is rarely used on its own but is used in some proprietary medicines for a variety of cerebral conditions. Although *Vinca* has been used as infusion for catarrh, dyspepsia and other stomach disorders its application in the home without medical supervision is *not recommended*.

Ⓜ *Centaurium erythraea* Rafn. *(C. umbellatum)* Gentianaceae

Common Centaury (July–Sept.) A delicate, usually single-stemmed annual herb, 24–35cm (up to 50cm) tall. The basal leaves are in a rosette, 1–5cm long, obovate to elliptic or paddle-shaped, obtuse; the stem leaves are shorter and narrower. The flowers are regular, hermaphrodite, arranged in a terminal dense corymb-like cyme. The corolla-tube is longer than the calyx; the lobes number 5, flat, 5–6mm long. The stamens number 5, twisted after splitting. The fruit is a capsule, longer than the calyx.

   Habitat grassland, margins of woods, dunes. **Distribution** throughout the region. **Active ingredients** centiopicrin, erythrocentaurine, traces of essential oil, resin, nicotinic acid. **Effect** as for *Gentiana lutea*. **Parts used** the dried flowering herb; dry quickly in shade or in a warm room (hang in fresh air). **Application M:** mainly to combat lack of appetite, anorexia and digestive disorders. An infusion (1–1½ teaspoons per cup water, allow to stand for 20 minutes) is taken before meals for arthritis and anaemia. In homoeopathy an essence prepared from the fresh herb is given for liver and gall bladder ailments.

Ⓜ *Gentiana lutea* L. Gentianaceae

Yellow Gentian (Sept.–Oct.) A robust long-living (up to over 50 years) perennial with a very strong tap root and 45–120cm tall, erect, unbranched stem. The basal leaves grow in a dense rosette, broadly ovate, elliptical or lanceolate, bluish-green, with 5–7 longitudinal veins; the stem leaves are opposite, sessile, small, but gradually becoming smaller. The flowers are arranged in terminal and axillary dense cymes, pedicelled. The calyx is herbaceous, pale yellow. The corolla-lobes number 5–6 (rarely up to 9), golden yellow, much longer than the tube. The anthers are almost as long as the corolla. The fruit is a many-seeded conical capsule.

   Habitat alpine meadows and pastures, usually on calcareous soil. **Distribution** mountains of C. and S. Europe; in the British Isles only grown for ornamental purposes. **Active ingredients** the bitter principles gentiopicrine and amarogentine, pectin, tannin, mucilage, sugar. **Effect** stimulates secretion of gastric juices; mildly increases blood pressure. **Parts used** the dried tap-root; wash, dry in the sun or a moderate heat. **Application M:** the drug is given as a maceration (put ½ teaspoon of finely shredded root into 2 cups of cold water, allow to stand for 8–12 hours, warm slightly) taken 30 minutes before meals, for lack of appetite; also given for dyspepsia and chronic gastritis, diarrhoea and heartburn. On the Continent the rhizome is used for the production of gentian brandy (Enzian schnaps) and bitter liquors which both are used as appetizers and also taken with heavy or fatty meals to aid digestion.

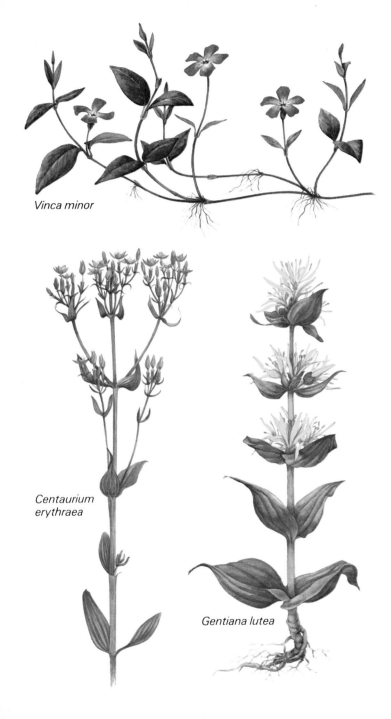

Vinca minor

Centaurium erythraea

Gentiana lutea

Ⓜ *Menyanthes trifoliata* L. Menyanthaceae

Buckbean, Bogbean (May–June) Aquatic perennial with a creeping rhizome. The leaves are alternate, raised above the water surface, ternate, the leaflets are 3–7·5cm long, ovate or elliptic, undivided, obtuse or subacute; the petiole is up to 22cm long, sheathing at the base. The flowers are arranged in a 10 to 20 flowered raceme on an up to 32cm tall leafless scape. The calyx lobes number 5, somewhat reflexed. The corolla is 5-lobed, 1·2–1·6cm in diameter, white usually pink outside, margin fringed. The fruit is a 2–valved, almost globular capsule.

Habitat fens, bogs, edges of ponds and lakes. **Distribution** throughout the region. **Active ingredients** menyanthine, bitter principles, tannin, alkaloids, saponin, pectin, traces of essential oil. **Effect** choleric, digestive, alleviates fever. **Parts used** the dried leaves, more rarely the entire flowering plant, dry as quickly as possible, do not press, keep in baskets. Application **M:** like *Gentiana* and *Centaurium* this drug stimulates secretion of stomach juices and is therefore given as a decoction (1 teaspoon per cup, boil for a moment, allow to stand for 10–15 minutes) before meals for anorexia, sluggish digestion, and dyspepsia; also for liver and gall disorders and chronic skin ailments.

Ⓜ *Cynoglossum officinale* L. Boraginaceae

Hound's tongue (herb: May–June; roots: April–Oct.) A biennial with stems that are usually erect, greyish-hairy, 25–65cm (up to 90cm) tall. The basal leaves are between 8–30cm long, lanceolate to ovate, petiolate, the stem leaves are alternate, shorter than the upper ones, sessile to clasping, oblong to lanceolate, softly hairy on both surfaces. The flowers are regular to slightly bilaterally symmetrical, arranged usually in cymes without bracts. The calyx is deeply 5-lobed, hairy; the lobes are 2·5–4mm long, ovate. The corolla is 4·5–6mm long, with a short cylindrical tube and a short 5-lobed limb, dull purple; the throat is closed by 5 scales. The fruit consists of ovoid, 5–8mm wide, bordered nutlets.

Habitat grassy dry localities; edges of and openings in woods, often near the sea. Distribution scattered throughout the British Isles; all over Europe. **Active ingredients** choline, essential oil, abundant mucilage, heliosupine, cynoglossine, consolidine, tannin, bitter principle. **Effect** astringent, antidiarrhoeal; also analgesic, wound-healing, stimulates gland secretion, mildly relieves spasms. **Parts used** the dried flowering plant or the dried or fresh root; dry in the shade or in a warm room. Application **M:** in the home a decoction (2–3 tablespoons per ½ litre of water, boil for 10 minutes) or an infusion (3 teaspoons per cup water, allow to stand for 15 minutes) is used either for compresses or for bathing slow-healing cuts, eczema or suppurating ulcers. Internally this drug should **not** be used in the home.

Ⓜ *Symphytum officinale* L. Boraginaceae
Ⓔ

Comfrey (April or Sept.– Oct.) An erect hairy perennial herb, 25–120cm tall, with a fleshy, branched, root stock. The leaves with their petiole-bases are broadly decurrent, 12–25cm long, ovate-lanceolate, to oblong-lanceolate. The flowers are nodding, regular, arranged in terminal branched, coiled cymes. The calyx is up to 8mm long, 5-lobed; the teeth are much longer than the tube. The corolla is 1·5–1·8cm long, funnel-shaped, whitish, yellowish-white, pink to purplish, 5-lobed, with 5 scales within the throat. The stamens are included. The fruit consists of glossy black nutlets.

Habitat damp localities, along ditches, rivers, streams, waste places in moist ground, roadsides, edges of woods and copses. **Distribution** throughout the region. **Active ingredients** a glycoside, allantoin, tannin, abundant mucilage, inulin, traces of essential oil. **Effect** anti-inflammatory, healing (cuts and grazes), anti-irritant, mildly purgative. **Parts used** the dried roots, dug up, cut lengthwise and dried in the sun or moderate heat (50°C). Application **M:** in allopathic medicine this herb is rarely used on its own but contained in numerous brands of proprietary medicine for phlebitis, eczema, mastitis, osteitis, haematoma, tendovaginitis, as an aid in the treatment of gastritis. In homoeopathy an essence from the fresh herb and root is prescribed for stomach and duodenal ulcers. In the home a compress (make a decoction from 3

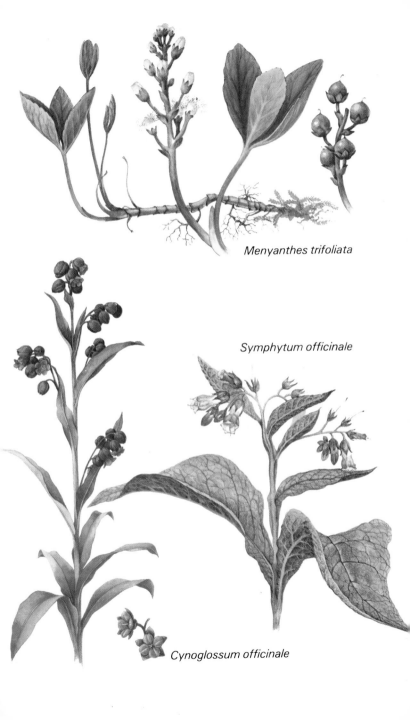

Menyanthes trifoliata

Symphytum officinale

Cynoglossum officinale

tablespoons shredded root per ½ litre water, boil for 5–8 minutes, allow to stand for 15 minutes) 2–4 times a day is applied for eczema, bruises and slow-healing wounds. Alternatively prepare a paste from the peeled fresh root and apply to affected parts of the skin for up to 60 minutes. An infusion of 2 teaspoons per cup water or a suspension of 1½–2 teaspoons in 1 cup of cold water can be taken as a purgative. **E:** the young shoots can be treated and eaten like asparagus or mixed in salads. Young leaves make an excellent vegetable or can be added to soups and stews.

Ⓜ *Borago officinalis* L. Boraginaceae
Ⓔ **Borage** (May–Sept.) A stout erect, 25–60cm tall, stiffly hairy annual herb. The leaves are up to 21cm long, ovate-elliptic, obtuse to acute, the basal ones petiolate, the upper ones sessile and clasping. The flowers are regular, arranged in loose bracteate cymes; the pedicels are up to 3cm long. The calyx is 5-lobed almost to the base, 0·7–1·4cm (up to 2cm in fruit) long, terminal. The corolla is short-lived, light blue or rarely white, 5-lobed, with a very short tube; the lobes are lanceolate, acute, 0·7–1·6cm long. The stamens are exserted. The fruit consists of ovoid, up to 1cm long nutlets.

Habitat waste ground, usually near human habitation, or in arable fields. **Distribution** C. Europe; in the British Isles only as a garden escape. **Active ingredients** mucilage, resin, saponin, tannin, traces of essential oil. **Effect** mildly diuretic, mild purifying agent and sweat inducement. **Parts used** the flowers or the entire flowering plant; dry quickly in the sun or, better, in moderate heat (not over 40°C). **Application M:** an infusion (2 teaspoons per cup water, allow to stand for 10 minutes) is taken 3–4 times a day for rheumatic conditions, pleurisy and affections of the mucous membranes. Old recipes recommend a concoction of flowers soaked in wine and drunk for melancholy and depression. **E:** young fresh leaves make a fine addition to salads and lend them a pleasant cucumber-like flavour. They can also be treated like spinach. The flower corolla can be used to colour vinegar blue.

Ⓜ *Anchusa officinalis* L. Boraginaceae
Ⓔ **Alkanet** (May–Sept.) A perennial with stems that are usually erect, stiffly hairy, 15–90cm (170cm) tall. The leaves are 4·5–12cm long, alternate, lanceolate to linear, usually ovate; the lower ones are petiolate, the upper ones sessile, hairy on both surfaces. The flowers are almost sessile, arranged in several dense axillary and terminal cymes. The calyx is 4–7mm (in fruit 1cm) long, deeply 5-lobed. The corolla is up to 1·5cm in diameter, usually violet or reddish, rarely white or yellow, 5-lobed; the tube up to 8mm long, as long or longer than the calyx; the throat is closed by scales. The fruit consists of obliquely ovoid, 1·5–2mm long nutlets.

Habitat roadsides, hedge banks, waste places, vineyards, pastures. **Distribution** E., W. and C. Europe; in Britain occasionally as an alien. **Active ingredients** the alkaloids cynoglossine and consolidine, tannin, mucilage, silicic acid. **Effect** expectorant, skin softener, purifying agent. **Parts used** the fresh or dried flowering herb; the root. **Application M:** in the past the plant was used externally in allopathic prescriptions for cuts, bruises, phlebitis. In homoeopathy an essence is still used for the same ailments as well as (internally) for the treatment of stomach and duodenal ulcers. In the home an infusion (2–3 teaspoons per cup water, allow to stand for 5 minutes) is given 3 times daily for bronchial catarrhs and coughs. **E:** young leaves and shoots (before flowering) are prepared and eaten like spinach.

Ⓜ *Pulmonaria officinalis* L. Boraginaceae
Ⓔ **Lungwort** (June–July) A perennial herb, with a creeping rhizome. The stem is simple, erect or ascending, 8–32cm tall. The basal leaves are ovate from a heart-shaped base (abruptly constricted into a winged petiole), 7–11cm long, usually with white spots; the stem leaves are sessile and clasping, ovate. The flowers are arranged in terminal short cymes. The calyx is 5 angled at the base, 5-lobed, 6–7mm long. The corolla is 8–10mm in diameter, at first pink then turning blue, 5-lobed; the throat is closed by scales or hairs. The fruit consists of ovoid, acute, up to 4mm long nutlets.

Habitat hedge banks, woods, railway cuttings and similar localities. **Distribution** most of Europe except the north. In the British Isles naturalized in many localities.

Borago officinalis

Pulmonaria officinalis

Anchusa officinalis

Active ingredients silicic acid, mucilage, tannin, saponin. **Effect** mildly expectorant. **Parts used** the fresh flowering herb (cut shortly before use), the dried upper part of the herb (shortly after flowering) and the leaves; dry in thin layers in fresh air. **Application M:** in homoeopathy an essence is prescribed for bronchitis, coughs, diarrhoea. In the home an infusion (2–3 teaspoons per cup water, allow to stand for 8–10 minutes) is given 3 times a day. **E:** the young basal leaves (March/April) can be used for salads or added to soups, stews or used with other vegetables.

Ⓜ *Lithospermum officinale* L. Boraginaceae

Gromwell A rough perennial herb growing from a stout rhizome. The stems are erect, 20–100cm long, lanceolate to ovate-lanceolate. The leaves are sessile, with distinct lateral nerves, rough to the touch, pubescent. The flowers are regular, arranged in terminal and axillary leafy dense cymes. The calyx is almost lobed to the base, the 5 lobes are oblong-linear. The corolla is 3–6mm in diameter, yellowish or greenish-white, not much longer than the calyx, 5–10 lobed; the tube is cylindrical, with hairy folds and small scales in the throat. The fruit consists of 4 ovoid white glossary nutlets.

Habitat hedges, thickets, edges of woods. **Distribution** throughout the region (but rare in Scotland). **Active ingredients** silicic acids and calcium-compounds. **Effect** diuretic, labour-inducing. **Parts used** the mature nutlets, powderized. **Application M:** in folk medicine it is given (1 teaspoon suffused in 1 glass of white wine) for bladder stones; mixed with a little water it is taken for arthritis and febrile condition.

Ⓔ *Echium vulgare* L. Boraginaceae

Viper's Bugloss (May–Aug.) A coarsely hairy biennial with erect, 25–90cm tall stems. The basal leaves are petiolate, 6–15cm long, broadly lanceolate to oblong-lanceolate; the stem leaves are sessile, 5–12cm long, lanceolate or oblong from a rounded base, obtuse. The flowers are almost sessile, arranged in dense, short one-sided cymes which in turn are in a large terminal panicle. The calyx is deeply 5-lobed. The corolla has a funnel-shaped tube and 5 unequal lobes, at first pink-purple, later bright blue or rarely white, with an open throat. The stamens number 4, long exserted. The fruit consists of 4 angular, rugose nutlets.

Habitat in dry grassy places, also on sea cliffs and dunes. **Distribution** scattered throughout the British Isles but rare in Scotland; in Ireland mainly confined to the coast. All over the rest of Europe. **Parts used** young leaves and shoots before flowering. **Application E:** treated and eaten like spinach. **Note** in the past this plant was used for medicinal purposes and given for purification of the blood, epilepsy and snake-bites. In the Tyrol people are warned not to eat this plant because it stimulates sexual desire.

Ⓜ *Convolvulus arvensis* L. Convolvulaceae

Bindweed, Cornbine (June–Sept.) A climbing or scrambling perennial, growing from stout, twisted, deep growing (over 2m) rhizomes. The stems are 20–80cm long, climbing by twisting anti-clockwise. The leaves are alternate, 1·5–5·5cm long, oblong to ovate from a base with lobes pointing backwards, obtuse, petiolate. The flowers are regular, hermaphrodite, solitary or in groups of 2–3; the pedicels have 2 bracteoles, not overlapping the calyx. The corolla is up to 2·5cm long, white or sometimes tinged with pink, short-lived, broadly funnel-shaped, shallowly 5-lobed. The stamens number 5. The fruit is a 3mm wide capsule.

Habitat hedges, waste places, as a weed in cultivated land, alongside roads and railway-lines. **Distribution** throughout the region, rare in Scotland. **Active ingredients** a glycoside, resin, a substance stimulating coagulation. **Effect** purgative and mildly diuretic. **Parts used** the fresh or dried flowering herb. **Application M:** in both allopathy and homoeopathy an essence prepared from fresh material, is prescribed for constipation and fevers. In the home an infusion (1 teaspoon per cup water, allow to stand for 5 minutes) is taken 3–4 times a day for the same ailments and uterine bleeding.

*Convolvulus
arvensis*

*Lithospermum
officinale*

Echium vulgare

Ⓜ *Calystegia sepium* (L.) R.Br. Convolvulaceae
Hedge Bindweed, Bellbine (July–Sept.) This perennial is related to the above species and is similar in appearance. It can be distinguished as follows: the bracteoles are large, overlapping the calyx; leaves are up to 15cm long.

Habitat hedges, edges of woods, garden fences, waste places, etc. **Distribution** most of the British Isles but more common in southern counties. All over Ireland and throughout the rest of Europe (not in the north). **Active ingredients** the glycoside jalapin, resins, tannins. **Effect** purgative (stronger than in the preceding species). **Parts use and application M:** as for the above species.

☠ *Atropa bella-donna* L. Solanaceae
Ⓜ **Deadly Nightshade, Dwale** A tall perennial herb with much-branched stems, 60–120cm (up to 150cm) tall, pubescent and glandular. The leaves are alternate, entire, 6–12cm long, ovate from a wedge-shaped base, acuminate. The flowers are drooping, hermaphrodite, usually solitary, axillary, 2·5–3cm in diameter. The calyx is bell-shaped, 5-lobed. The corolla is a little bilaterally symmetrical, bell-shaped, lurid violet or violet-green, with 5 short obtuse lobes. The stamens are subequal, slightly extended with whitish anthers. The fruit is a globose, 1–2cm wide, shining black conspicuous berry (in appearance similar to a cherry and therefore a lure for children).

Habitat woods, thickets, hedges, mainly on calcareous soil. **Distribution** scattered throughout the British Isles but usually rare and local (from Westmorland southwards); over most of the rest of Europe; cultivated and often naturalized. **Active ingredients** atropine sulphate, hyoscyamine, scopolamine, belladonnine and derivatives, flavone glycosides, tannin. **Effect** relieves spasms; analgetic, dilates the pupil, paralysing the parasympathetic nerve system. **Parts used** the fresh or dried leaves; the roots. **Application C:** this drug is of paramount importance for the preparation of numerous brands of proprietary medicine for myocardial infarction, hypotension, abdominal spasms, stomach ulcers, hyperacidity, constipation and many other disorders; it is also used as an aid in ophthalmic diagnosis and surgery. **Note** on no account should this drug be used for domestic purposes. Even a small dose leads to *severe poisoning* (flushed skin, dry mouth, widened pupils, delirium and respiratory failure leading to death).

☠ *Hyoscyamus niger* L. Solanaceae
Ⓜ **Henbane** A sticky, softly hairy, fetid-smelling annual to biennial herb. The stems are 20–80cm tall, woody at the base, erect. The leaves are alternate, entire, deeply incised or with a few marginal teeth, 5–20cm long, ovate to ovate-oblong; the basal ones petiolate; the stem leaves sessile and clasping. The flower is almost sessile, arranged (usually in 2 rows) in dense one-sided spikes. The calyx is 1–1·5cm long, pitcher-shaped, 5-toothed. Corolla slightly bilaterally symmetrical, 2–3cm in diameter, lurid yellow with purplish venation, 5-lobed. The anthers are purple. The fruit is a many-seeded capsule, enclosed in the constricted calyx.

Habitat waste places (often near farms), sandy places (roadsides, railway embankments, dunes near the sea). **Distribution** widely scattered throughout the British Isles and Ireland; all over the rest of Europe. **Active ingredients** hyoscyamine, atropine, scopolamine, tannins, traces of essential oil, a glycoside (in the seed). **Effect** similar to above. **Parts used** the dried leaves, seeds and more rarely the entire flowering herb. **Application C:** as indicated for *A. bella donna,* above. The drug is also contained in preparations for insomnia, sedatives, various forms of tremor (especially senile tremor), rheumatic conditions, sea-sickness and others. **Note** this drug is *poisonous* and should never be used for domestic purposes.

Calystegia sepium

Hyoscyamus niger

Atropa bella-donna

☠ *Solanum dulcamara* L. Solanaceae

Bittersweet, Woody Nightshade A usually scrambling perennial. The stems are up to 200cm long, woody in the lower parts, glabrous to tomentose. The leaves are alternate or in pairs, 3–9cm long, ovate from a truncate, heart-shaped base, entire or 1 to 4 lobed, and often with a basal leaflet; the petiole is up to 3cm long. The flowers are 0·8–1·1cm in diameter, regular, arranged in loose, many-flowered, leaf-opposed peduncled cymes. The calyx is 2·5–3·5mm long, 5-lobed. The corolla is rotate, 5-lobed, purple or white, 3–4 times as long as the calyx. The anthers are yellow, opening by pores, sticky and forming a cone. The fruit is a many-seeded 0·8–1cm wide red cherry.

Habitat hedges, edges of woods and copses, waste grounds, beaches. **Distribution** throughout the region (absent from the N. Scotland). **Active ingredients** glycosidic bitter principles, solaceine, solaneine, solasonine, saponin, tannin. **Effect** mildly diuretic, stimulates central nervous system, aids blood disorders. **Parts used** the dried second-year stems; collect in spring or after the leaves are shed. **Application C:** in allopathy the drug is used either as a powder or in brands of proprietary medicine for skin-diseases caused by metabolic disorders (chronic eczema, psoriasis, etc.), auto-intoxication, rheumatic conditions and blood disorders. In homoeopathy an essence (fresh plant) is prescribed for the same ailments. **Note** an overdose of this drug leads to paralysis of the tongue and finally loss of speech.

Ⓜ *Solanum nigrum* L. Solanaceae
Black Nightshade (July–Sept.) This annual is related to the above and can be distinguished as follows: not woody at base, up to 60cm tall, usually erect. The flowers are only 4–6mm wide. The fruit is a black berry.

Habitat arable fields, waste places, gardens (weed). **Distribution** scattered in Wales, S. Scotland and Ireland. Otherwise almost cosmopolitan. **Active ingredients** solanine, saponin. **Effect** relieves spasms, sedative. **Parts used** the entire fresh flowering herb. **Application M:** in homoeopathy an essence is prepared for spasms and epilepsy. In the home an infusion was given in the past for the same conditions. The berries are supposed to be *poisonous*; they certainly should not be eaten.

Note *S. tuberosum* L., the cultivated potato, is often used for medicinal purposes. **Active ingredients** mucilage, solanic, starch, sugar, vitamin C. **Effect** relieves spasms, neutralizing acidity of gastric juices. **Parts used** the freshly pressed juice of the 'potato' (tuber). Make sure the potato is not green and free of sprouts. **Application** 1–2 tablespoons of juice after meals, for stomach complaints and hyperacidity.

☠ *Datura stramonium* L. Solanaceae

Thorn-apple (leaves: June–Sept; seeds: Sept.–Oct.) A stout annual herb, branched, erect, 15–70cm (up to 100cm) tall. The leaves are alternate, 0·5–2cm long, ovate from a usually asymmetric base, coarsely toothed; the petiole is 2–7cm long. The flowers are showy, regular, erect, solitary. The calyx is tubular, 3–4cm long, 5-angled, green, splitting transversely in fruit. The corolla is white or rarely purple, funnel-shaped, with a long cylindrical tube and 0·8–1·1cm long erect acuminate lobes. The stamens are not protruding. The fruit is a many-seeded spiny capsule, 3·5–5cm wide, opening by 4 valves. The seeds are small, black.

Habitat waste and cultivated ground. **Distribution** introduced and scattered as a casual all over the British Isles. Throughout the temperate and sub-tropical regions of the northern hemisphere. Cultivated for medicinal purposes. **Active ingredients** hyoscyamine, hyoscine, scopolamine, atropine, traces of essential oils. **Effect** relieves spasms, anaesthetic (similar to *Atropa bella-donna*). **Parts used** the leaves, fresh or dried; the seeds. **Application C:** thorn-apple is *one of our most poisonous plants* and should *never* be used for domestic purposes. The drug is widely used in allopathy and homoeopathy for asthma, neuralgia, Parkinson's disease and other disorders.

Solanum dulcamara

Solanum nigrum

Datura stramonium

Ⓜ *Physalis alkekengi* L. Solanaceae

Chinese Lantern A perennial growing from a horizontal rhizome. The stem is erect, simple or branched, 25–75cm tall. The leaves are usually alternate, 4–15cm long, broadly ovate from a truncate or wedge-shaped base, acuminate, entire or sinuate, slightly pubescent; the petiole is 1–6cm long. The flowers are regular, solitary, axillary, pedicelled. The calyx is 5-lobed, green and up to 1·8cm long, red to orange and up to 5·5cm long and inflated balloon-like in fruit. The corolla is 1·5–2·5cm in diameter, 5-lobed, whitish. The stamens number 5, exserted. The fruit is a 1·3–1·8cm wide red or orange berry.

Habitat waste places, hedges, gardens. Distribution in the British Isles occasionally naturalized or as a garden escape. Most of the rest of Europe except for the north. Active ingredients citric acid, sugar, vitamins A and C, the bitter glycoside physaline. Effect strongly diuretic. Parts used the fresh or dried berry (freed from the calyx). Application M: in homoeopathy for kidney and bladder disorders, arthritis and rheumatism. In the home a decoction (1–2 teaspoons per cup water, bring to the boil, allow to stand for 10 minutes) 3 times a day for the same ailments and jaundice.

Ⓜ *Verbascum densiflorum* Bertol. *(V. thapsiforme)* Scrophulariaceae

Mullein (July–Sept.) A greyish-white or yellow-tomontose biennial herb with stout, erect 30–120cm tall stems. The basal leaves are 5–45cm long, oblong-elliptic, entire or crenate; the upper stem leaves are shorter, ovate to lanceolate, acuminate, toothed or crenulate, long decurrent. The bracts are 1·5–4cm long. The flowers are arranged in a large terminal spike-like raceme. The calyx is deeply 5-lobed, up to 1·3cm long. The corolla is 2·2–5·6cm in diameter, flat, the outside tomentose, yellow, with 5 lobes and a short tube. The stamens number 5, the upper ones with white or yellow hairs, the lower glabrous and with decurrent anthers. The fruit is an up to 9mm wide elliptic-ovoid capsule.

Habitat waste places, railway embankments, in similar sunny dry localities. Distribution in the British Isles only as a casual. Throughout Europe, in the north as far as S. Sweden. Active ingredients mucilage, traces of saponins, sugar, yellow pigments, hesperidin, verbascoside, aucubin. Effect expectorant, softens the skin. Parts used the dried flowers without the calyx – collect on a sunny day, dry quickly (not over 40°C) as moisture turns the flowers brown and renders them ineffective; the fresh herb before flowering. Application M: in the home an infusion (2 teaspoons of flowers per cup water) 3 times daily for bronchitis, coughs, and throat irritations. In homoeopathy an essence, based on the fresh herb, is prescribed for gastritis, neuralgias, rheumatic conditions (with doubtful effect) and externally – for septic cuts. The drug is contained in a few brands of proprietary medicine (mainly cough mixtures) and is usually more effective in conjunction with others.

Ⓜ *Linaria vulgaris* Mill. Scrophulariaceae

Toadflax (July–Oct.) A bluish-green perennial herb, growing from a creeping rhizome. The stems are several, erect, 25–60cm (up to 80cm) tall. The leaves are alternate, 2·5–8cm long, linear-lanceolate, sometimes lanceolate. The flowers are bilaterally symmetrical, arranged in a many-flowered terminal dense raceme, pedicelled. The calyx is deeply 5-lobed. The corolla is distinctly 2-lipped; the lower lip is 3-lobed, forming a lip, the upper lip is 2-lobed; the tube is slender, at the base extended into a pointed spur. The stamens number 4, not exserted. The fruit is a capsule, exceeding the calyx, opening by several apical valves.

Habitat grassy places, hedgerows, along roads and railways, waste places. Distribution common throughout the region (rare in N. Scotland). Active ingredients flavone glycosides. Effect diuretic, induces sweating, purgative. Parts used the dried flowering herb (cut 10cm above ground), dry in shade. Application M: in homoeopathy an essence, based on fresh material, is prescribed for diarrhoea and cystitis. For domestic purposes an infusion (1 teaspoon per cup water, allow to stand for 5 minutes) is given 3–4 times a day for constipation, dropsy, jaundice, haemorrhoids and – drunk hot – to induce perspiration.

Physalis alkekengi

Verbascum densiflorum

Linaria vulgaris

(M) *Scrophularia nodosa* L. Scrophulariaceae

Figwort (June–Sept.) A perennial herb with a short, swollen, knotty rhizome. The stem is quadrangular (not winged), 35–65cm (up to 85cm) tall, erect. The leaves are opposite, 5–13·5cm long, ovate, acute, irregularly serrate, with a truncate and usually somewhat decurrent base; the petiole is not winged. The flowers are bilaterally symmetrical, arranged in a loose panicle, composed of cymes and supported by leaf-like bracts; the inflorescence-axis and pedicels are glandular. The calyx is 5-lobed, the lobes ovate, obtuse. The corolla is 0·8-1cm long, green or with a red-brown upper lip, 5-lobed (the 2 upper lobes united below). The fruit is ovoid, 0·6–1cm wide capsule.

Habitat on damp ground in woods, hedge banks, alongside streams and in similar localities. **Distribution** throughout the region (except Shetland). **Active ingredients** saponins, glycosides, resin, sugar, organic acids. **Effect** diuretic, mildly purgative, mild wormer. **Parts used** the fresh or dried flowering herb; more rarely the dried rhizome. **Application M:** the drug is contained in a few brands of proprietary medicine for constipation. In homoeopathy an essence, prepared from the fresh herb, is prescribed for mastitis, glandular swellings and eczema. In the home an infusion (1–2 teaspoons per cup water, allow to stand for 8 minutes) is given 2–3 times daily for the same disorders as well as (the rhizome) for worms.

☠ (M) *Digitalis purpurea* L. Scrophulariaceae

Foxglove A biennial with stems 45–120cm (up to 150cm) tall, erect, simple, usually greyish tomentose. The leaves are alternate, the basal ones forming a rosette, 15–30cm long, ovate to lanceolate, at the base tapering into the winged petiole, crenate. The flowers are bilaterally symmetrical, nodding, and arranged in a large terminal, many-flowered raceme, pedicelled, devoid of bracts. The calyx is deeply 5-lobed, the lower lobes ovate, the upper lobes lanceolate. The corolla is showy, up to 5·5cm long, pink-purple (rarely white) inside with dark purple spots on a white ground, hairy within. The stamens number 4, not exserted. The fruit is a many-seeded, ovoid capsule, exceeding the calyx.

Habitat on acid soil in openings and in clearings and edges of woods, in mountain grassland, on rocks, heaths. **Distribution** throughout the region (except Shetland). Often cultivated for medicinal purposes. **Active ingredients** heart glycosides digitoxin and gitoxin and derivatives, saponins, mucilage, organic acids, tannin. **Effect** stimulating and regulating cardiac function; strongly diuretic. **Parts used** the dried leaves, either collected in late summer of first year or when flowering the second year; dry as quickly as possible in fresh air. **Application C:** *Digitalis* provides one of our most important drugs for the treatment of cardiac disorders and dropsy. In homoeopathy an essence is prepared from fresh leaves. *Digitalis* is one of the most *poisonous* native plants and *should on no account be used in the home.* **Note** the Yellow Foxglove (*D. lutea*) and *D. lanata* possess the same properties and are also used for medicinal purposes.

(M) (E) *Veronica beccabunga* L. Scrophulariaceae

Brooklime (May–Sept.) An aquatic fleshy perennial herb. The stems are 15–60cm long, decumbent and ascending, rooting at the nodes. The leaves are glabrous, opposite, thick, broadly elliptic to oblong from a rounded base, obtuse, shortly petiolate. The flowers are slightly bilaterally symmetrical, arranged in up to 30-flowered, opposite axillary racemes. The calyx is 4-lobed. The corolla is 6–8mm wide, blue, tube very short; limb 4-lobed (the upper-lobe larger than the others). The stamens number 2. The fruit is a laterally compressed capsule, circular, shorter than the calyx.

Habitat in streams, ditches, ponds, etc. **Distribution** throughout the region. **Active ingredients** saponin, tannin, aucubine. **Effect** very mildly diuretic. **Application M:** the plant is of no importance as a medicinal herb but its properties are beneficial as a mild purgative when eaten. **E:** the young shoots before flowering and the leaves of flowering plants are eaten as a salad (best mixed with water-cress). Finely chopped one can eat them in sandwiches. When used as a vegetable they should be mixed with other herbs to mask their somewhat bitter taste.

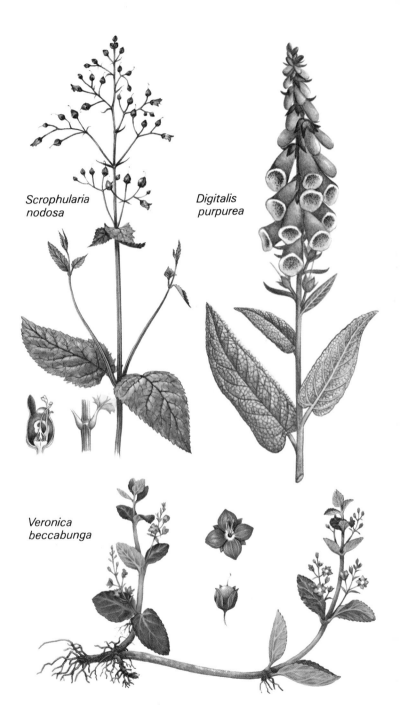

Scrophularia nodosa

Digitalis purpurea

Veronica beccabunga

Ⓜ *Veronica officinalis* L. Scrophulariaceae

Common Speedwell This perennial is related to the above but is not fleshy and of terrestrial habit. It also possesses axillary inflorescences and creeping stems which are rooting at the nodes and hairy all over. The leaves are opposite, 1·5–3cm long, oblong to obovate-elliptic from a wedge-shaped base, hairy on both surfaces. Corolla 5–6mm wide, lilac. The anthers and filaments are also lilac. The capsule is obovate to heart-shaped in outline, longer than the calyx.

　　Habitat meadows, pastures and usually dry grassy places, also in open woods and heaths. **Distribution** throughout the region. **Active ingredients** tannins, bitter principles, the glycoside aucubine, traces of essential oil. **Effect** mildly diuretic, mildly expectorant, antidiarrhoeal. **Parts used** the fresh or dried flowering herb, dry in shade or well ventilated warm room. **Application M:** the drug is contained in a few herbal tea mixtures. In homoeopathy an essence, made from fresh material, is prescribed for chronic skin ailments. In the home an infusion (1–2 teaspoons per cup water, allow to stand for 5–8 minutes) is taken 2–3 times a day for the same disorders as well as for stomach upset, arthritis and rheumatic conditions.

Ⓜ *Euphrasia rostkoviana* Hayne Scrophulariaceae

Eyebright (June– Oct.) A delicate annual herb with stems ascending to suberect from a decumbent base, slender and wavy, branched, 8–50cm long; the internodes are usually much longer than the leaves. The leaves are small, 0·5–1·1cm long, thinly herbaceous, with distinct veins, covered with glandular hairs on both surfaces, the lower ones oblong from a wedge-shaped base, obtusely toothed; the upper ones broader and more acutely toothed. The flowers are axillary. The calyx is bell-shaped with 4 teeth. The corolla is much larger than the calyx, bilaterally symmetrical, 0·8–1·2cm long, white with the upper lip often tinged with lilac; the lower lip is long with spreading lobes. The fruit is a capsule.

　　Habitat in moist grassland. **Distribution** throughout most of Europe; locally in the British Isles. **Active ingredients** essential oil, tannin, bitter principle, the glycoside aucubine, resins. **Effect** astringent, skin softener (pharmacologically not fully explored). **Parts used** the dried or fresh flowering herb; cut above the ground, dry in shade, store in the dark. **Application M:** as the vernacular name indicates this plant is a time-honoured remedy for eye-disorders. Externally an infusion (3 teaspoons per 2 glasses water, allow to stand for 8–10 minutes) is used in an eyebath or applied as compress for styes, blepharitis and conjunctivitis. Internally a weaker infusion (1–1½ teaspoons per cup water) is taken 3–4 times a day for the same ailments, jaundice, and abdominal spasms.

☠ *Gratiola officinalis* L. Scrophulariaceae
Ⓜ

Hedge Hyssop (June– Aug.) A perennial with glabrous stems, ascending to erect from a creeping base, hollow, quadrangular in the upper part, 12–60cm (up to 80cm) tall. The leaves are opposite, 1·5–5cm long, linear to lanceolate from a semi-clasping base, dotted with glands. The flowers are bilaterally symmetrical, axillary, solitary. The calyx is distinctly 5-lobed. The corolla is 1·1–1·9cm long, white tinged with purple or purple-red, slightly 2-lipped with a wide tube, the upper lip is 2-lobed and flat, the lower lip 3-lobed and somewhat larger. The stamens number 5, not exserted (only 2 are fertile). The fruit is a many-seeded 4-valved capsule.

　　Habitat wet grassland, fens, river banks, ditches, etc. **Distribution** S. and C. Europe, northwards to the Netherlands. **Active ingredients** essential oil, gratioside, gratiogenin, gratiotoxin, resin. **Effect** violently purgative, diuretic, cardiac stimulant. **Parts used** the fresh (for homoeopathic use) or dried flowering herb; to be cut above the ground and quickly dried in heated room. **Application C:** homoeopathic prescriptions are given for cystitis, pyelitis, abdominal pain (colics) and certain stomachic disorders. In the home an infusion was used in the past as a purgative and wormer. The drug must *never be used without medical supervision* and should be avoided in pregnancy and when breast-feeding.

Veronica officinalis

Gratiola officinalis

Euphrasia rostkoviana

Ⓜ *Pinguicula vulgaris* L. Lentibulariaceae

Common Butterwort (May–Aug.) An insectivorous perennial bog-plant, overwintering as a bud. The leaves all form a basal rosette, 1·8–8cm long, ovate-oblong, pale yellow-green, the margins are involute, the surface covered by sticky glands. The flowers are bilaterally symmetrical, solitary and terminal on a leafless, glandular 8–20cm tall scape. The calyx is unequally 5-lobed and 2-lipped. The corolla is 0·9 –1·6cm long, 2-lipped, spurred, violet but with a white blotch at the open mouth; the upper lip is 2-lobed, the lower 3-lobed. The stamens number 2. The fruit is an ovoid capsule, opening by 2 valves.

Habitat bogs, heath, wet grassy slopes, wet rocks. **Distribution** common throughout the region. **Active ingredients** an enzyme which makes milk coagulate, mucilage. **Effect** very mildly expectorant, skin softener. **Parts used** the flowering herb; dry quickly in the sun. **Application M:** in homoeopathy an extract, prepared from fresh material, is prescribed for whooping cough and nervous throat-irritations. In the home an infusion (2 teaspoons per cup water, allow to stand for 2–3 minutes) 3–4 times a day can be used for colds and coughs.

Ⓜ *Verbena officinalis* L. Verbenaceae

Vervain A stout dull green perennial herb, growing from a woody stock. The stems are stiff, erect, 25–65cm tall, branched above, stiffly hairy. The leaves are opposite, 2–7·5cm long, oblanceolate to diamond-shaped in outline, more or less deeply pinnatifid (the upper ones sometimes entire). The flowers are slightly bilaterally symmetrical, arranged in slender terminal spikes (at first dense, elongated in fruit). The calyx is unequally 5-toothed, 2–3mm long, ribbed. The corolla is 3·5–4·5mm in diameter, 2-lipped and 5-lobed, pale lilac, the tube twice as long as the calyx. The stamens number 4 (sometimes 2). The fruit consists of 4 red-brown nutlets.

Habitat roadsides, embankments, waste places. **Distribution** scattered throughout England and Wales, in Scotland only in Fife; over most of the rest of Europe except the north. **Active ingredients** the glycosides verbenaline and verbenine, tannin, bitter principles, traces of essential oil, mucilage. **Effect** astringent, mildly diuretic, aids menstrual flow and milk secretion, antidiarrhoeal. **Parts used** the flowering plant; dry in the sun or in artificial heat (40–45°C). **Application M:** the drug is contained in a herbal tea-mixture for stimulating the metabolism, for stomach disorder, rheumatic pain and skin ailments. In homoeopathy an essence from fresh material is prescribed for dropsy, painful menstruation. In the home an infusion (1–2 teaspoons per cup water, allow to stand for 10–12 minutes) is given 1–3 times a day for insomnia, nervous exhaustion, and disorders connected with stone-formation.

Ⓜ *Mentha aquatica* L. Labiatae

Water Mint (July–Oct.) This strongly scented perennial herb is closely related to the above species but is easily distinguished from it by the fact that the calyx-tube is not hairy within and the calyx teeth are equal. It also differs from similar species by only having very small and inconspicuous bracts (never leaf-like). The stems are usually erect, often reddish. The leaves are 3–9cm long, ovate to ovate-lanceolate from a truncate base, petiolate. The flowers are arranged in 2–3 very dense whorls, forming a terminal head-like inflorescence up to 2cm in diameter. The corolla is lilac. The nutlets are brown.

Habitat swamps, fens, marshes, near streams, rivers and ponds, in wet woods. **Distribution** throughout the region. **Active ingredients** essential oil with menthol, carvone, tannin. **Effect, parts used and application M:** similar to *M. piperita* and used by the pharmaceutical industry for the production of gargles, mouth-washes, and for flavouring liquors.

Ⓜ *Mentha pulegium* L. Labiatae

Ⓔ **Penny-royal** (Aug.–Oct.) A perennial herb with a pungent scent. The stems are 8–40cm tall, prostrate to ascending, not mat-forming. The leaves are opposite, 0·8–3cm long, narrowly elliptical from a tapering base, sometimes subcircular, shortly petiolate, hairy (at least on the lower surface). The flowers are arranged in many-flowered distant axillary whorls. The calyx is 2–3mm long, slightly 2-lipped, with 5

Pinguicula vulgaris

Verbena officinalis

Mentha aquatica

teeth; the throat is hairy within. The corolla is 4–6mm long, lilac, with a gibbous tube, and 4 subequal lobes. The fruit consists of 4 pale brown, 0·75mm long nutlets.

Habitat in wet sandy soil, moist meadows, along streams, etc. Distribution throughout C. and S. Europe. Scattered in S. England, becoming rarer northwards; very rare in Scotland (Ayr and Berwick). Active ingredients essential oil, tannin, flavone glycosides. Effect sedative, relieves spasms and flatulence. Parts used the fresh or dried flowering herb; cut 8–10cm above the ground and dry in shade. Application M: the use of this plant for medicinal purposes goes far back in history. Nowadays in homoeopathy an essence prepared from fresh material is prescribed for asthmatic conditions, coughs, various stomach and abdominal disorders and arthritis. In the home an infusion (1 teaspoon per cup water, allow to stand for 8–12 minutes) is taken 2–3 times a day for the same purpose. E: although the strong aroma of Penny-royal is not to everyone's taste it can be used as a condiment for flavouring various dishes (soups, stews, stuffings) and especially sprinkled over buttered new potatoes.

Ⓜ *Mentha x piperita* L. Labiatae

Peppermint (July–Oct.) This perennial is the hybrid between the preceding species and *M. spicata* L. (Spearmint). The most important distinguishing feature is that this plant is always sterile. The flowers are arranged in an oblong, 30–80cm long spike consisting of numerous congested whorls; the bracts are also inconspicuous and never leaf-like. The calyx-tube is never hairy within. The herb has a pungent (peppermint!) scent. The stems are erect, usually branched, reddish or purple, often thinly hairy, 24–90cm tall. The leaves are 40–90cm long, ovate-lanceolate, or (rarely) ovate from a wedge-shaped to almost heart-shaped base, long petiolate. The corolla is lilac-pink.

Habitat mainly in cultivation but locally naturalized in ditches, damp waste places, roadsides, etc. Distribution all over Europe but usually as a garden escape; locally in the British Isles. Active ingredients essential oil with menthol, menthone, jasmone, tannin, bitter principle. Effect relieves spasms and flatulence, stimulates bile flow and production, antiseptic, anaesthetic. Part used leaves, fresh or dried. Application M: peppermint, one of the most important members in the arsenal of healing plants is contained in numerous brands of proprietary medicine (tinctures, salves, essences, inhalents, herbal pills and tea-mixtures, etc.). The drug is extensively used in both allopathic and homoeopathic medicine for gastritis, abdominal colics, disorders of the gall bladder, indigestion; also in embrocations for the relief of rheumatic pain, in snuffs and other preparations. For domestic purposes an infusion (2 teaspoons per cup water, allow to stand for not longer than 10 minutes) 2–3 times a day for indigestion, disorders of the gall bladder, nausea, or as a digestive and stimulating beverage.

Ⓜ *Lycopus europaeus* L. Labiatae

Gipsy-wort A perennial herb with a creeping rhizome. The stems are 25–75cm (up to 100cm) tall, erect, hairy, branched. The leaves are opposite, 2·5–10cm long, ovate-lanceolate to elliptic, pinnately lobed (the lobes acute, triangular). The flowers are bilaterally symmetrical, small, arranged in axillary whorls. The calyx has 13 nerves and 5 equal sharply pointed teeth, hairy. The corolla is 2-lipped, with a tube not exceeding the calyx, 2·5–3·5mm long and in diameter, white and purplish dotted on the lower lip. The stamens number 2, exserted. The fruit consists of 4 small, tetrahedral nutlets.

Habitat alongside rivers, streams, ditches, in marshes and fens. Distribution throughout England and Wales, Ireland, scattered in Scotland. All over the rest of Europe and the Mediterranean area. Active ingredients lycopine, essential oil, tannin. Effect inhibits iodine conversion in the thyroid gland. Parts used the fresh or dried flowering herb. Application M: the effective ingredient is (besides *Crataegus, Posmarinus*) contained in various brands of proprietary medicine prescribed for hyperthyroidism and related disorders such as Basedow's disease.

Mentha pulegium

Lycopus europaeus

Mentha x *piperita*

Ⓜ ***Origanum vulgare*** L. Labiatae
Ⓔ **Marjoram** (July–Sept.) An aromatic slightly hairy perennial herb with a woody rhizome and 25–60cm (up to 80cm) tall, erect stems, branched above. The leaves are opposite, petiolate, 1–4·8cm long, ovate, entire, slightly appressed hairs on both surfaces. The flowers are bilaterally symmetrical, arranged in dense cymes, forming a terminal panicle. The calyx is 13-nerved, bell-shaped, with 5 almost equal short teeth, hairy within. The corolla is 5·5–8·5mm long, 2-lipped, rose-purple, the tube longer than the calyx. The stamens number 4, exserted, the anther-cells divergent. The fruit consists of 4 ovoid, smooth nutlets.

Habitat dry grassy areas (hedge banks, downs, etc.), usually on calcareous soil. **Distribution** common throughout England, Wales, and S. Ireland, more scattered and local in Scotland and N. Ireland. S. and S. C. Europe. **Active ingredients** essential oils with thymol and carvacrol, tannin, bitter principle. **Effect** mildly expectorant, stimulates bile production, relieves spasms, mildly diuretic. **Parts used** the fresh and dried flowering herb; cut 10cm above ground, dry in shade. **Application M:** in allopathic medicine this drug is virtually obsolete (only contained in a few cough mixtures). In the home and in homoeopathy an infusion (1–1½ teaspoons per cup water, allow to stand for 10 minutes) is given 3–4 times daily for bronchial catarrh and stomach or intestinal spasms, and as a diuretic. For inflammations of throat and mouth it is used as a gargle. In cosmetics and perfumery the essential oil extracted from this plant is used in the production of colognes and for scenting soaps. **E:** although plants growing in the British Isles are much less aromatic than those in S. Europe they can be used as a spice for various dishes (pizza, pastas, lamb dishes Greek style, stews, casseroles, and sauces) **Note** not to be confused with 'Oregano' which is a C. American spice (*Lippia graveolens*).

Ⓜ ***Thymus serpyllum*** L. Labiatae
Wild Thyme (July–Aug.) A mat-forming, slightly aromatic perennial herb. The stems are long, creeping, with ascending to upright 5–10cm tall flowering shoots; the flowering shoots are finely and evenly hairy all round (but not in opposing rows) below the inflorescence, usually rounded in cross-section or indistinctly angled. The leaves are opposite, very shortly petiolate, 3·5–7mm long, oblanceolate to paddle-shaped, glabrous, but with margins fringed with hairs usually more or less upright. The flowers are bilaterally symmetrical, small, arranged in head-like dense terminal inflorescences. The calyx is 2-lipped, 3–4mm long. The corolla is rose-purple, 2-lipped. The stamens number 4, exserted. The fruit consists of 4 tiny nutlets.

Habitat dry grassland, heath, on sandy soil. **Distribution** in the British Isles confined to East Anglia; common over most of Europe from S. Sweden southwards. **Active ingredients** essential oils with cymol and thymol, tannins, bitter principles. **Effect** expectorant, mildly relieves spasms. **Parts used** the flowering fresh or dried herb; dry in shade. **Application M:** the drug is contained in a variety of brands of proprietary medicine for tracheobronchitis, bronchitis, bronchialitis and also chronic stomach ailments. A homoeopathic essence, prepared from the fresh herb, is prescribed for nervous disorders. In the home an infusion (2 teaspoons per cup water, allow to stand for 5 minutes) is taken internally 3 times a day for the same ailments and externally as a herbal bath and for herbal cushions. **Note** the garden or French Thyme (*T. vulgaris* L.) has the same but quantitatively stronger properties and is more widely used in medicine; it is extensively cultivated for this as well as for culinary purposes.

Origanum vulgare

Thymus serpyllum

Ⓜ️ *Hyssopus officinalis* L. Labiatae

Hyssop An aromatic perennial herb, stems slightly woody at the base, 20–65cm high, green, almost glabrous. The leaves are opposite, 1·5–2·75cm long, linear of oblong-lanceolate, somewhat obtuse, sessile. The flowers are bilaterally symmetrical, arranged in unilateral spike-like, long and dense inflorescences, with bracts as long as the flowers. The calyx is 4–5mm long, tubular, 15-nerved, with 5 almost equal teeth. The corolla is 2-lipped, up to 1·3cm long, violet-blue. The stamens number 4, exserted; the anther cells are diverging. The fruit consists of 4 smooth, ovoid-triangular nutlets.

Habitat old walls and buildings, stony places. **Distribution** in the British Isles found in S. England as an escape or naturalized (e.g. Beaulieu Abbey). In the rest of Europe native in the E. Mediterranean region; widespread in S. Europe as a garden escape. **Active ingredients** essential oils, tannins, the glycoside diosmin. **Effect** relieves spasms, stimulates appetite, astringent, suppresses perspiration, mildly expectorant. **Parts used** the flowering herb; cut 5cm above the ground and dry in shade. **Application M:** as an infusion (2 teaspoons per cup water, allow to stand for 8–12 minutes, or add to cold water, bring to the boil, and allow to stand for 5 minutes) 3–4 times daily for bronchitis, flatulence, anorexia, dropsy, and excessive perspiration (thyrotoxicosis, infectious diseases, hyperhidrosis, etc.). **Note** in perfumery the essential oil extracted from Hyssop is used in perfume-types such as Fougère and Chypre; it is also used to flavour liqueurs.

Ⓜ️ *Satureja montana* L. Labiatae
Ⓔ

Savory An aromatic perennial subshrub with ascending or trailing stems and 10–45cm high, erect branches. The leaves are opposite, 0·8–2·2cm long, lanceolate-linear, acute, sessile or very shortly petiolate, leathery, entire, pointed. The flowers are bilaterally symmetrical, arranged in small cymes forming a large unilateral terminal inflorescence. The calyx is 10-nerved, with 5 almost equal triangular teeth. The corolla is 2-lipped, with a straight 6–7mm long tube, white or tinged with pink, hairless within. The stamens number 4, not exserted. The fruit consists of 4 ovoid smooth nutlets.

Habitat old walls and buildings, stony places (in Europe on dry stony hillsides and calcareous soil). **Distribution** native to S. Europe; in the British Isles formerly cultivated as a pot herb, naturalized in a few localities in S. England (e.g. Beaulieu Abbey). **Active ingredients** essential oils with carvacrol and cymol, tannin, mucilage. **Effect** astringent, mildly antiseptic, relieves flatulence, stimulates appetite, mildly expectorant. **Parts used** the fresh or dried flowering shoots; dry in shade or in a warm, well-ventilated room. **Application M:** this drug is given as an infusion (3 teaspoons per cup water, allow to stand for 8–10 minutes; never boil) taken 3 times daily for gastro-enteritis (especially when the stools smell obnoxious), also for cystitis and bronchitis. **E:** this species is sometimes cultivated as a condiment but normally only used in mixed herbs. **Note** the widely cultivated condiment Summer Savory (*S. hortensis* L.) posses-ses the same properties but is quantitatively stronger. It is also used for medicinal purposes. As a spice, it is mainly used with beans but can also be added (sparingly) to stews, casseroles and sauces.

Hyssopus officinalis

Satureja montana

Ⓜ️ *Melissa officinalis* L. Labiatae

Ⓔ **Balm** (June–Sept.) A scented perennial herb with a short rhizome. The stems are 25–65cm tall, erect, branched, hairy. The leaves are opposite, 2·7–7·5cm long, ovate from a wedge-shaped or rounded base, crenate, petiolate. The flowers are bilaterally symmetrical, arranged in axillary whorls. The calyx is 13-nerved, bell-shaped, 2-lipped; the upper tooth broad-triangular; the lower lanceolate-triangular, all pointed. The corolla is 2-lipped, white or flushed pink, 1–1·3cm long; the tube is upwardly curved and dilated in the upper half. The stamens number 4, not exserted. The fruit consists of 4 obovoid smooth nutlets.

Habitat waste places, derelict land, near human habitation, gardens. **Distribution** S.E. and C. Europe. In Britain frequently found as a garden escape and naturalized in some localities. **Active ingredients** essential oils with gein, geraniol, citronellal and citral, tannin, bitter principle. **Effect** mainly sedative, also relieves spasms and flatulence. **Parts used** the fresh or dried leaves collected just before or after flowering; dry in shade. **Application M:** as an infusion (3 teaspoons per cup water, allow to stand for 8–12 minutes; never boil) 2–3 times daily for nervous tension, mild insomnia, headache, stomach or abdominal pain, indigestion. A stronger infusion (2 cups of dried herb per 1 litre of water) can be added to the bath water (take several baths a week for nervous conditions). Dried leaves can also be sewn into linen bags and placed under the pillow at night. The drug is contained in many brands of proprietary medicine for the above conditions; the best form of application is either pressed juice or a spirit-extraction, both are commercially available. **E:** young leaves can be added to sweet salads, soups, custards, or eaten in sandwiches. Bruised leaves lend a special flavour to spring cups (dry white wine, mineral water, serve chilled).

Ⓜ️ *Salvia officinalis* L. Labiatae

Ⓔ **Sage** (May–July) An aromatic perennial undershrub, growing from a tap root. The stems are often woody at the base, 30–80cm tall, erect, square, densely hairy. The leaves are opposite, persistent, 3–10cm long, oblong, from a wedge-shaped base, with finely toothed margins, petiolate, thickly herbaceous or leathery, greyish-green, hairy. The flowers are arranged in axillary whorls of 4–8. The calyx is tubular to bell-shaped, 2-lipped; the upper lip has 3, the lower 2 teeth. The corolla is 2·8–3·5cm long, violet-blue, pinkish or white, 2-lobed, the upper lip straight or somewhat sickle-shaped; the lower lip is 3-lobed. The stamens number 2, with a complex connective.

Habitat grassland, slopes and in warm positions on calcareous soil. **Distribution** native in the Mediterranean region; widely cultivated in S. and C. Europe as a pot herb and frequently naturalized. **Active ingredients** essential oils with campher, borneol, cineol, linalool, thujone, triterpenic acids, ursolic acid, bitter principle, resin, tannin. **Effect** anti-inflammatory, mildly antiseptic, astringent, relieves spasms and suppresses perspiration. **Parts used** the dried (fresh in homoeopathy) leaves collected before flowering; dry in shade or warm room. **Application M:** as an infusion (2 teaspoons per cup water, allow to stand for 15 minutes; never boil) 3–4 times daily to reduce perspiration (at night) accompanying nervous hyperhidrosis, tuberculosis, and thyrotoxicosis. A slightly stronger infusion is used as a gargle for laryngitis, tonsillitis or as a mouthwash for oral infections (Salvia oil is added to some brands of toothpaste). In homoeopathy the drug (essence) is prescribed for menopause complaints, circulatory disorders and it is also used as an agent in the treatments of diabetes. **E:** sage leaves fresh or dried are an indispensible condiment.

Melissa officinalis

Salvia officinalis

Ⓜ *Prunella vulgaris* L. Labiatae

Ⓔ **Self-heal** (April–May/Sept.) A slightly pubescent perennial herb, growing with a short rhizome and erect or ascending, 5–30cm tall stems. The leaves are opposite, petiolate, 1·5–5·5cm long, narrowly ovate from a wedge-shaped or rounded base, entire, subacute to obtuse. The flowers are bilaterally symmetrical, arranged in whorls in dense terminal cylindrical to almost globular inflorescences. The calyx is distinctly 2-lipped, closed after flowering; the upper lip has 1 developed and 2 suppressed lateral teeth and the lower lip has 2 teeth fringed with hairs. The corolla is 2-lipped, 1·1–1·5cm long, violet or (seldom) pink or white, with a concave upper lip. The stamens number 4, the outer pair longer than inner. The fruit consists of 4 smooth nutlets.

Habitat open grassland, forest clearings, edges of woods, waste places, etc. **Distribution** common throughout the region. **Parts used** young shoots and leaves before flowering. **Application M:** the plant has slightly astringent properties and an infusion is sometimes used as a gargle or mouthwash for laryngitis. **E:** as an addition to salads, also in soups, stews, or as a vegetable mixed with other wild or cultivated plants.

Ⓜ *Betonica officinalis* L. *(Stachys officinalis)* Labiatae

Betony (June–Sept.) A stout perennial herb with a short woody rhizome. The stems are erect, somewhat hairy; usually simple, 15–60m tall. The leaves are mostly arranged in a basal rosette, 2·5–7cm long, ovate-oblong or obtuse, the margins crenate, long petiolate; the stem leaves are few, rather distant, smaller than the basal ones, the uppermost sessile. The flowers are bilaterally symmetrical arranged in whorls in a dense cylindrical terminal inflorescence. The calyx is up to 1cm long, with 5 equal, narrow, awned teeth. The corolla is 2-lipped, bright red-purple; the tube exceeds the calyx, the upper lip is flat. The anther cells are not diverging. The fruit consists of 4 nutlets.

Habitat grassland, hedge banks, heath, open woods. **Distribution** throughout England, Ireland and Wales, rare and scattered in Scotland. All over Europe (except the north). **Active ingredients** abundant tannin, bitter principle, several alkaloids. **Effect** mainly astringent. **Parts used** the fresh or dried flowering herb; dry in shade or sun. **Application M:** in homoeopathy an essence, prepared from fresh material, is prescribed for asthma and excessive perspiration. For domestic purposes an infusion (2 teaspoons per cup water, allow to stand for 12–15 minutes) is taken internally 2–3 times a day for diarrhoea, arthritis, abdominal colics, flatulence or externally for phlebitis or slow-healing cuts and grazes.

Ⓜ *Lamium album* L. Labiatae

White Dead-nettle (May–Sept.) A hairy perennial herb with a long-creeping rhizome. The stems are usually erect, rarely ascending, 15–65cm tall. The leaves are opposite, petiolate, ovate from a heart-shaped base, crenate-serrate, or double-serrate. The flowers are arranged in small distant axillary whorls usually leaf-like with bracts. The calyx is tubular to bell-shaped, 0·8–1·1cm long, with 5 almost equal teeth longer than the tube. The corolla is 2-lipped, up to 2·2cm long, white; the upper lip is hood-like, the lower lip has 1 large and 2 very small, 2 to 3 toothed lateral lobes. The stamens number 4, not exserted. The fruit consists of 4 trigonous nutlets.

Habitat hedge banks, edges of woods, forest clearings, waste places. **Distribution** throughout the region. **Active ingredients** mucilage, tannin, tyramine, methylamine, choline, traces of fatty oils, saponin, flavone-glycoside. **Effect** astringent, diuretic. **Parts used** the flower corolla and also the flowering shoots; collect when the plants are dry and dry quickly in shade. **Application M:** in homoeopathy an essence, prepared from fresh material, is prescribed for amenorrhoea or kidney and bladder complaints. In the home an infusion (2 teaspoons of flowers per cup, allow to stand for 8–12 minutes) 2–3 times daily is taken internally for the same disorders as well as for catarrhs, or for a vaginal douche; externally it is used for bathing burns or septic cuts. **E:** the young shoots and leaves (March–April) can be used for salads or mixed with spinach or other leaf vegetables; young leaves can also be added to soups or sauces.

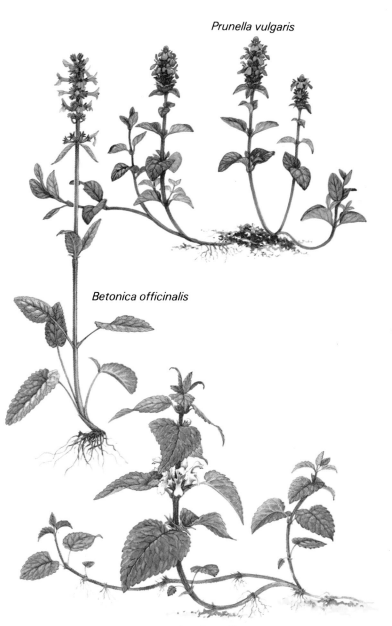

Prunella vulgaris

Betonica officinalis

Lamium album

Ⓜ *Leonurus cardiaca* L. Labiatae

Motherwort (June–Sept.) A pubescent perennial herb with a stout rhizome. The stems are 45–95cm (up to 120cm) tall, branched. The leaves are opposite, 5–12cm long, petiolate; the lower ones are ovate to ovate-circular from a heart-shaped base, more or less deeply palmately 5–7-lobed; the upper ones lanceolate from a wedge-shaped base, 3-lobed. The flowers are arranged in numerous distant axillary many-flowered whorls, bilaterally symmetrical. The calyx is 5-angled, bell-shaped, with 5 equal ovate-lanceolate teeth. The corolla is 1–1·3cm long, white to pale pink, with purplish dots; the tube is shorter than the calyx. The stamens number 4, the outer pair longer than the inner. The fruit consists of 4 trigonous nutlets.

Habitat waste places, hedge banks, along roads and railways. **Distribution** scattered all over the British Isles and throughout the rest of Europe. **Active ingredients** glycosides, bitter principle, essential oil, alkaloids, tannin, resin, acids. **Effect** sedative, relieves spasms, aids menstrual flow. **Parts used** the fresh or dried flowering herb; cut above ground and dry in shade. **Application M:** in homoeopathy an essence, prepared from fresh material, is prescribed for cardiac disorders, amenorrhoea, flatulence, and menopause complaints. For domestic purposes an infusion (1 teaspoon per cup water, allow to stand for 10 minutes) or a maceration (2 teaspoons per cup water) is taken 2–3 times a day for the above disorders as well as for stomach complaints and anxiety.

Ⓜ *Galeopsis segetum* Neck. *(G. ochroleuca)* Labiatae

Downy Hemp-nettle (July–Sept.) An annual herb, 10–60cm (up to 80cm) tall, with usually pubescent erect stems. The leaves are opposite, 1·5–8cm long, ovate, ovate-oblong or ovate-lanceolate from a cuneate base, softly (velvety) silky (especially on the lower surface), petiolate, crenate. The flowers are bilaterally symmetrical, arranged in dense axillary and terminal whorls; the bracts are leaf-like. The calyx is velvety silky, glandular, tubular to bell-shaped, with 5 slightly unequal sharp teeth. The corolla is 2-lipped, light yellow, up to 4 times as long as the calyx; the upper lip is helmet-shaped; the lower lip is 3-lobed, with small conical bosses at the base. The fruit consists of 4 nutlets.

Habitat in fields, meadows and waste places. **Distribution** locally in England and Wales, more rare towards the north. Throughout W. and C. Europe. **Active ingredients** silicic acid, tannin, saponin, fatty oils, wax, resin, traces of essential oil, bitter principle. **Effect** astringent, mildly expectorant, diuretic. **Parts used** the fresh or dried flowering herb; cut above ground, dry in shade. **Application M:** in homoeopathy an essence, based on fresh material, is prescribed for disorders of the spleen. A decoction (1½–2 teaspoons per cup water, bring to the boil quickly) is taken 2–3 times a day for bronchitis, whooping cough and tracheitis.

Ⓜ *Nepeta cataria* L. Labiatae

Cat-mint (July–Sept.) A scented perennial herb with 30–80cm (up to 100cm) tall, erect, branched, pubescent stems. The leaves are petiolate, 2·5–7·5cm long, ovate from a cordate base, whitish-tomentose on the lower surface. The flowers are bilaterally symmetrical, arranged in axillary whorls in a terminal inflorescence. The calyx is pubescent, 5-toothed, the upper tooth longer than the lower. The corolla is 2-lipped, 1–1·3cm long, white with purple dots; the upper lip is flat, the tube is curved in, widened at the middle. There are 4 stamens, the outer pair shorter than the inner. The fruit consists of 4 obovoid smooth nutlets.

Habitat hedge banks, roadsides, along railways, etc., usually on calcareous soil. **Distribution** in England locally as far as Northumberland, in Scotland only in Wigtown and Stirling; locally in Ireland. Common over most of the rest of Europe. **Active ingredients** essential oils with carvacrol, nepetol, thymol, bitter principle. **Effect** relieves flatulence and spasms, aids menstrual flow and stimulates stomach functions. **Parts used** the fresh or dried flowering herb; cut 10cm above the ground, dry in shade. **Application M:** an infusion (1–2½ teaspoons per cup, allow to stand for 10 minutes) is given 3–4 times a day for chills, flatulence, anaemia, abdominal colics and amenorrhoea or other female complaints.

Galeopsis segetum

Leonurus cardiaca

Nepeta cataria

Ⓜ️ *Glechoma hederacea* L. Labiatae
Ⓔ **Ground Ivy** (March–May) A perennial herb with creeping and rooting non-flowering stems and 10–60cm tall ascending or erect flowering stems. The leaves are opposite, 0·3–7cm long, subcircular-cordate or reniform, usually obtuse, crenate, usually glabrous. The flowers are bilaterally symmetrical, arranged in 1-sided 2 to 5-flowered whorls. The calyx is hairy, often with yellow glands, tubular to bell-shaped, up to 7mm long, 2-lipped; the upper lip has 3 teeth, the lower 2 teeth. The corolla is 2-lipped, 1–2·3cm long, pale violet, rarely pinkish or white; the tube is straight, the upper lip flat, the lower lip 3-lobed. The fruit consists of 4 smooth, 2mm long nutlets.

Habitat grassland, woods, waste places, usually in damp soil. **Distribution** all over Europe; in the British Isles, rare in Scotland, absent from Orkney and the Outer Hebrides. **Active ingredients** essential oil, tannin, bitter principle, resin, saponin. **Effect** astringent, anti-inflammatory, diuretic. **Parts used** the fresh (in homoeopathy) or dried flowering herb; dry in shade. **Application M:** in homoeopathy an essence is prescribed for haemorrhoids. In the home an infusion (2–3 teaspoons per cup water, allow to stand for 5 minutes) is taken internally 2–3 times a day for bronchial catarrhs and abdominal or stomach disorders; externally as a gargle for sore throat and mouth infections or for bathing cuts and bruises. **E:** young shoots and leaves, collected before flowering in spring, lend a special flavour to vegetable soups; they can also be treated and eaten like spinach.

Ⓜ️ *Marrubium vulgare* L. Labiatae
White Horehound (June–Sept.) A perennial, whitish-tomentose herb with a short rhizome. The leaves are opposite, 1·8–4·5cm long, circular or broadly ovate from a heart or wedge-shaped base, crenate, petiolate (the lower ones much longer than the upper). The flowers are bilaterally symmetrical, arranged in many-flowered axillary whorls. The calyx is 10-nerved, with 10 teeth curved at the point. The corolla is 2-lipped, white or rarely pinkish white, 1–1·6cm long, with the upper lip almost flat; the tube does not exceed the calyx. The fruit consists of 4 ovoid, smooth nutlets.

Habitat waste places, roadsides, grassy slopes. **Distribution** over most of Europe; in the British Isles from Moray southwards; in Ireland from Dublin and Galway southwards. **Active ingredients** essential oil, bitter principle, tannin. **Effect** stimulates bile flow; expectorant. **Parts used** the flowering herb; cut above ground, dry in shade. **Application M:** the drug is mainly used for disorders of the gall bladder (more rarely for catarrhs) but usually in herbal remedies with a mixture of other herbal remedies such as *Mentha, Taraxacum* and *Agrimonia*. In the home an infusion (2 teaspoons per cup water, allow to stand for 10–12 minutes) or a decoction (1 teaspoon per cut water, bring to the boil, allow to stand for 15 minutes) 2–3 times a day is used for the same disorders and (taken 30 minutes before meals) for lack of appetite. It can be applied externally to slow-healing cuts and skin disorders.

Ⓜ️ *Scutellaria galericulata* L. Labiatae
Skull-cap (June–Aug.) A perennial, usually slightly pubescent herb with a creeping rhizome. The stems are simple or branched, 12–55cm tall. The leaves are lanceolate to oblong-lanceolate from a heart-shaped base, distantly toothed, slightly petiolate. The flowers are bilaterally symmetrical, usually arranged in axillary pairs, almost sessile. The calyx is distinctly 2-lipped, closed in fruit; the upper lip has a small scale-like appendage; both lips are entire. The corolla is 2-lipped, 1·2–2cm long, blue or blue-violet, long-exceeding the calyx; the tube is curved. The fruit consists of 4 almost globose nutlets.

Habitat in moist places; along streams and ditches, waterlogged meadows, fens, etc. **Distribution** all over the region except in Shetlands. **Active ingredients** scutellarine (a flavone glycoside). **Effect** anti-inflammatory; alleviates fever. **Parts used** the flowering herb. **Application M:** in both allopathic and homoeopathic medicine this drug is now obsolete. In the past it was used as a remedy for malaria. In the home an infusion (1–2 teaspoons per cup water, allow to stand for 8–12 minutes) taken 2–3 times a day is sometimes used for throat infections.

Glechoma hederacea

Marrubium vulgare

Scutellaria galericulata

Ⓜ *Teucrium chamaedrys* L. Labiatae

Wall Germander (June–Sept.) A perennial with stems that are often woody at the base, ascending and usually rooting below, 8–35cm long, hairy. The leaves are opposite, 0·8–3·2cm long, ovate from a wedge-shaped base, shortly petiolate, somewhat lobed or crenate, dark green and glossy on the upper surface, hairy on the lower surface. The flowers are bilaterally symmetrical, arranged in 2 to 6 flowered whorls forming a terminal, slightly one-sided spike-like raceme. The calyx is 4–6·5mm long, 5-toothed. The corolla is pink-purple, rarely white, 0·9–1·6cm long, consisting of one 5-lobed hairy lip. The fruit consists of 4 obovoid nutlets.

Habitat roadsides, open woodland, dry grassy slopes, in hedges, on (mainly calcareous) rocks and walls. **Distribution** Europe north to the Netherlands, in the British Isles occasionally naturalized on old walls. **Active ingredients** essential oil, tannin, bitter principle. **Effect** diuretic; stimulates stomach functions and gland secretions. **Parts used** the flowering herb; cut a few centimetres above ground, dry in shade or in a well-ventilated room. **Application M:** in the home the infusion (2 teaspoons per cup water, allow to stand for 10–12 minutes) is drunk 2–3 times a day as a diuretic or for a weak stomach and lack of appetite.

Ⓜ *Ajuga reptans* L. Labiatae

Bugle (May–July) A perennial herb with a short rhizome and long rooting stolons. The stem is usually erect, 8–30cm tall, usually hairy on two opposite sides (rarely all-round). The basal leaves form a rosette, 3·5–7·5cm long, obovate or oblong-ovate, tapering into a long petiole; the stem leaves are opposite, much shorter, almost sessile. The flowers are bilaterally symmetrical, arranged in many-flowered axillary whorls forming a terminal spike; the bracts are tinged blue. The calyx is 5–7cm long, 5-toothed. The corolla is 2-lipped (the upper lip very short; the lower 3-lobed), blue or pinkish, rarely white. The fruit consists of 4 veined nutlets.

Habitat woods, meadows, pastures, usually on moist ground. **Distribution** throughout the region. **Active ingredients** not well-identified tannins and perhaps a glycoside. **Effect** astringent; stimulates bile flow. **Parts used** the flowering herb; cut above the ground, dry in shade or sun. **Application M:** given as an infusion (1–1½ teaspoons per cup, allow to stand for 5–8 minutes), mixed with *Mentha piperita*, 2–3 times a day for dyspepsia and gall disorders.

Ⓜ Ⓔ *Rosmarinus officinalis* L. Labiatae

Rosemary (June–Sept.) An evergreen aromatic shrub, 30–150cm (up to 300cm) tall, with erect or ascending branches. The leaves are opposite, 1·3–4cm long, linear or narrowly oblong, leathery, green and wrinkled on the upper surface, white-tomentose on the lower surface, margins revolute. The flowers are bilaterally symmetrical, arranged in few-flowered whorls in short axillary and terminal racemes. The calyx is 2-lipped, 3–4·5mm long (5–7mm in fruit), sometimes purplish, initially tomentose, the upper lip entire, the lower 2-lobed. The corolla is 2-lipped, exceeding the calyx, up to 1·3cm long, pale blue, sometimes pink or white, upper lip concave. The 2 stamens are exserted. The fruit consists of 4 brown nutlets.

Habitat dry grassland, amongst rocks, often near the seashore. **Distribution** in most parts of Europe, the British Isles and Ireland; cultivated in gardens for ornament, culinary or medicinal purposes. **Active ingredients** essential oil with so-called rosemary-camphor, borneol, cineol, tannin, carboxylic acids, bitter principle, resin. **Effect** diuretic; antiseptic; prevents or relieves flatulence and spasms, stimulates bile flow and causes redness of the skin. **Parts used** the dried leaves at flowering time; dry in shade or in a well-ventilated room. **Application M:** in allopathic medicine the drug is very rarely used on its own but contained in a number of brands of proprietary medicine for circulatory disorders, heart-failure (especially in old age), liver and gall bladder ailments and – externally – muscular and rheumatic pain, pleurisy. The fresh leaves are used in homoeopathy for amenorrhoea, nervous stomach disorders, restlessness, anxiety and ulcers. In the home an infusion (1–1½ teaspoons per cup water, allow to stand for 10 minutes) 2–3 times a day for the above mentioned complaints as well as

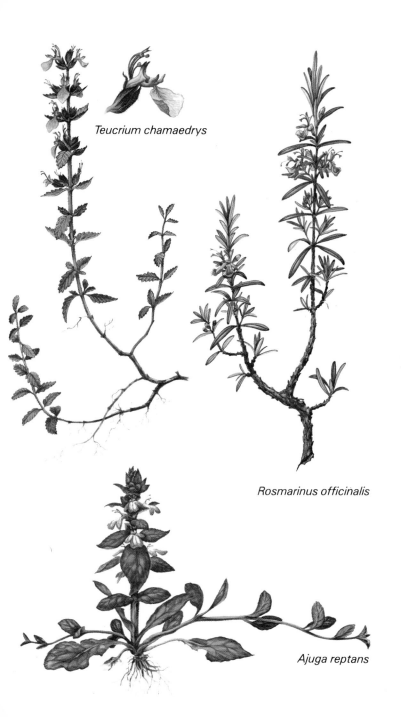

Teucrium chamaedrys

Rosmarinus officinalis

Ajuga reptans

low blood pressure and tiredness. For circulatory disorders use rosemary wine: put one handful of dried leaves into 750ml–1 litre of dry white wine allow to stand in a warm place for 7–10 days. Externally the infusion (made up to 1 litre) is added to the bath water (take 2–3 times weekly) for circulatory disorders or nervous exhaustion. **E:** rosemary leaves are a time-honoured condiment for flavouring various dishes (eggs, fish, poultry and meat). Because of its strong aromatic flavour they should be used sparingly. The essential oil of rosemary is also used in rosemarin-spirit and in the production of toilet waters, bath-essences, Eau de Cologne, and for scenting soap.

Ⓜ *Lavandula angustifolia* Miller Labiatae

Lavender (June/July–Sept.) A small aromatic evergreen shrub, 25–150cm (200cm) tall, with erect or ascending branches, tomentose. The leaves are opposite, 1·8–5cm long, narrowly oblong, linear or lanceolate, entire, at first white-tomentose, later green. The flowers are bilaterally symmetrical, arranged in whorls in usually dense 2–9cm long spikes; the bracts are different from the leaves, rhombic or ovate, up to 8mm long. The calyx is 13-veined, 5–7·5mm long, with small teeth. The corolla is purple or purplish-blue, 9–13mm long, 2-lipped; the upper lip is 2-lobed, the lower 3-lobed. The fruit consists of 4 very small nutlets.

Habitat dry grassy slopes, amongst rocks. **Distribution** native to the Mediterranean region and widely cultivated for ornamental purposes all over Europe as well as for perfumery (mainly in S. France but formerly also in England). **Active ingredients** abundant essential oil, tannin, a glycoside, saponin. **Effect** mildly sedative; prevents or relieves flatulence and spasms, and stimulates bile flow. **Parts used** the fresh or dried not fully opened flowers; dry in shade. **Application M:** this drug is contained in a number of brands of proprietary medicines for muscular and rheumatic pain (externally) and for disorders of the gall bladder, insomnia, nervous disorders, migraine. In the home an infusion (1–1½ teaspoons per cup water, allow to stand for 12 minutes) 2–3 times a day is taken for persistent headaches, nervous heart-ailments, flatulence or diarrhoea. The infusion can also be added to the bathwater as indicated for rosemary. Lavender is widely used for perfume notably Eau de Cologne.

Ⓜ *Plantago lanceolata* L. Plantaginaceae
Ⓔ

Ribwort (May–Sept.) A perennial herb with 20–47cm tall flower-scape and a short, silkily hairy stem. The leaves are all basal, 3–30cm long, lanceolate to ovate-lanceolate, usually entire, rarely toothed, distinctly 3 to 5-nerved, tapering into a usually long petiole at the base. The flowers are very small, regular, arranged in a dense 1–5cm long, cylindrical spike; the scape is always longer than the leaves, deeply grooved. The corolla is 4-lobed, 3·5–4mm in diameter, brownish; the lobes are acute, with a brown midrib. The 4 white stamens are inserted in the corolla-tube. The fruit is a 4–5mm wide 2-seeded capsule.

Habitat grassland, roadsides, river banks, hedges, etc. **Distribution** throughout the region. **Active ingredients** mucilage, silicic acid, aucubine, ursolic acid, tannins, vitamin C. **Effect** mildly expectorant, mildly purgative and (perhaps) diuretic. **Parts used** the dried leaves; dry as quickly as possible in the sun or shade (leaves which are black should be discarded); store in sacks suspended in well-ventilated rooms. **Application M:** the drug is contained in some cough mixtures. In the home an infusion (2 teaspoons per cup water, allow to stand for 12–15 minutes) is taken 2–3 times a day for bronchitis and coughs; it is also taken as a spring tonic (to purify the blood), for disorders of the liver and diarrhoea. The freshly pressed juice can also be taken for coughs. **E:** The young leaves are occasionally eaten. They are, however, rather bitter and tedious to prepare since their fibrous strands have to be removed before use.

Ⓜ *Plantago major* L. Plantaginaceae

Great Plantain (June–Oct.) This perennial is closely related to the above but can be distinguished from it as follows. The leaves are ovate or elliptic from a broadly rounded base. The scape is not grooved. The corolla lobes are without a prominent brown midrib. The anthers are lilac to yellowish. Otherwise as for the preceding species. The dried, mature inflorescences can be used as food for cage birds.

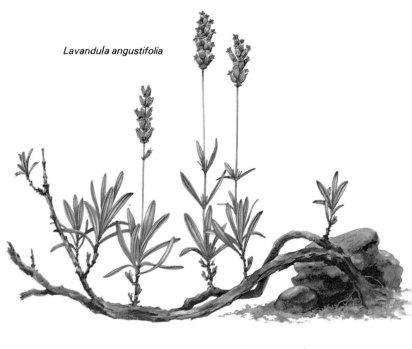

Lavandula angustifolia

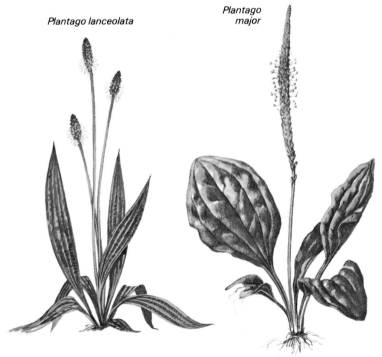

Plantago lanceolata

Plantago major

(M) *Plantago arenaria* L. *(P. indica, P. psyllum)* Plantaginaceae
Fleawort (Aug.–Sept.) An annual herb, 8–40cm tall, with a slender, tapering root. The stems are erect or spreading, usually branched, leafy and hairy. The leaves are opposite, 2·5–10cm long, linear, entire or sometimes obscurely toothed; the lower ones most often have axillary shoots. The flowers as in the preceding species are 3·5–4mm in diameter, arranged in compact, 0·8–1·2cm long, almost globular spikes; corolla brownish-white. The fruit is a capsule; the 2 boat-shaped seeds (smooth above, concave below) in both colour and shape are reminiscent of a flea.

Habitat waste places, disturbed ground, often on dunes. **Distribution** throughout S and C. Europe (widely cultivated especially in S. France for medicinal purposes). **Active ingredients** abundant mucilage (the seeds swell when in contact with water and increase their volume several times), aucubine. **Effect** purgative, skin softener **Parts used** the mature seeds. **Application M:** this drug represents a most useful and mild laxative for constipation and flatulence. It is best taken by mixing 1–2 teaspoons with one cupful of soup, milk, unsweetened pudding or fruit juice. There are a few brands of pharmaceutical preparations on the market which contain it in one form or another.

(E) *Campanula rapunculus* L. Campanulaceae
Rampion (leaves: June–Sept; roots: April/May–Sept/Oct.) A biennial herb with a turnip-like root stock. The stems are erect, simple, 25–80cm (up to 100cm) tall, sometimes slightly hairy. The basal leaves are obovate from an abruptly contracted base, obtuse to acuminate, petiolate; the stem leaves are sessile, lanceolate to linear-lanceolate, with the margins crenate. The flowers are regular, sessile or shortly pedicellate, arranged in a simple or branched (in the lower part) racemose inflorescence. The calyx has 5 very long, erect teeth. The corolla is 1·1–2·2cm long, pale blue or sometimes white, funnel-shaped, exceeding the calyx-teeth slightly, the 5 lobes about half as long as the tube, acute. The fruit is an obconical capsule opening near the apex.

Habitat at the edges of woods and forests, meadows, hedge banks, fields. **Distribution** in the British Isles scattered all over England and S. Scotland. In the rest of Europe southwards from the Netherlands. **Parts used** the leaves before flowering, the roots either in spring or the autumn. **Application E:** the leaves are used for salads either on their own or mixed with other wild or cultivated salad plants. The roots must be thoroughly cleaned and boiled. Since they possess a mild and sweetish taste they are better mixed with other root-vegetables for salad.

Plantago arenaria

Campanula rapunculus

Ⓜ *Asperula odorata* L. *(Galium odoratum)* (L.) Scop. Rubiaceae

Ⓔ **Sweet Woodruff** (May–June) A perennial herb with a slender, branched, creeping rhizome, pleasantly (hay) scented when dried. The stems are erect, unbranched, quadrangular, 10–45cm tall, glabrous but hairy beneath the nodes. The leaves are arranged in distant whorls, 2–4·2cm long (the lower ones smaller than the middle ones), lanceolate to elliptical, usually cuspidate, the margins with forwardly-directed prickles. The flowers are regular, 5·5–6·5mm in diameter, shortly pedicelled, arranged in a complex umbel-like inflorescence. The calyx is minute, ridge-like. The corolla is funnel shaped, white, 4-lobed; the lobes obtuse, about the same length as the tube. The fruit is 2–3mm wide, with hooked bristles.

Habitat in woods, usually on damp calcareous soil. **Distribution** throughout the region except in Orkney and the Outer Hebrides. **Active ingredients** coumarin glycoside, asperuloside, tannins, bitter principle, vitamin C. **Effect** sedative, diuretic; prevents and relieves spasms. **Parts used** the fresh or dried herb; cut shortly before (best) or at flowering time; dry in shade. **Application M:** the drug contained in some brands of proprietary medicine for haemorrhoids, circulatory disorders and as a prophylactic for thrombosis. In the home an infusion (2 teaspoons per cup water, allow to stand for 10–12 minutes) can be taken 2–3 times a day for nervous tension and insomnia (1 cup in the evening). There are no known harmful side effects. **E:** The fresh herb lends its flavour to liquors and especially to May-cups.

Ⓜ *Galium verum* L. Rubiaceae

Lady's Bedstraw (May–Sept.) A sweet-scented perennial, stoloniferous herb with a slender creeping rhizome. The stems are decumbent to erect, 10–80cm (up to 100cm) long, quadrangular. The leaves, arranged in whorls of 8–18, are 0·5–2·6cm long, linear, 1-veined, dark green, with revolute margins. The flowers are regular, 2–4mm in diameter, arranged in a many-flowered, complex, panicle-like inflorescence. The calyx is minute, ridge-like. The corolla is yellow, wheel-like with 4 pointed lobes. The fruit consists of two, 1·5mm wide, glabrous, smooth, 1-seeded mericarps.

Habitat in grassland, downs, hedge banks, dunes. **Distribution** throughout the region. **Active ingredients** silicic acid, glycosides, tannins, traces of essential oil, organic acids. **Effect** diuretic; prevents or relieves spasms. **Parts used** the dried flowering herb; cut, bundle and hang up in the sun or shade. **Application M:** in both allopathic and homoeopathic medicine this drug is obsolete. For domestic purposes an infusion (2 teaspoons per cup water, allow to stand for 8–12 minutes) is taken 3–4 times a day for dropsy, kidney and bladder disorders and stomach upsets. In the past it has also been applied externally to skin infections and septic or slow healing cuts and grazes.

Ⓜ *Galium aparine* L. Rubiaceae

Goosegrass, Sticky Willie (not illustrated) This annual is related to the above but can easily be distinguished: the stems are never erect, scrambling to ascending, set with distinct recurved prickles along the angles; the leaves are narrowly elliptic or linear-oblanceolate; the corolla is whitish; the fruit is up to 6mm wide, greenish or purplish, covered with white hooked prickles.

Habitat hedges, along fences, waste places, scree, shingle, etc. **Distribution** all over Europe and the British Isles. **Active ingredients, effect, parts used** and **application** as for the preceding species. **Note** a strong decoction (both species) makes milk coagulate.

Galium verum

Asperula odorata

Ⓜ *Rubia tinctorum* L. Rubiaceae

Madder A perennial herb with a long-creeping, yellow root stock with bright red fibrous roots. The stems are quadrangular, climbing, 25–100cm long. The leaves, arranged in whorls of 4–6, are 2–10cm long, lanceolate or oblong-elliptical, light green with distinct lateral venation on the lower surface. The flowers are arranged in axillary, 5–30cm long, many-flowered cymes. The calyx is minute or completely absent. The corolla is up to 6·2mm in diameter, light yellow; the tube is short, the lobes 2·5–3·5mm long, acuminate. The fruit is a fleshy, usually only 1-seeded mericarp.

Habitat hedges, along fences, thickets, waste places. **Distribution** naturalized after extensive cultivation – as a dye-plant – in S. and C. Europe; in the British Isles only found as a casual (formerly cultivated). **Active ingredients** anthraquinone glycosides, tannins, organic acids, fatty oil, pectin, sugar. **Effect** prevents or relieves spasms; perhaps mildly diuretic. **Parts used** the root stock; clean, take off roots, peel off outer skin, dry quickly to prevent mould. **Application M:** in homoeopathy a tincture is prepared and prescribed for anaemia, amenorrhoea, anorexia and disorders of the spleen. The drug is contained in a number of brands of proprietary medicine for bladder stones (mainly prophylactic or post-operative) and kidney colics. A maceration (1 teaspoon shredded root, per cup of cold water, allow to stand for 8–10 hours) 2–3 times a day can be taken for the same complaints. **Note** the drug stains the urine red.

Ⓜ Ⓔ *Sambucus nigra* L. Caprifoliaceae

Elder (flowers: June–July; fruits: Sept.–Oct.) A deciduous shrub or small tree, 2–10m tall, with arching branches and a cork-like brownish-grey bark, the younger branches and twigs with conspicuous lenticels. The leaves are pinnate, the leaflets number 3–9, ovate, ovate-elliptic or ovate-lanceolate, sometimes dissected, 2·5–9cm long. The stipules are absent or very small. The flowers are regular, arranged in large, flat-topped, umbel-like inflorescences (up to 21cm in diameter). The calyx has a very narrow limb. The corolla is 4–5·5mm in diameter, cream-white, with a short tube and a spreading 5-lobed limb. The anthers cream-coloured. The fruit is a fleshy drupe, globose, 6–8mm in diameter, black.

Habitat scrub, woods, roadsides, waste places. **Distribution** all over the region. **Active ingredients** essential oil, glycoside sambunigrine, rutin, tannin, traces of essential oil, anthocyanine. **Effect** stimulates sweating (flowers and fruit); purgative, diuretic (fruit). **Parts used** the flowers – collect the entire inflorescence and dry and comb off the flowers; the mature berries – dry in shade or in artificial heat (not over 40°C); also (sometimes) the leaves and bark. **Application M:** this time-honoured drug is used whenever perspiration is required for speeding the healing-process. It is taken as hot as possible as an infusion: 2 teaspoons per cup water, or better 1 teaspoon *Sambucus* and 1 teaspoon *Tilia* flowers, allow to stand for 8–12 minutes, taken 2–3 times a day for the common cold, other febrile conditions and to activate kidney-functions. The freshly pressed juice of the berries acts as a laxative or is taken for bronchitis and coughs. **E:** The juice mixed with equal parts of honey is used as a spread or for puddings and other sweets; it can also be blended with other fruit juices (prunes, apples, pears, etc.). **Note** *All green parts of this plant are poisonous.*

Ⓜ Ⓔ *Sambucus racemosa* L. Caprifoliaceae

Red-berried Elder (fruit: June–July) This perennial is related to *S. nigra* (above) and *S. ebulus* (below). It can be distinguished from both by its panicle-like inflorescence (not flat-topped) and scarlet berries.

Habitat open woods, edges of beech-forests, usually in mountain areas. **Distribution** C, and S. Europe; in the British Isles planted and occasionally naturalized. **Active ingredients** fatty oils, vitamin C. **Effect** emetic, purgative. **Parts used** the oil extracted from the seeds. **Application M:** in the home a decoction of the berries has been used for constipation or to induce vomiting; this use is, however, inadvisable. **E:** the mature berries are a fine source of vitamin C and can also be turned into a jelly but only after the seeds have been completely removed.

Sambucus racemosa

Rubia tinctorum

Sambucus nigra

Ⓜ️ *Sambucus ebulus* L. Caprifoliaceae

Dwarf Elder, Danewort This perennial is related to the Elder but, besides being a herb, can be distinguished by the following characteristics. It has a stout creeping rhizome. The leaves smell unpleasant and have conspicuous ovate to elliptic stipules. The flowers are usually reddish-white.

Habitat clearings in forests, roadsides, waste places, hedges, ditches. **Distribution** S. Europe and in C. Europe as far as the Netherlands. Scattered over most of the British Isles but rare in Scotland. **Active ingredients** bitter principles, tannin, traces of essential oil. **Effect** mildly diuretic, emetic; stimulates perspiration. **Parts used** the dried rhizome and roots; clean, cut into small pieces or shred; dry quickly in a warm room and store in a dark place. Rarely the mature berries, or fresh bark of young branches. **Application M:** in homoeopathy an essence, prepared from fresh berries or the bark, is prescribed for dropsy. In allopathy the drug is contained (usually with *Convallaria, Scilla* and *Chimaphila*) in a few brands of medicine for diuretics. In the home an infusion (½ teaspoon per cup water, allow to stand for 12–15 minutes) is taken 1–2 times a day for dropsy, kidney complaints or rheumatic pain. This remedy should, however, only be taken under medical supervision; it may cause nausea or vertigo.

Ⓜ️ *Viburnum opulus* L. Caprifoliaceae

Guelder Rose (March–April/Oct) A deciduous shrub, 2–4m high, with glabrous, angled twigs. The buds are without scales. The leaves are opposite, simple, 3–12cm long, with up to 5 irregularly toothed lobes, oval to heart-shaped in outline, glabrous on the upper surface, pubescent on the lower surface, turning red in the autumn; the petioles are up to 3·5cm long; the stipules are thread-like. The flowers are regular, arranged in 4–10cm wide cymose corymbs. The calyx is 5-lobed. The corolla is 5-lobed, white (the central ones fertile, 4·5–7·5mm in diameter; the outer ones larger and showy, sterile). The stamens number 5. The fruit is a drupe, red, subglobose, 6–8·5mm in diameter.

Habitat hedges, scrub, woods. **Distribution** all over the region. **Active ingredients** viburnin, baldrianic acid, resin, pectin, sugar. **Effect** astringent, sedative; prevents or relieves spasms. **Parts used** the fresh bark. **Application M:** in homoeopathy an essence, prepared from fresh bark, is prescribed for menstrual pain and spasms after birth. In the past a decoction has been used in the home for the same complaints and for abdominal haemorrhages. **Note** the North American species *V. prunifolium* L., which is an up to 8m-tall tree and cultivated for ornament, has similar properties.

Ⓜ️ *Valeriana officinalis* L. Valerianaceae

Valerian (Sept.–Oct.) A perennial herb with a short, unbranched rhizome, rarely stoloniferous. The stems are erect, robust, glabrous or hairy below, 15–80cm (up to 150cm) tall. The leaves are pinnate with a terminal leaflet, 5–22cm long, petiolate, the upper ones almost sessile; the leaflets are lanceolate, sometimes irregularly toothed. The flowers are regular, hermaphrodite, arranged in a terminal cymose inflorescence. The calyx forms a pappus in fruit. The corolla is 4–5·5mm in diameter, white-pink, funnel-shaped, 5-lobed; 3 stamens. The fruit is a 1-seeded, ovate-oblong, 2·5–4mm long nut.

Habitat grassland, scrub, meadows, woods, on dry or damp soil. **Distribution** all over the region (as far north as Sweden). **Active ingredients** essential oil, valepotriate, resin, starch, sugar, traces of alkaloids. **Effect** sedative (acting on the central nervous system); prevents or relieves spasms. **Parts used** the roots; collect after the leaves have died, wash, remove small roots, dry in shade or at 30°C. Store in tight-lidded containers. **Application M:** a maceration (1–1½ teaspoons per cup of cold water, allow to stand for 8–9 minutes) is taken 1–2 times a day for headaches, nervous heart-disorders, insomnia (1 cup before bedtime), and neurasthenia. The drug is contained in many brands of proprietary medicine prescribed for these and other disorders. There are no known harmful side effects but use of the drug can become addictive.

Sambucus ebulus

Valeriana officinalis

Viburnum opulus

(E) *Valerianella locusta* (L.) Betcke *(V. olitoria)* Valerianaceae

Lamb's Lettuce, Corn Salad (April– May) A small annual herb, 5–40cm tall, with brittle, branched stems. The lower stem leaves are 1·5–7cm long, paddle-shaped, obtuse, entire or toothed; the upper stem leaves are shorter, lanceolate, obtuse or sharply acute. The flowers are very small, regular, arranged in cymose heads. The calyx is almost absent, or appearing as a 1-toothed rim. The corolla is funnel-shaped, pale lilac, not spurred, 5-lobed. The stamens number 3. The fruit is a 1-seeded nut, 2–2·6mm long, subcircular, compressed.

Habitat on cultivated ground, waste places, hedge banks, dunes, usually in dry soil. **Distribution** all over the region (except the extreme north). **Parts used** the young lower leaves, collected before the flowering stem develops. **Application E:** widely cultivated, it provides an excellent and tasty spring salad and can be eaten on its own or mixed with other salad plants (it makes a fine addition to potato salad!). In cultivation several harvests over the year are possible; it is usually sown as a second crop in August/September and gathered over the autumn and winter until the shoots develop in the spring.

(M) *Knautia arvensis* (L.) Coul. Dipsacaceae

Field Scabious A perennial herb with a stout, almost erect, branched stock, usually with underground stolons. The stem is erect, 10–80cm (up to 100cm) tall, rounded in cross-section, with bristles below. The basal leaves form an overwintering rosette, oblanceolate, simple or pinnatifid or crenate, shortly petiolate; the stem leaves are deeply pinnatifid to (rarely) entire and all the leaves are hairy. The flowers are arranged in dense, flat heads with an involucre formed by numerous ovate-lanceolate bracts (in 2 rows), bluish-lilac, the peripheral flowers larger than the central ones. The calyx has 8 teeth. The corolla is unequally 4-lobed. The fruit is densely hairy, 4–6cm long.

Habitat meadows, pastures, hedge banks and similar grassy places; usually in dry soil. **Distribution** all over the region (absent from Shetland and the Outer Hebrides). **Active ingredients** tannins, bitter principle, sugar. **Effect** astringent, mildly diuretic. **Parts used** the fresh or dried flowering herb, with or without roots. **Application M:** in homoeopathy an essence, prepared from fresh material, is prescribed for purifying the blood, eczema and other skin-disorders. In the home an infusion (2–3 teaspoons per cup water, allow to stand for 5 minutes) is taken 2–3 times daily for purifying the blood or used externally for cuts, burns and bruises.

(M) *Succisa pratensis* Moench Dipsacaceae

Devil's-bit Scabious (June– Oct.) A perennial herb with a short erect root stock. The stems are ascending to erect, 10–80cm (up to 100cm) tall. The leaves are arranged in opposite pairs; the basal ones are arranged in a rosette, 5–30cm long, narrowly obovate to narrowly elliptic from a tapering base, obtuse to acute; the stem leaves are few, often only bract-like. The flowers are arranged in dense hemispherical, long-pedunculate heads, 1·5–2·7cm in diameter. The bracts of the involucre are in 2–3 rows, herbaceous. The calyx is cup-shaped with 4 seta-like teeth. The corolla has 4 almost equal lobes, lilac to dark violet-blue, sometimes white. The fruit is unopening, 1-seeded, crowned by the persistent calyx.

Habitat meadows, pastures, fens, damp woods and similar localities. **Distribution** throughout the region. **Active ingredients** saponins, tannin, sugar, scabioside, amidon. **Effect** diuretic, mildly expectorant; stimulates stomach functions and kills worms. **Parts used** the dried flowering herb and rhizome plus roots; dig up in spring, cut or shred and dry in a warm room. **Application M:** drug is obsolete in homoeopathy and allopathy. In the home it can be given as an infusion (1 teaspoon per cup water, allow to stand for 10–12 minutes) 1–3 times a day for coughs, bronchitis, asthma, diarrhoea and skin disorders. A stronger infusion (2 teaspoons per cup water) is used as a gargle for mouth and throat infections.

Valerianella locusta

Succisa pratensis

Knautia arvensis

Ⓔ *Galinsoga parviflora* Cav. Compositae

Gallant Soldier, Joey Hooker (April–Oct.) An annual weak herb with erect, branched, usually glabrous 8–60cm (up to 80cm) tall stems. The leaves are opposite, 1·5–9cm long, simple, ovate-acuminate, shortly petiolate, the margins toothed. The flower heads are rather small, 2·5–5mm in diameter, globular, arranged in dichasial cymes. The bracts of the involucre are few, in 1–2 rows, broadly ovate. The ray florets number 4–8, white; the female are ligulate; the disc florets are few, tubular, hermaphrodite, yellow. The fruit is a 1–1·5mm long, obovoid-prismatic, somewhat compressed achene.

Habitat arable land, waste places, along fences, pavements in towns, etc. Distribution in the British Isles mainly in S. England and as a weed around and in London. Parts used the young leaves and tips of shoots, before flowering. Application E: can be used like spinach or added to soups and stews; it is also a fine salad plant either on its own or mixed with other wild or cultivated salads. The fresh juice can be drunk mixed with tomato or other vegetable juices.

☠ *Senecio jacobaea* L. Compositae

Ⓜ **Ragwort** (July–Aug.) (Not illustrated) A biennial to perennial herb with an erect, short root stock, without stolons. The stems are 23–120cm (up to 150cm) tall, erect, furrowed, branched above; the leaves are spirally arranged; the basal ones arranged in a rosette, short-lived, petiolate, lyrate to pinnatifid; the stem leaves are pinnatifid to double-pinnatifid, with the terminal lobe longest; all the leaves are softly and thinly woolly beneath. The flower heads are 1·2–2.5cm in diameter, arranged in a large, flat, dense corymb. The bracts of the involucre are oblong-lanceolate. The ray florets and disc florets are golden-yellow. The fruit is a 1·8–2·2mm long achene with a long pappus.

Habitat roadsides, waste places, pastures, similar grassy places and dunes. Distribution throughout the region. Active ingredients essential oil, rutin, an alkaloid, mucilage, mineral salts. Effect astringent, expectorant; aids menstrual flow, stops bleeding and causes softening of the skin. Parts used the fresh or dried flowering herb. Application C: in homoeopathy an essence, based on fresh material, is prescribed for dysmenorrhoea and other female complaints, internal haemorrhages and circulatory disorders. Note all species of this genus are *poisonous* and may cause severe damage to the liver (including primary cancer) and should therefore *never be used for domestic medicinal purposes*.

☠ *Senecio vulgaris* L. Compositae

Ⓜ **Groundsel** (all year) This species is related to the above but differs mainly by being an annual (sometimes overwintering) and usually having no ray florets.

Habitat as a weed on cultivated ground, roadsides, waste places. Distribution throughout the region. Active ingredients the alkaloids senecionin and senecin, inulin. Effect mainly aids menstrual flow and stops bleeding. Parts used the fresh or dried flowering herb. Application C: in homoeopathy an essence, prepared from fresh material, is prescribed for menstrual disorders and nose bleeds. *Not to be used for domestic purposes.*

Galinsoga parviflora

Senecio vulgaris

Ⓜ *Tussilago farfara* L. Compositae
Ⓔ **Coltsfoot** (flowers: March – April; leaves: May – July) A robust perennial herb with white, scale-clad stolons. The leaves are all basal, appearing long after the flowers, 8 – 30cm wide, almost circular in outline but polygonal, with up to 12 acute lobes, at first whitish-tomentose or both, later only on the lower surface. The flower heads are solitary, terminal on 3 – 17cm tall white or purplish shoots. The bracts of the involucre are numerous but usually in 1 row, green or purplish linear. The ray florets are numerous (over 200), yellow, in many rows, female. The disc florets are few, male, yellow. The fruit is a 0·6 – 1·1cm long, glabrous achene with a much longer white pappus.

    Habitat neglected fields, waste ground, roadsides, banks, cliffs, scree, dunes, etc. **Distribution** throughout the region. **Active ingredients** abundant mucilage, rutin, inulin, bitter glycosidal principle, tannin, essential oil. **Effect** expectorant, anti-inflammatory, anti-irritant, mildly astringent; relieves or prevents spasms. **Parts used** mainly the fresh or dried leaves but also the dried flower heads before they are fully opened; dry in thin layers in shade. **Application M:** in the home an infusion (1 teaspoon per cup water, allow to stand for 5 – 8 minutes) 2 – 3 times a day is taken for bronchitis, cough and tracheitis as well as for stomach and abdominal disorders. The bruised leaves can also be applied to slow-healing cuts and grazes. **E:** the young leaves, flower buds and young flowers lend salads a distinctive aromatic flavour; they can also be used for soups and like spinach.

Ⓜ *Petasites hybridus* (L.) Gaertn., Mey. and Scherb. Compositae
Butterbur (leaves: June – July; root stock: Aug. – Oct.) A perennial herb with a stout, branched, almost 2m long, horizontal rhizome. The leaves are very large, almost all basal, 8 – 90cm wide, long petiolate, circular from a pronounced heart-shaped base, green on the upper surface, greyish on the lower surface; the petioles are hollow. The flowering stems are 10 – 50cm tall (taller in fruit). The flower heads number 1 – 3, in the axils of reddish-violet bracts; the predominantly male heads are up to 1·3cm in diameter, with up to 3 female and up to 40 sterile florets; the predominantly female heads are up to 7mm wide, with about 100 female and a few sterile florets. The fruit is a cylindrical 2 – 3·5mm long achene, yellow-brown with a whitish pappus.

    Habitat in moist soil. **Distribution** throughout the region. **Active ingredients** traces of essential oil, tannin, mucilage, resin, petasitine, petasine-S, inulin, pectin, glycosidal bitter principle. **Effect** analgesic, diuretic; stimulates perspiration and prevents spasms. **Parts used** the fresh or dried leaves and the root stock; dry in the shade, sun or a warm room. **Application M:** in the home a decoction (½ teaspoon per cup of cold water, bring to the boil, allow to stand for 15 minutes) or an infusion (1 – 1½ teaspoons per cup water, allow to stand for 8 – 10 minutes) 2 – 3 times a day for gall-stone colics, coughs and as a diuretic.

Ⓜ *Inula helenium* L. Compositae
Elecampane (Sept. – Oct.) A perennial herb with a single or branched tuberous root stock. The stems are erect, stout, 40 – 120cm (up to 150cm) tall, furrowed, softly hairy. The leaves are spirally arranged, simple; the basal ones are 20 – 42cm long, elliptical from a tapering base, long petiolate; the stem leaves are usually sessile, oval to heart-shaped from a clasping base; all the leaves are tomentose on the lower surface. The flower-heads are large and showy, up to 8·5cm in diameter, either solitary or a few arranged in a corymb. The bracts of the involucre are in many rows, the outer ones leaf-like. The ray florets are in 1 row, female, narrow, spreading, yellow. The disc florets are tubular, hermaphrodite, yellow. The fruit is a 4-ribbed, 4 – 5mm long achene.

    Habitat roadsides, neglected fields, waste places, open woods. **Distribution** throughout the region. **Active ingredients** essential oil, inulin, bitter principle, mucilage, resin. **Effect** mildly expectorant, prevents or relieves spasms, stimulates metabolism. **Parts used** the root stock; dig up, clean, cut or shred, dry in the sun or artificial heat (45 – 60°C). **Application M:** mainly used in the home as an infusion (1 teaspoon per cup water, allow to stand for 8 – 18 minutes) 2 – 3 times daily for bronchitis, disorders of the stomach, intestines or the gall bladder, lack of appetite and anorexia.

Tussilago farfara

Petasites hybridus

Inula helenium

Ⓜ️ *Antennaria dioica* (L.) Gaertn. Compositae

Cat's Foot (June–July) A greyish woolly perennial herb growing from a creeping woody overground stock and with rooting stolons. The stems are 3–22cm tall, erect. The leaves are mostly arranged in basal rosettes, 0·5–4cm long, obovate to paddle-shaped; the stem leaves are usually appressed, lanceolate or linear, acute. The flower-heads are dioecious, arranged in terminal umbel-like inflorescences (in female plants 0·9–1·2cm in diameter, in male plants 4·5–6·5cm in diameter). The bracts of the involucre are densely overlapping, woolly below, glabrous above, white or pinkish. The female heads have very narrow tubular florets; the pappus of the 1mm long achenes have hairs in several rows.

Habitat dry hills and mountain-slopes, pastures, heaths, etc. **Distribution** all over the British Isles and most of N. and C. Europe. **Active ingredients** essential oil, tannin, resin, mucilage. **Effect** diuretic, antidiarrhoeal; stimulates bile flow and kills worms. **Parts used** the dried, not fully opened flower heads; collect on a dry sunny day and dry in shade or sun. **Application M:** in the home an infusion (1½–2 teaspoons per cup water, allow to stand for 5–8 minutes) 2–4 times a day is taken for diarrhoea, gall bladder ailments and worms.

Ⓜ️ *Solidago virgaurea* L. Compositae

Golden-rod (July–Oct.) A perennial herb with a stout, ascending stock. The stems are up to 85cm tall, erect, simple or branched, rounded in cross-section, often pubescent. The leaves are alternate, mostly sessile; the basal ones are 2–12cm long, obovate from a tapering base; the stem leaves oblong-lanceolate to elliptical, entire or slightly toothed, acute. The flower heads are 0·5–1·1cm in diameter, shortly peduncu-late, arranged in a raceme or panicle. The bracts of the involucre are linear, in many rows, greenish, with scarious margins. The ray florets are in 1 row, yellow, female, spreading. The disc florets are yellow, hermaphrodite. The fruit is a 2·7–3·2mm long, brown, pubescent achene; the pappus greyish-white.

Habitat dry grassland, open woods, hedge banks, cliffs, etc. **Distribution** through-out the region. **Active ingredients** essential oil, saponins, tannin, bitter principle, catechin, organic acids. **Effect** mildly diuretic, antidiarrhoeal. **Parts used** the flowering herb; collect before the flower heads are fully developed, dry in shade. **Application M:** this drug is contained in numerous brands of proprietary medicine which are prescribed for kidney and bladder disorders, arthritis and rheumatism. In homoeopathy an essence, based on fresh material, is given for the same ailments. In the home an infusion (2 teaspoons per cup water, allow to stand for 10–12 minutes) is mainly taken 2–4 times a day as a diuretic or externally (use a stronger infusion) for bathing slow-healing cuts, burns and eczema. There are no known harmful side effects.

Ⓜ️ *Conyza canadensis* (L.) Cronq. *(Erigeron canadensis L.)* Compositae

Canadian Fleabane (June–Oct.) An annual herb with stems from 5–110cm tall, erect, stiff, leafy throughout. The leaves are arranged spirally; the basal ones are petiolate, usually entire, obovate-lanceolate, short-lived; the stem leaves are 1–5cm long, linear to narrowly lanceolate, acute, entire or slightly toothed and fringed with hairs. The flower heads are up to 5·5mm in diameter, numerous, arranged in a terminal panicle. The bracts of the involucre are linear, with scarious margins. The tubular florets are yellow (the central ones hermaphrodite, the outer female). The fruit is a 1–1·6mm long yellow achene; the pappus is yellowish, long.

Habitat waste places, neglected fields, roadsides, on dunes and walls, and as garden weed. **Distribution** throughout the region (rare in Scotland). **Active ingredients** essential oil, tannin, gallic acid, choline. **Effect** diuretic; stops bleeding and kills worms. **Parts used** the fresh flowering herb. **Application M:** in homoeopathy an essence is prescribed for haemorrhoids and painful menstruation. In the home an infusion (2 teaspoons per cup water, allow to stand for 5–8 minutes) is taken 2–3 times a day for uterine bleeding, diarrhoea, enteritis and dropsy.

Solidago virgaurea

Antennaria dioica

Conyza canadensis

Ⓜ *Bellis perennis* L. Compositae

Ⓔ **Daisy** (Feb./March– Oct./Nov.) A perennial herb with an erect stock and stout roots. The leaves are all in a basal rosette, obovate to paddle-shaped, shortly petiolate, 1·5–9cm long, scattered hairs, crenate to toothed. The flower heads are terminal on a 4–22cm long scape, 1·5–2·7cm in diameter. The receptacle is conicle, pitted. The bracts of the involucre are obtuse, usually arranged in 2 rows, green, with black apices. The ray florets are white or tinged red, spreading in 1 row, female. The disc florets are yellow, hermaphrodite. The fruit is a 1·5–2·5mm long achene, compressed, bordered, without ribs and pappus.

Habitat meadows and similar grassland. **Distribution** throughout the region. **Active ingredients** saponins, tannin, organic acids, essential oil, bitter principle, flavones, mucilage. **Effect** expectorant, mildly analgesic, anti-diarrhoeal, cures coughs and prevents or relieves spasms. **Parts used** the fresh or dried flower heads. **Application M:** this drug is used in the home as an infusion (1 teaspoon per cup water, allow to stand for 5–8 minutes) 2–4 times a day for catarrhs, arthritis, rheumatism, liver and kidney disorders, diarrhoea, and for purifying the blood. No harmful side effects. **E:** the young flower buds and young basal leaves can be eaten on sandwiches, in soups, and in salads. Preserved in vinegar the buds can be used as a substitute for capers.

Ⓜ *Eupatorium cannabinum* L. Compositae

Hemp Agrimony (July– Sept./Oct.) A large perennial herb with a woody root stock. The stems are 25–80cm (up to 125cm) tall, usually simple, softly hairy to glabrous. The leaves are opposite; the basal ones are oblanceolate, petiolate, the stem leaves almost sessile, 3-partite, 3–11cm long, dotted with glands. The flower heads are arranged in many-flowered, dense corymbs. The involucre has 10 bracts arranged in 2 rows, with purple tips, the outer shorter than the inner. The florets are all tubular, hermaphrodite, numbering 5–7, white or mauve. The fruit is a 5-angled achene, dotted with glands; the pappus is whitish, its hairs in 1 row.

Habitat in moist soil in woods, fens, marshes and along streams and ditches. **Distribution** throughout the region (rare in Scotland). **Active ingredients** essential oil, resin, tannin, inulin, euparin. **Effect** diuretic; stimulates bile flow. **Parts used** usually the fresh or dried flowering herb; cut above the ground, dry quickly in the sun or artificial heat (not over 40°C); sometimes the root stock. **Application M:** in homoeopathy an essence, prepared from fresh material, is prescribed for disorders of the liver, spleen and gall bladder and for dropsy. In the home an infusion (2 teaspoons per cup water, allow to stand for about 10 minutes) 2–3 times a day is given for the same complaints as well as for colds and influenza.

Ⓜ *Chamaemelum nobile* (L.) All. *(Anthemis nobilis* L.*)* Compositae

Chamomile (June– July) An aromatic perennial herb with a short much-branched creeping rhizome. The stems are 8–36cm long, decumbent or ascending, branched, hairy. The leaves are spirally arranged, sessile, oblong in outline, 2–3 pinnatisect; the lobes are linear, spine-tipped. The flower heads are 1·8–2·7cm in diameter, solitary, long-pedunculate. The bracts of the involucre are in 2-several rows, oblong, with broad scarious margins, glossy. The ray florets are female, spreading, white. The disc florets are yellow, tubular, with their enlarged base covering the apex of the achene, hermaphrodite. The fruit is a slightly compressed 1–1·5mm long achene with 3 stripes on the inner face.

Habitat roadsides, waste places, pastures and similar grassy places. **Distribution** in Belgium, France, S. England and S. Ireland. In the past widely cultivated for ornament, medicinal use and for lawns. **Active ingredients** essential oil with angelica-acid, apigenin, bitter principle, resin. **Effect** similar to *Chamomilla recutita* but only mildly relieves or prevents spasms. **Parts used** the flower heads; collect on a dry sunny day and dry in shade. **Application M:** this drug can be used as indicated for *C. recutita* but is not equally effective. A strong infusion (4 teaspoons per cup water, allow to stand for 10 minutes) is used for rinsing hair, has a mildly bleaching effect and heightens its blondness.

190

Bellis perennis

Eupatorium cannabinum

Chamaemelum nobile

Ⓜ ***Achillea millefolium*** L. Compositae
Ⓔ **Yarrow, Milfoil** (June– Oct.) A stoloniferous scented perennial herb. The stems are erect, unbranched, covered with woolly hairs, 10–65cm tall. The leaves are alternate, 2–3 times pinnatisect, 3–16cm long, lanceolate in outline, the basal ones petiolate, the upper ones sessile. The 4–7mm wide flower heads are arranged in terminal corymbs; the bracts of the involucre are in several rows, stiff, keeled, with brown or blackish scarious margins. The ray florets are female, usually numbering 5, white or sometimes pink or red; the disc florets are hermaphrodite, cream-coloured or white. The fruit is an achene, compressed, 1·75–2·25mm long, glossy, grey, slightly winged.

Habitat meadows, pastures, hedge banks along railway lines and similar grassy places. **Distribution** throughout the region. **Active ingredients** essential oil with chamazulene and cineole, tannin, achilleine, resin. **Effect** astringent, antiseptic, anti-inflammatory; stimulates stomach functions and bile flow, and prevents or relieves spasms. **Parts used** the flowering herb and the flowers; cut the herb 8–10cm above the ground, dry in shade or artificial heat (not over 35°C). **Application M:** mainly used in the home as an infusion (2 teaspoons per cup water, allow to stand for 8–10 minutes) 2–3 times a day for menstrual pain, indigestion and other stomach disorders. As an inhalant (boil 1 handful of the herb in 1½–2 litres of water and inhale hot steam) for infections of the respiratory tract. Externally it is used for bathing wounds and haemorrhoids (1–2 handfuls per litre) but this should be done in moderation (although the drug is harmless it may cause skin-irritation in some people). **E:** the young leaves (before the new flowering stems develop) can be eaten as salad (best mixed with other wild salad plants) or used as a vegetable.

Ⓜ ***Achillea moschata*** Wulfen *(A. erba-rotta* All. **subsp. *moschata*)** Compositae
Iva or Musk-Yarrow An aromatic perennial herb with a much-branched rhizome. The stems are 5–20cm tall, erect with scattered hairs, in the upper part also glandular to hairy. The leaves are lanceolate-oblong to oblong in outline, almost to the midrib pinnatifid, glabrous or with scattered hairs; the lobes number 6–12 on either side, entire or rarely 2 to 3 toothed, 0·5–1·5mm broad. The flower heads number 3–25, arranged in a terminal corymb, up to 1·5cm in diameter. The bracts of the involucre are 4–5mm long, with dark-brown margins. The ray florets number 6–8, white, spreading, the female disc florets are tubular, hermaphrodite, yellowish-white. The fruit is a 2mm long achene, ovate in outline, compressed, without ribs.

Habitat rocky slopes, alpine grassland, scree. **Distribution** eastern Alps (France and Germany), rare in the rest of the Alps. **Active ingredients** essential oil with cineole, bitter principles. **Effect** digestive, diuretic; stimulates appetite. **Parts used** the flowering herb; dry in shade. **Application M:** rarely used on its own in allopathic medicine, but is contained in a number of brands of proprietary medicine for lack of appetite, anorexia, physical and nervous exhaustion, irritability and nervous headaches. It is also used in the preparation of 'Iva-liquor', a medicinal aperitive, and for perfumery. In the home an infusion (1–1½ teaspoons per cup water, allow to stand for 10 minutes) is taken 2–3 times a day for the above complaints, as well as for haemorrhages, liver and kidney disorders and menstrual pains.

Ⓜ ***Chamomilla recutita*** (L.)Rauschert *(**Matricaria recutita**, **M. chamomilla**)* Compositae
Wild (German) Chamomile (May– Aug.) An annual soothingly aromatic herb. The stems are 10–60cm tall, erect, glabrous, much-branched. The leaves are alternate, 2–3 times pinnate, lanceolate-elliptic in outline; the final segments are narrowly linear ending in a fine bristle-like point. The flower heads are dense, 1·2–2·4cm in diameter, long peduncled. The receptacle is conical, hollow; the bracts of the involucre are linear, obtuse, greenish-yellow, with narrow, scarious greenish margins. The 12–16 ray florets are white, 5–10mm long, first spreading, later reflexed. The disc florets are yellow, 5-lobed. The fruit is a 1–2·25mm long achene, greyish, truncate, 4–5 ribbed on the ventral side, without outside oil-glands.

Habitat arable land, waste places, along roads. **Distribution** all over the region (rare

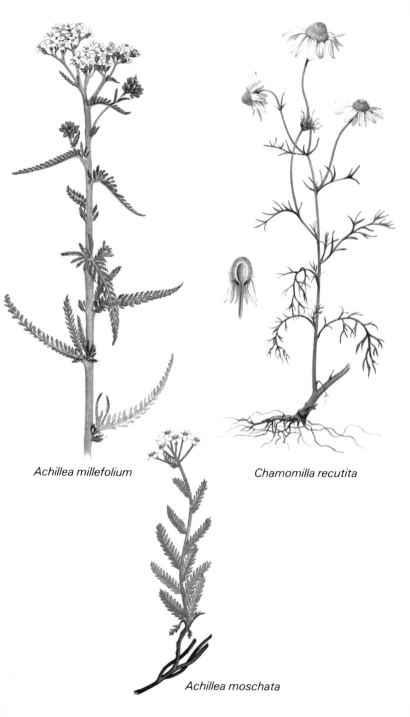

Achillea millefolium

Chamomilla recutita

Achillea moschata

in Scotland); often cultivated as a medicinal plant and naturalized. **Active ingredients** essential oil with bisabol oil and chamazulene, mucilage, flavone glycosides, coumarin, fatty acids. **Effect** antiseptic, analgesic, relieves flatulence and spasms, promotes perspiration, promotes healing of cuts and grazes. **Parts used** the fully developed flower heads; collect on dry day, dry in shade or artificial heat (not over 30°C). **Application M:** ancient and most widely used herb. An infusion (2 teaspoons dried flowers to 1 cup of boiling water) is taken after meals for disorders of the intestines, flatulence and peptic ulcers; a slightly stronger infusion is used for gargling against sore throats or as a mouthwash for gingivitis. As an inhalant (½ cup of dried flowers boiled in 4 pints of water – cover head with towel and inhale steam) against catarrh or as a steambath against inflamed haemorrhoids. Externally a hot compress (¼ cup of dried flowers before using) is used for healing cuts and bruises and against eczema.

Ⓜ *Chamomilla suaveolens* (Pursh) Rydb. *(Matricaria matricarioides)*
Compositae
Pineapple Weed (June–July) This strongly aromatic annual herb is related to the above species but can be easily distinguished from it by its much stronger and less pleasant smell, the absence of ray florets and by its 4-lobed tubular florets.

  Habitat roadsides, paths, in neglected fields, waste places, farmyards, etc. **Distribution** as a weed throughout the region. **Active ingredients** essential oils. **Effect** prevents or relieves spasms and kills worms. **Parts used** the flower heads or the entire flowering herb. **Application M:** obsolete in both allopathy and homoeopathy, is occasionally used in the home as an infusion (1 teaspoon per cup water, allow to stand for 8–10 minutes) 2–3 times a day for intestinal worms and as sedative. There are no harmful side effects.

Ⓜ *Tanacetum parthenium* (L.) Schultz Bipont.
(Chrysanthemum parthenium) Compositae
Feverfew (June–Aug.) A strongly aromatic perennial herb, growing from a usually vertical root stock. The stems are erect, 15–70cm tall, branched above, often downy. The leaves are spirally arranged, yellowish-green, 2–9cm long, narrowly-ovate to ovate in outline, pinnate with pinnatifid lobed or toothed leaflets, the lower ones long petiolate, the upper ones shortly petiolate and less divided. The flower heads are 1–2·4cm in diameter, arranged in loose corymbs. The bracts of the hemispherical involucre are keeled, with scarious edges and lanciniate tips. The ray florets are spreading, white, rather short, female; the disc florets are tubular hermaphrodite, yellow. The fruit is a 1·2–1·6mm long, 5–10 ribbed achene; the pappus is a membranous corona.

  Habitat mountain scrub, rocky slopes, walls, waste places, hedgerows, gardens. **Distribution** naturalized over most of Europe including the British Isles (not in Orkney and Shetland). **Active ingredients** essential oil, parthenolide, cosmosiine, borneol, bitter principle. **Effect** digestive, revulsive; kills worms. **Parts used** the dried flower head. **Application M:** this drug is no longer used in allopathic medicine and rarely for homoeopathic preparations. In the home it is occasionally used as a digestive (1 teaspoon per cup water) or as a mild worm killer.

Ⓔ *Leucanthemum vulgare* Lam.
(Chrysanthemum leucanthemum) Compositae
Marguerite, Ox-eye Daisy This well-known perennial is distinguished from the other species of the genus described here by having 2·5–5·5cm wide flower heads with white ray florets. The basal leaves are sub-circular from an obovate-paddle-shaped from an abruptly contracted base above the long petiole.

  Habitat meadows, pastures and other types of grassland. **Distribution** all over the region. **Parts used** young leaves and flower heads. **Application E:** the young leaves can be used for salads or eaten in sandwiches, omelettes etc.; but since they are rather pungent one should use them sparingly. They are best mixed with other salad plants either wild or cultivated. The flower heads can be used in the same way as *Taraxacum* for home winemaking.

Tanacetum parthenium

Chamomilla suaveolens

Leucanthemum vulgare

☠ *Tanacetum vulgare* L. *(Chrysanthemum vulgare)* Compositae

Ⓜ **Tansy** (April–Sept.) A slightly fragrant perennial herb, with a creeping root stock. The stem is erect, 25–90cm (up to 110cm) tall, stiff, branched above, usually tinged with red. The leaves are spirally arranged, 10–27cm long, oblong to elliptic in outline, pinnate; the lower ones are petiolate, the upper ones sessile and semi-clasping; the segments are in 8–12 pairs, sharply toothed, dotted with glands. The flower heads are 0·6–1·3cm in diameter, many arranged in a flat-topped terminal corymb. The bracts of the involucre are glabrous, with scarious margins. The florets are all tubular; the outer ones bilaterally symmetrical, female; the inner ones regular, hermaphrodite; all are golden-yellow. The fruit is a 1·3–1·9mm long, 5-ribbed achene; the pappus is very short and membranous.

Habitat waste places, hedgerows, roadsides. **Distribution** throughout the region. Widely cultivated for ornament and frequently naturalized. **Active ingredients** essential oil with β-thujone, bitter principle tanacetine, glycosides, resin, tannin. **Effect** digestive; kills worms and stimulates stomach functions. **Parts used** the dried flowers and leaves and the flowering herb; dry in shade, or artificial heat (under 35°C). **Application C:** in the past this drug was used in medicine as a wormer but is now substituted by less dangerous drugs. In homoeopathy a preparation of fresh material is prescribed for menstrual pain and worms. Its use for domestic purposes (internally) is not advisable but bruised fresh leaves can be applied to bruises and varicose veins.

Ⓜ *Artemisia absinthium* L. Compositae

Wormwood (July–Sept.) An aromatic perennial herb with barren rosettes and flowering stems. The stems are erect, 25–80cm (up to 100cm) tall, angled and furrowed, usually woody towards the base, silky hairy. The leaves are spirally arranged, 2–11cm long; the lower ones and those of the sterile branches are tri-pinnate; the upper ones range from bipinnate to entire; all the leaves are silky hairy and dotted on both surfaces. The flower heads are 2·8–4·2mm in diameter, broader than long, drooping, arranged in dense racemose panicles. The bracts of the involucre are silky hairy, with scarious edges. All the florets are tubular, the outer ones female, the inner hermaphrodite, all yellow. The fruit is a 1·5mm long glabrous achene without pappus.

Habitat waste places. **Distribution** all over Europe including the British Isles as far north as Ross and Aberdeen. **Active ingredients** essential oil with thujone, thujol, phellandrene, proazulene, bitter principle (absinthin), tannins. **Effect** disinfectant; stimulates gland secretions, stomach functions and bile production, and relieves flatulence and spasms. **Parts used** the flowering herb; cut the flowering twigs and dry in shade. **Application M:** in homoeopathy an essence is prescribed for the stimulation of bile and gastric juice production and for disorders of the liver and gall bladder. In the home an infusion (½–1 teaspoon per cup water, allow to stand for 8-10 minutes) 2–3 times a day for indigestion, lack of appetite, chronic stomach disorders or as a tonic. **Note** in normal use and taken for short periods this drug is harmless, but the alcoholic extraction ('absinth') will cause *severe brain damage*. For this reason its use in aperitifs and other alcoholic beverages is prohibited by law.

Ⓜ *Artemisia vulgaris* L. Compositae

Ⓔ **Mugwort** (July–Sept.) This perennial is related to the above and can be distinguished as follows: the stems are glabrous or thinly pubescent, reddish. The leaves are usually glabrous on the upper surface, and white-tomentose on the lower surface; the lower leaves are lyre-shaped pinnatifid, auricled; the upper leaves sessile, clasping, bipinnate to pinnate. The inflorescence branches are rather stiff. The florets are reddish-brown. The achenes are only 0·8–1mm long.

Habitat waste places, roadsides, hedgerows. **Distribution** all over the region. **Active ingredients** essential oil, with thujone and cineole, bitter principle, tannin, resin, inulin. **Effect** mainly stimulation of stomach functions (similar to the above species but weaker). **Parts used** the flowering herb; cut the flowering shoots and dry in shade or in artificial heat (not over 30°C). **Application M:** contained in a number of brands of proprietary medicine for dyspepsia and gastritis. In the home an infusion (1 teaspoon

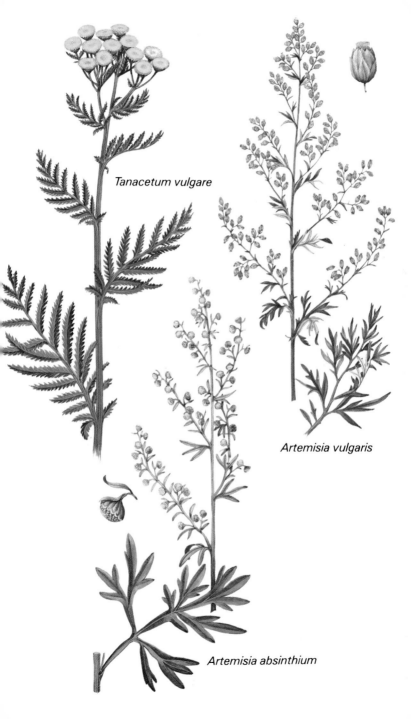

Tanacetum vulgare

Artemisia vulgaris

Artemisia absinthium

per cup water, allow to stand for 8–10 minutes) is taken 2–3 times a day for the same conditions as well as for menstrual pains, flatulence and diarrhoea. **Note** this drug should not be taken for long periods. **E:** Mugwort is an indispensable condiment for fat poultry such as geese and ducks as well as fat pork, mutton and eel. It can also be used for sauces or salads and be added to goose and/or pork dripping.

Ⓜ *Carlina acaulis* L. Compositae
Stemless Carline Thistle (Sept.–Oct.) A stemless perennial herb with a long (over 20cm) tap root. The leaves are 5–35cm long, elliptic-oblong, pinnatifid or pinnatisect, with spine-tipped segments or lobes, shortly petiolate or sessile, glabrous or softly hairy on the lower surface. The flower head is very showy, 2·5–6cm in diameter. The bracts of the involucre are in several rows; the outer ones up to 5·5cm long, the inner ones slightly shorter, silvery-white or whitish-pink, tinged purple-brown beneath. The florets are all hermaphrodite, tubular, 5-lobed. The fruit is an oblong, hairy, 4–5mm long achene, with a 1–1·4cm long pappus.

    Habitat dry short grassland, mountain slopes, usually on calcareous soil. **Distribution** in C. Europe, from France to Russia. **Active ingredients** essential oil with carlina oxide, tannin, inulin, resin. **Effect** mildly diuretic, antibiotic; stimulates perspiration and relieves spasms. **Parts used** the dried root stock; dig up the root stock, cut into small pieces or shred, dry in sun or shade. **Application M:** the drug is contained in a few brands of proprietary medicine for gall bladder disorders and spasms of the digestive tract. The infusion (1–2 teaspoons per cup) 2–4 times a day is taken for the same ailments as well as dropsy, bronchitis and sweat stimulation.

Ⓜ *Arctium lappa* L. Compositae
Ⓔ **Great Burdock** (July–Sept.) A bushy biennial herb with a long (sometimes over 50cm) stout tap root. The stems are 70–140cm tall, with many ascending branches, usually tinged with red. The leaves are arranged spirally, large, ovate from a heart-shaped base, without spines, entire or somewhat toothed, green; on the lower surface with a whitish cottony indumentum, slightly cottony on the upper surface; the petiole is robust, 12–34cm long, solid furrowed above. The flower heads are 2·5–4·5cm in diameter, long-pedunculate, arranged in terminal groups. The bracts of the involucre are green, numerous, awl-shaped, hooked at the spreading apex. The florets are all tubular, hermaphrodite, purplish; upper part of the corolla shorter and wider than the lower. The fruit is a compressed 4·5–7·25mm long achene.

    Habitat growing along roads and in waste places, sometimes in meadows and woods. **Distribution** all over the region (except N. Scotland). **Active ingredients** inulin, mucilage, tannin, traces of essential oil, glycoside, antibiotic substances. **Effect** diuretic; stimulates perspiration. **Parts used** the root; collect the roots in the autumn of the first or spring of the second year, wash, split lengthwise and dry in moderate heat (not over 45°C). **Application M:** as a decoction (2 teaspoons per cup of water, boil for 8–12 minutes) or as a powder (1 teaspoon) 2–3 times a day internally against chronic catarrh, onset of colds, influenza or disorders of the gall bladder, and rheumatic pain; externally it is used for bathing cuts, abscesses and skin eruptions. **E:** the young leaves are boiled in water like spinach. Young stalks and branches can be peeled and used raw as a salad or boiled like asparagus. For the root: peel off thick rind, cut pith in pieces, boil in salted water (add pinch of sodium carbonate) for 30 minutes, pour away water, stew in butter for fifteen minutes, season and serve.

Ⓔ *Cirsium arvense* (L.) Scop. Compositae
Creeping Thistle (Aug.–Sept.) A perennial herb with a slender tap root producing whitish creeping horizontal roots. The stems are 25–100cm (up to 150cm) tall. The lower leaves are not in a rosette, are oblong-lanceolate from a narrow petiole-like base, pinnatifid to a varying degree, with spine-pointed lobes; the upper leaves are sessile to almost clasping, not, or only slightly, decurrent, usually deeply pinnatifid, glabrous on both surfaces or softly hairy on the lower. The flower heads are 1·25–2·6cm in diameter, solitary or arranged in terminal groups of 2–4. The bracts of the involucre are numerous, usually purplish; the outer ones with spiny spreading tips; the inner ones

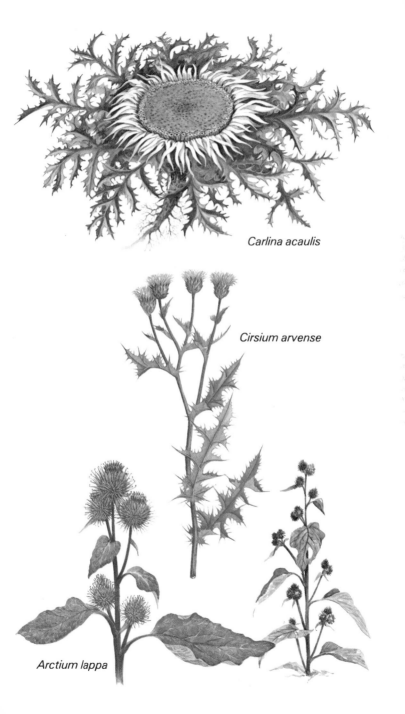

Carlina acaulis

Cirsium arvense

Arctium lappa

are lanceolate, with erect tips. The florets are all tubular, purplish or whitish. The fruit is a 3–4mm long brown achene with a pappus of several rows of feathery brownish hairs.

Habitat waste places, arable land, road-sides etc., usually an obnoxious weed. **Distribution** throughout the region. **Parts used and application E:** the young shoots as well as the flower stalk of this plant can be eaten as a vegetable (for treatment see under *Onopordum*). The roots of first year plants can also be used and treated in the same way; they are nutritious but of a rather bland taste and are therefore best eaten mixed with other root vegetables. They may also be eaten raw.

(E) *Cirsium vulgare* (Savi) Ten. Compositae

Spear Thistle (Aug.– Oct.) This biennial is closely related to the above species, but its decurrent leaves are covered with rough hairs and prickles on the upper surface. The stem has a spiny wing. The flower heads are longer, 2–4·2cm in diameter. The achenes are yellowish with black markings.

Habitat, distribution, parts used and **application E:** as for the above species.

(M) *Silybum marianum* (L.) Gaertn. Compositae

Milk Thistle (Aug.– Sept.) An annual to biennial herb with a 35–125cm stem, not winged, erect, furrowed, with a cottonwool-like indumentum. The leaves are alternate, oblong, pinnatifid or with undulated spiny margins, pale glossy green with white along the veins; the lower ones are sessile, the upper ones clasping and auriculate. The flower heads are 1–2·5cm in diameter, solitary, erect or drooping. The bracts of the involucre are in many rows, spiny, long, spreading to recurved, with a sharply pointed yellowish apex. The florets are all tubular, hermaphrodite, red-purple. The fruit is a compressed, 5·5–7·5mm long, blackish, speckled achene with a long white pappus.

Habitat waste places, arable land. **Distribution** native to S. Europe, introduced to C. Europe. Naturalized in the British Isles northwards to Aberdeen. **Active ingredients** silymarin, silydianin, silychristin, bitter principle, essential oil, mucilage, fatty oil. **Effect** stimulates bile production and gland secretions, relieves spasms. **Parts used** the mature achenes; cut the flower heads just before they are fully mature and keep in a thin layer in a warm dry place until the achenes fall off (tap lightly); store in a dark place. **Application M:** more recently this drug has again gained importance in allopathic medicine and is contained in numerous brands of proprietary medicine for the treatment of various liver ailments. It is also used (as a tincture) in homoeopathy for liver and abdominal disorders. In the home an infusion (1 teaspoon per cup water, allow to stand for 15 minutes) is taken 3 times a day before meals for the same complaints. There are no known harmful side effects.

(M) *Onopordum acanthium* L. Compositae

(E) **Scotch Thistle, Cotton Thistle** A very large biennial thistle, growing from a stout tap root. The stems are 50–180cm tall, branched above, white-woolly, winged. The leaves are narrowly elliptic to elliptic-oblong, decurrent, with triangular spine-tipped lobes or sharply toothed, with a cotton-like indumentum on both surfaces. The flower heads are usually solitary, terminal, up to 5·5cm in diameter. The bracts of the globose involucre in many rows, lanceolate to awl-shaped, with yellowish spines. The florets are all tubular, hermaphrodite, pale purple or rarely white. The fruit is a compressed, quadrangular, 3·5–5mm long, mottled achene; the pappus is rather long, with toothed hairs.

Habitat waste places, roadsides, arable land, gardens. **Distribution** from S. Europe to S. Scandinavia. Naturalized in the British Isles (rare in Scotland). **Active ingredients** traces of alkaloids, flavone glycosides. **Effect** heart tonic. **Parts used** the flowering herb. **Application M:** the drug is contained in a few brands of proprietary medicine prescribed for heart disorders. **E:** the young plants, before the flower develops, can be eaten (remove prickles, boil in salted water, sauté in butter and serve as a vegetable). They can also be mixed with other vegetables and eaten like spinach. The receptacle of the flower heads can be prepared and eaten in the same way as artichokes.

Cirsium vulgare

Silybum marianum

Onopordum acanthium

Ⓜ **_Cnicus benedictus_** L. Compositae

Blessed Thistle (July: herb; Aug.–Sept: fruit) The stem of this thistle-like annual herb is 8–65cm tall, covered with a spider web-like indumentum. The leaves are alternate, oblong, with conspicuous white veins on the lower surface; the lower ones are 10–30cm long, pinnatifid with the lobes pointing downwards, petiolate. The stem leaves are smaller, sessile and semi-clasping, ovate lanceolate, with a spiny apex. The flower heads are solitary, 2–3cm in diameter, enveloped by upper leaves. The bracts of the involucre are brown; the inner ones with a comb-like apical appendage. The central florets are hermaphrodite, the outer ones sterile and very small, all yellow. The fruit is a ribbed, 6–8.5mm long, brown achene with a yellow pappus.

Habitat arable land, waste places. **Distribution** widely cultivated as a medicinal herb in Europe and often naturalized. In the British Isles only as a casual. **Active ingredients** cnicin, tannin, traces of essential oil, abundant mucilage, flavonoids, linoleic acid, resin. **Effect** digestive; stimulates bile flow. **Parts used** the dried herb; collect shortly before flowering, dry not too fast to avoid brittleness; the dried mature achenes. **Application M:** the drug is contained in several brands of proprietary medicine or in herbal tea-mixtures for disorders of the liver, the gall bladder, dyspepsia, sluggish digestion or lack of appetite. It is also prescribed in homoeopathy (essence) for the same ailments. In the home an infusion (2–3 teaspoons per cup water, allow to stand for 15 minutes) is taken 2–3 times a day for the same complaints as well as for arthritis, heartburn and (externally) for bathing wounds. There are no known toxic effects.

Ⓜ **_Centaurea cyanus_** L. Compositae

Cornflower, Bluebottle An annual herb with 15–75cm (up to 95cm) stems, erect, branched, with a cottonwool-like indumentum. The leaves are spirally arranged, lyre-shaped pinnatifid, or oblanceolate and toothed or entire, 8–20cm long, the upper stem leaves smaller, sessile, linear-lanceolate, the petiole with a greyish woolly indumentum on both surfaces. The flower heads are 1·5–3·25cm in diameter, solitary, on long peduncles. The bracts of the ovoid involucre are numerous, densely overlapped, in several rows, with decurrent deeply toothed appendages: the outer ones silverish; the following rows brown with white-marginal teeth. The florets are all tubular; the peripheral ones large and showy, bright blue, the inner purple-red. The anthers are purple. The fruit is a compressed 2·7–3·2mm long silverish achene with a short reddish pappus.

Habitat as a weed in cornfields, waste places, roadsides, etc. **Distribution** throughout the region. **Active ingredients** a glycoside, tannin, cyanine, mucilage. **Effect** astringent, weakly diuretic, very mildly purgative. **Parts used** the dried florets; cut the flower heads, dry quickly in shade, pluck out the florets. **Application M:** in the home it can be used as an infusion (2–3 teaspoons per cup water, allow to stand for 3–5 minutes) 2–3 times a day for dropsy, constipation or as a mouthwash for bleeding gums, and for conjunctivitis (eye-bath or compress).

Ⓜ **_Centaurea montana_** L. Compositae

Mountain Cornflower Related to _C. cyanus_ but this is a perennial with creeping rhizomes and broadly winged stems. The soft leaves are usually entire (the lower ones are sometimes lobed) and floccose-tomentose on the lower surface. The central florets of the flower head are violet, the outer blue.

Habitat open woods and meadows. **Distribution** mountains of Europe from the Ardennes to the Pyrenees. The plant is widely cultivated in gardens for ornament (also in Britain). **Parts used** and **application M:** the plant has similar properties as _C. cyanus_ and is, albeit rarely, used for the same purpose.

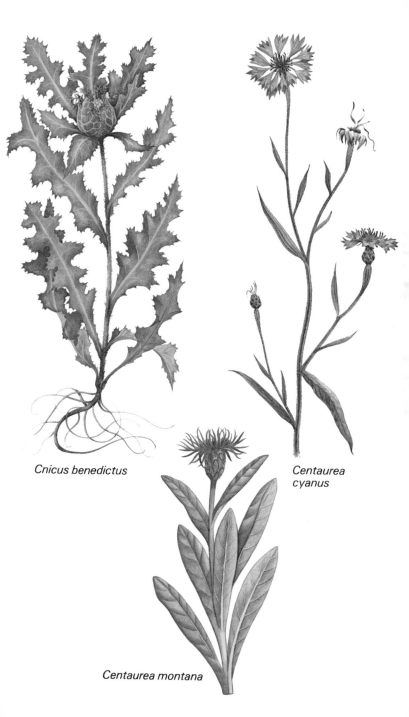

Cnicus benedictus

Centaurea cyanus

Centaurea montana

Ⓜ Ⓔ *Cichorium intybus* L. Compositae

Chicory, Wild Succory (herb: Aug.–Sept; root: Oct.) A tough perennial herb with a long stout tap root and a short vertical stock. The stems are erect, stiff, 20–85cm (up to 120cm) tall, furrowed, branched, hairy to glabrous. The leaves are spirally arranged; the basal ones are oblanceolate, pinnatifid or coarsely toothed, shortly petiolate; the lower stem leaves are sessile, clasping, the upper ones lanceolate from a widened auriculate, sessile base, all glandular. The flower heads are 2–4·25cm in diameter, terminal and axillary (often in groups of 2–3). The bracts of the cylindrical involucre are in 2 rows, all green, the outer spreading above. The florets are all ligulate, light blue, sometimes white or pinkish; the ligules are 5-toothed. The fruit is an obovoid, 2–3mm long achene crowned by a minute scaly pappus.

Habitat arable land, roadsides, pasture, etc. **Distribution** throughout the region. **Active ingredients** inulin, choline, intybin cichorin, fatty oil, sugar. **Effect** digestive; stimulates gland secretion and bile production, **Parts used** the tap root; dig up, wash, cut into small sections and dry slowly in the sun or in a warm room. The flowering herb; dry in the sun. **Application M:** in the home the decoction of an equal mixture of *Cichorium* and *Taraxacum* (1 tablespoon per cup water, boil for 5 minutes) 2–3 times a day is taken for gall bladder, gall stones, dyspepsia and haemorrhoids. **E:** the very young leaves (best cut above the stock after they have appeared) make a fine spring-salad, vegetable, or sandwich filler. The larger leaves are rather bitter but can be mixed with milder vegetables. The tap root is eaten as a vegetable and is ideal for diabetics (inulin content). The dried and shredded tap root is widely used in ersatz coffee (to be roasted).

Ⓔ *Lapsana communis* L. Compositae

Nipplewort (June–Sept.) An annual with 10–90cm tall stems, erect, branched above, usually hairy below. The lower leaves are long-petiolate, pinnatifid with the terminal lobe much longer than the lateral ones; the upper stem leaves are shortly petiolate, ovate-rhombic to lanceolate, entire or sinuous to toothed, all thinly herbaceous, more or less hairy. The flower heads are many, 1·3–2·25cm in diameter, arranged in corymbose panicles. The bracts of the ovoid involucre are up to 10 in 1 row, strongly keeled, abruptly obtuse. The florets number 8–15, all ligulate, light yellow. The fruit is a 2·5–5·25mm long, compressed, many-ribbed, brown achene without a pappus.

Habitat waste places, on walls, roadsides, hedges, open woods, etc. **Distribution** all over the region. **Parts used** the young leaves and shoots before flowering (the leaves can also be used at flowering time). **Application E:** can be eaten in salads, on sandwiches or in omelettes. Also added to soups, casseroles or treated like spinach.

Ⓔ *Tragopogon pratensis* L. Compositae

Jack-go-to-bed-at-noon, Goat's Beard (leaves: May–June; roots Sept.–Oct.) An annual to perennial herb containing a white sap, growing from a long brown tap root crowned by the persistent leaf bases. The stem is 20–70cm tall, usually simple, linear-lanceolate from a slightly sheathing base, tapering to a long soft point, distinctly white-veined; the upper stem leaves are usually semi-clasping. The flower heads are large and showy, solitary and terminal, closing around midday. The conical bracts of the involucre number about 8–10, arranged in 1 row, up to 3·5cm long, lanceolate-acuminate from a united base. The florets are all ligulate, yellow, usually slightly shorter than the involucral bracts. The fruit is a spindle-shaped, many-ribbed, 1·1–2·3cm long, yellowish achene; the pappus is conspicuous, with feathery hairs.

Habitat pastures, meadows, waste places, road-sides, hedgerows and similar grassy localities. **Distribution** throughout Europe northwards as far as Denmark, S. Sweden and Karelia. In the British Isles northwards as far as Sutherland and Caithness. **Parts used** the young leaves and stems before flowering; the tap root in the autumn. **Application E:** stems with young buds are treated like asparagus. Young leaves, tips of shoots and diced tap root can be mixed with other salads. The whole plant is also usable as a vegetable, in stews and soups. The fully developed tap root is blanched, peeled and then treated and eaten like salsify.

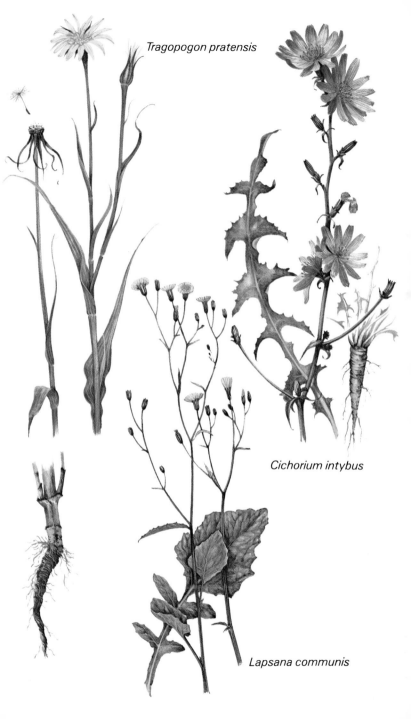

Tragopogon pratensis

Cichorium intybus

Lapsana communis

Lactuca virosa L. Compositae

Great Lettuce (July–Sept.) An annual to biennial herb containing copious latex, growing from a usually branched tap root. The stems are erect, leafy throughout, 50–180cm (up to 210cm) tall, often prickly below, whitish or reddish. The leaves are spirally arranged, bluish-green, stiff, entire or pinnatifid to a varying degree, with prickles on the midrib and lateral veins beneath; the lower ones with a false petiole; the stem leaves are clasping and auriculate. The flower heads are 0·8–1·1cm in diameter, arranged in large ovate to pyramidal panicles. Bracts of the involucre are about 1cm long, numerous, overlapping, in many rows, with white margins and reddish-purple tips. The florets are all ligulate, yellow, longer than the involucre. The fruit is a 3mm long, blackish, many-ribbed, beaked achene; pappus whitish.

Habitat along roads, railway lines, canals, and other grassy places, also on banks near the sea. **Distribution** native in S.W. Europe, spreading over most of Europe and the British Isles as far as C. Scotland. **Active ingredients** bitter principle, an alkaloid, organic acids, mucilage. **Effect** sedative, narcotic. **Parts used** the fresh or dried flowering herb; the dried latex. **Application C:** in homoeopathy an essence, prepared from fresh material, is prescribed for chronic catarrhs, coughs, swollen liver, flatulence and ailments of the urinary tract. However, it is *not recommended for domestic purposes.*

Ⓜ *Lactuca serriola* L. (*L. scariola*) Compositae

Prickly Lettuce (July–Sept.) This biennial is related to the above species and characterized by the fact that all the leaves are positioned vertically and most of the time in one plane. The mature achenes are greenish-grey.

Habitat waste places, roadsides, along and on walls, on dunes, etc. **Distribution** S. and C. Europe spreading northwards to Denmark and C. England. **Active ingredients, effect, parts used** and **application M:** similar to the preceding species.

Ⓔ *Sonchus arvensis* L. Compositae

Field Milk-Thistle A perennial herb with a creeping rhizome. The stems are 50–120cm (up to 160cm) tall, erect or ascending, furrowed, glandular-hairy above. The basal leaves are lanceolate to oblong, pinnately lobed; the lobes are triangular-oblong with spiny teeth and fringed with spiny hairs; the petiole is winged; the stem leaves are less pinnate, sessile with a heart-shaped, clasping base and rounded auricles. The flower heads are 3·5–5·25cm in diameter, arranged in a loose corymb (its branches and axis like the involucre with yellow glandular hairs). The bracts of the 1·5–2cm long bell-shaped involucre are in several rows, oblong-lanceolate, obtuse. The florets are all ligulate, golden yellow. The fruit is a 2·75–3·5mm long, brown, 10-ribbed achene; the pappus has 2 rows of hairs.

Habitat arable land, waste places, along streams and ditches, marshes. **Distribution** throughout the region. **Parts used** young leaves (rich in mineral salts and vitamin C); it may be best, but not necessary, to cut off the marginal prickles. **Application E:** eaten raw in salads; since the leaves are somewhat bitter they should be mixed with other salad plants either wild or cultivated (if desired the bitter taste can be eliminated by parboiling the leaves in as little water as possible for about 2 minutes – pour water away).

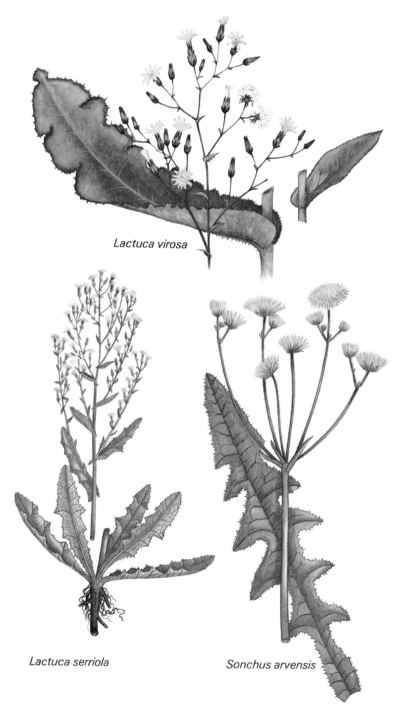

Lactuca virosa

Lactuca serriola

Sonchus arvensis

ⓔ **Sonchus oleraceus** L. Compositae

Milk- or Sow-Thistle This annual is related to the above and can be distinguished by the pointed auricles at the base of the stem leaves, and the achene which has only 3 ribs on one each face (5 in the above species).

Habitat waste places, arable land, roadsides, etc. **Distribution, parts used** and application **E:** as for the preceding species.

Ⓜ **Hieracium pilosella** L. Compositae

Mouse-ear Hawkweed (May–Sept./Oct.) An annual herb with a long slender rhizome, producing many long stolons with terminal rosettes. The leaves are all in a basal rosette (rarely 1–3 small stem leaves present), linear-lanceolate to ovate-oblong, rarely linear, from a wedge-shaped base, obtuse. The flower heads are solitary on a 3–30cm long scape (covered with basally black glandular hairs). The bracts of the involucre are in several irregular rows, lanceolate-oblong covered with basally black glandular and ordinary white hairs. The florets are all ligulate, light yellow, the outer reddish on the lower surface. The fruit is a 2mm long blackish-purple achene with hairy pappus.

Habitat meadows, pastures, heaths, roadsides, banks, on walls, etc. **Distribution** throughout most of Europe. **Active ingredients** tannin, mucilage, a glycosidal bitter principle (umbeliferone), resin. **Effect** mildly diuretic, mildly astringent, anti-inflammatory; stimulates bile flow; **Parts used** the fresh and dried flowering herb; dry in the sun or shade. **Application M:** an infusion (2–3 teaspoons per cup water, allow to stand for 5 minutes) 2–4 times a day is taken for enteritis, influenza, pyelitis and cystitis; externally it can be used for bathing (or as a compress) of cuts and eye-infections.

Ⓜ **Taraxacum officinale** Weber Compositae
ⓔ

Common Dandelion (leaves: April–Aug.; roots: Sept.–Oct./Nov.) A very variable robust perennial herb containing a white latex and growing from a fleshy, long, simple or branched tap root. The leaves are spirally arranged, confined to a dense basal rosette, entire to more or less deeply pinnately lobed, with the terminal lobe the largest. The flower heads are 2·5–6·5cm in diameter, solitary, terminal on a hollow, 2–40cm tall scape. The bracts of the cylindrical involucre are in 2 rows; the inner ones erect; the outer ones are shorter spreading to reflexed (rarely erect); all are lanceolate to linear. All the florets are ligulate, yellow, numerous, hermaphrodite. The fruit is a 3·5–4·25mm long, ribbed, brown, greenish or greyish, beaked (up to 4 times as long as achene), rough achene with short projections, the pappus forms many rows of rough white hairs.

Habitat meadows, pastures, lawns, roadsides, banks, waste places, pavements, etc. **Distribution** throughout most of Europe. **Active ingredients** inulin, bitter principle, taraxin, choline, taraxerine, resin, traces of essential oil, sugar, vitamin C (leaves) and vitamin A, nicotinic acid, mucilage. **Effect** diuretic, digestive tonic; stimulates stomach and bile secretion. **Parts used** the young herb before flowering; dry in a warm room. The tap-root; dig up, clean with a brush (but do not wash), split lengthwise and dry thoroughly; keep in insect-proof containers. **Application M:** in allopathic medicine a decoction of 2 teaspoons mixed herb and root per cup water, bring quickly to the boil, allow to stand for 12–15 minutes taken 2–3 times a day is prescribed for disorders of the gall-bladder and dyspepsia. In homoeopathy an essence, prepared from fresh material, is given for rheumatism, neuralgia and stomach complaints. The time-honoured home-remedy is either as the above decoction or the freshly pressed juice (commercially available) 1 tablespoon, 3 times a day for the same ailments as well as a diuretic; it should be taken over a period of several weeks to be effective. **E:** the young leaves are eaten as salad or vegetable (the bitter taste can be alleviated by putting them into cold water 2 hours before use). Very young flower buds can be preserved in vinegar and used like capers. The developing shoots, before the scape begins to grow, also make a fine vegetable and are used like brussel sprouts. Tap roots, dug up in the autumn, are used like salsify.

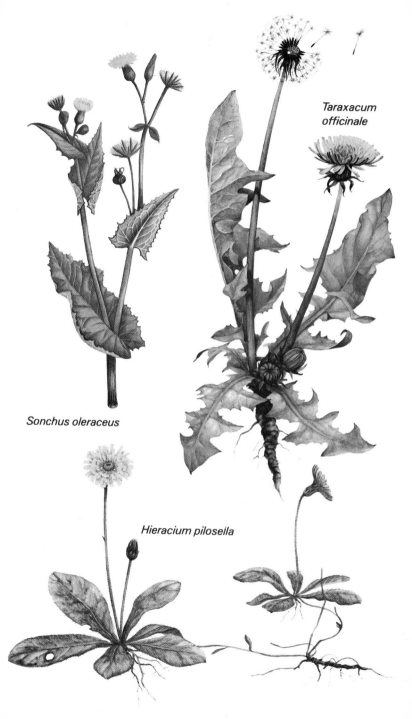

Taraxacum officinale

Sonchus oleraceus

Hieracium pilosella

Ⓜ️ *Arnica montana* L. Compositae

Arnica (flowers: June–July; roots: April–May or Sept.–Oct.) A perennial herb with a stout creeping rhizome. The stems are 12–60cm tall. The basal and lower stem leaves are 5–17cm long, obovate to elliptical or oblanceolate, usually densely glandular-pubescent, all crowded near the stem base; the stem leaves are few, opposite, much smaller, usually ovate-lanceolate. The flower heads number 1–3 (rarely more), their peduncles having 2 alternate bracts. The bracts of the 1·2–1·7cm long involucre are lanceolate, usually arranged in 2 rows. The ray florets are female, 1·8–3cm long, yellow, irregularly reflexed. The disc florets are tubular, yellow, hermaphrodite. The fruit is a 7–9mm long ribbed achene, the pappus has 1 long row of hairs.

Habitat meadows, pastures, heaths, usually in mountainous areas. **Distribution** from Norway and Latvia across Europe to Portugal. **Active ingredients** essential oil, bitter principle, tannin, arnidendiol, the flavone-glycosides astralagin and isoquercetin. **Effect** anti-inflammatory, dilates the blood vessels. **Parts used** the florets; cut the flower heads, dry quickly in shade (±30°C), pluck out the florets. The root stock; dig up, clean, dry in artificial heat at ±35°C. **Application M:** arnica is mainly used in a tincture for bathing wounds or preparing cold compresses for phlebitis, tenosynovitis, epicondylitis, bruises, hematomes, rheumatic pain, and contusions (use about 3 teaspoonsful of tincture per half litre of cold or lukewarm water); it can also be used as a mouthwash for inflammation of the gums. Internally it is applied (always under strict medical supervision) for angina pectoris and other heart conditions (especially those connected with old age). **Note** the undiluted tincture causes severe skin irritations. Internal overdoses leads to enteritis, tachycardia and collapse.

Ⓜ️ *Calendula officinalis* L. Compositae

Marigold (June–Sept.) An attractive ornamental perennial, sticky to the touch, with a slender tap root. The stems are fragile, erect, 25–70cm tall, branched above. The lower leaves are oblong-ovate to paddle-shaped; the stem leaves are much smaller and narrower, sessile, semi-clasping, subacute; all the leaves are spirally arranged, hairy and glandular. The flower heads terminal and solitary, large and showy, 2·75 –5·5cm in diameter. The bracts of the involucre are numerous, in 1–2 rows, lanceolate, acute. The ray florets are spreading, ligulate, female, orange-yellow, in most forms in several rows. The disc florets are few, tubular, hermaphrodite, not producing mature fruits, darker in colour. The fruit is an irregular boat-shaped achene, without a ring of hairs.

Habitat usually cultivated in gardens, rarely as an escape along roads, in waste places, along hedges. **Distribution** naturalized or as an escape all over the region; widely grown as a garden plant. **Active ingredients** essential oil, bitter principle, carotenoids, flavone glycosides, resin, mucilage, organic acids, saponin. **Effect** anti-inflammatory; prevents spasms, stimulates bile flow and perspiration. **Parts used** the florets; cut the flower heads, dry carefully in shade, pluck out the ray florets. Also the fresh flowering herb (cut 5cm above ground). **Application M:** the drug is contained in several brands of proprietary medicine for spasms of the digestive tract, liver and gall bladder disorders, gastritis, cystitis, cystopyelitis as well as in salves and tinctures for external use. In the home the infusion (2 teaspoons per cup water, allow to stand for 12 minutes) is occasionally used for dropsy, spasms of the digestive tract and for worms. It can be used for bathing or applied as compress to slow-healing cuts, eczema, bruises, or as a gargle for pharyngitis, bleeding gums.

Ⓜ️ *Helichrysum arenarium* (L.) Moench Compositae

'Everlasting Flower' (July–Oct.) A perennial herb with a stout branched root stock. The non-flowering shoots form rosettes of paddle-shaped leaves. The stems are 8–50cm tall, erect or ascending, greyish-white with appressed hairs. The leaves are spirally arranged, 5–7cm long, obovate-oblong, 1-nerved, densely whitish-tomentose (the upper ones narrower, oblong-lanceolate to thread-like). The flower heads are 4–5·5mm in diameter, almost globose to hemispherical, yellow to reddish-orange, glossy. The bracts of the involucre are numerous, overlapping, the inner ones several

Calendula officinalis

Arnica montana

Helichrysum arenarium

times longer than the outer, gold to lemon-yellow. The florets are all tubular. The fruit is an achene with a pappus of rough hairs.

Habitat dry sandy places, heaths, dunes, pine forests, etc. Distribution in Europe from the Netherlands southwards to Germany and Bulgaria. In Britain cultivated for ornament. Active ingredients helichrysine and other flavonoids, coumarin, bitter principle, traces of essential oil, resin. Effect mildly stimulates bile production. Parts used the fresh or dried flowers or the entire flowering herb. Application M: in allopathic medicine the infusion (2 teaspoons per cup water, allow to stand for 5 minutes) is prescribed 2–3 times a day for the treatment of gall bladder disorders. In homoeopathy an essence, prepared from fresh material, is given for chronic gall ailments and lumbago. In the home the above infusion is taken as a diuretic and for arthritis, rheumatism, cystitis, and for stimulating gastric secretion.

Ⓔ *Triglochin maritima* L. Juncaginaceae

Sea Arrow-grass   A robust perennial herb with a short, stout rhizome with fibrous roots. The leaves are all basal, erect, linear in outline from a sheathing base, sometimes awl-shaped, 1·75–3·2mm wide, semicylindrical. The inflorescence is a raceme terminating a leafless scape, together 10–75cm tall. The pedicels are 0·7–2·2mm long. The flowers are regular, with 3 deciduous perianth segments. The carpels number 6, all fertile and separating after opening. The entire fruit is 2·8–4·2mm long, cylindrical-ovoid, not appressed to the axis of the raceme.

Habitat salt marshes, grassy places at the shore. Distribution all along the British and European coasts (including the Baltic) and inland near salt mines. Parts used the entire plant before flowering. Application E: the plant is either added to soups or stews or eaten as a vegetable like spinach.

☠ *Convallaria majalis* L. Liliaceae

Ⓜ Lily of the Valley (May–June)   A perennial with a long creeping rhizome. The leaves are in pairs, 6–21cm long, ovate-lanceolate, the lower enveloping the upper, sheath-like, parallel-nerved, glabrous; the petiole is always longer than the blade. The flowers are sweet-scented, nodding, arranged in 1-sided racemes. The raceme has an 8–40cm tall peduncle. The perianth is white, globular to bell-shaped, 6–8·5mm in diameter, with the segments united to about the middle, the stamens are inserted at the perianth-base, not protruding. The fruit is a 2–6 seeded red berry.

Habitat woods, hedgerows, in dry calcareous soil. Distribution throughout most of Europe; scattered in the British Isles. Active ingredients glycosides, saponin, resin, asparagin, chelidonic and other organic acids, essential oil with farnesol. Effect heart tonic, diuretic. Parts used the flowering herb; to be dried as quickly as possible in shade. Application C: the drug is used both in homoeopathy and allopathy for various heart conditions. Note it must never be used without *strict medical supervision*.

☠ *Polygonatum odoratum* (Mill.) Druce *(P. officinale)* Liliaceae

Ⓜ Angular Solomon's Seal (Sept.–Oct.)   An elegantly arching perennial herb, growing from a long and thick creeping rhizome. The stems are 15–25cm tall, angular in cross-section, leafy throughout. The leaves are alternate, 3–12cm long, ovate to elliptic or elliptic-oblong, sessile, nearly positioned in opposite rows. The flowers are pleasantly scented, single or in a pair, axillary, pendulous. The perianth is 1·6–2·3cm long, cylindric to bell-shaped, green-white, the segments united except for a short apical part. The stamens are not protruding. The fruit is a berry, globular, bluish-black, 5–6·5mm in diameter.

Habitat woods, copses, usually on limestone. Distribution throughout the region. Active ingredients asparagin, mucilage, saponin, tannin, a glycoside. Effect diuretic, stimulates healing. Parts used the rhizome with roots. Application C: this drug is used only in domestic medicine: the infusion (1 teaspoon per cup water, allow to stand for 5–8 minutes) is taken internally as a diuretic and metabolism stimulant (do not take more than 3 cups a day and only over short periods!). A slightly stronger infusion (2–3 teaspoons per cup water) is applied as a compress to cuts, eczema, bruises and other skin disorders. Note *the berries are poisonous.*

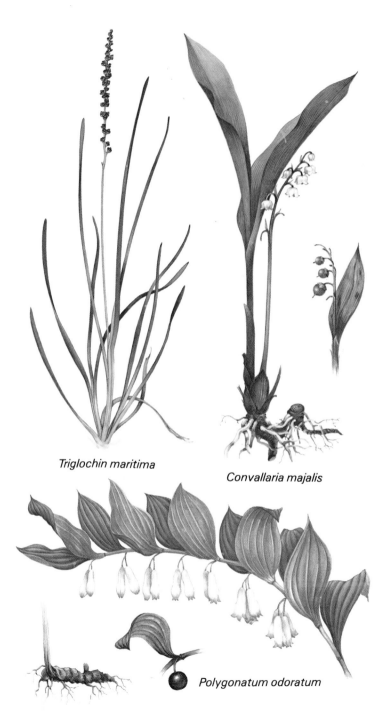

Triglochin maritima

Convallaria majalis

Polygonatum odoratum

Ⓜ **Allium ursinum** L. Liliaceae
Ⓔ **Ramsons** (April–June) A fragrant bulbous perennial herb, 8–45cm tall. The leaves appear in spring, usually 2 but sometimes 3, basal, 8–27cm long, ovate-elliptic, acute, bright green with parallel venation; the petiole is 3–21cm long, twisted. The flower scape is angular, with basal sheaths. The flowers are arranged in a flat-topped umbel enveloped by a 2-valved, ovate, scarious, acuminate spathe. The perianth-segments are spreading, up to 1·1cm long, lanceolate, acute. The ovary is deeply 3-lobed, the seeds are black.

Habitat in damp soil in woods, copses, valleys and similar moist shady localities. Distribution throughout the region (absent from Shetland, Orkney, and the Channel Islands). Active ingredients essential oil, vitamin C. Effect antibiotic; stimulates gland secretion and bile production, prevents spasms, and kills worms. Parts used the flowering fresh herb. Application **M & E**: the fresh leaves can be taken for high blood-pressure or progressive arterio-sclerosis. They are best used raw, bruised or finely chopped in salads or in buttered sandwiches. They can, of course, also be used for flavouring soups or in vegetables but are then medicinally less effective. Note the same properties – and more effective – are present in garlic cloves (*Allium sativum* L.) which are commercially available fresh throughout the year.

Ⓔ **Allium schoenoprasum** L. Liliaceae
Chives A tufted perennial herb with bulbs arranged on a short rhizome. The leaves are 8–25cm long, cylindrical, 0·8–3mm wide, tapering to a fine point, hollow, sheathing at the base. The flower scape is 10–40cm tall, rounded in cross-section. The flowers have bulbils between them, arranged in an almost globular dense umbel surrounded by a 2-valved, shortly acuminate scarious spathe. The perianth-segments are usually spreading, 0·6–1·2cm long, pink or pale purple. The stamens are much shorter than the perianth. The seeds are angular.

Habitat dry rocky pastures, meadows or similar grassland. Distribution throughout Europe; locally in Wales and N. England. Widely and extensively cultivated as a herb and condiment. Parts used the leaves before flowering. Application **E**: chives are easily cultivated (even on the window-sill) and are one of our most popular condiments for flavouring salads, cottage cheese, omelettes, soups, sauces, etc. It should always be used fresh and only sparingly when applied to fine-tasting vegetables, otherwise its flavour will dominate the dish.

☠ **Colchicum autumnale** L. Liliaceae
Ⓜ **Meadow Saffron, Naked Ladies, Autumn Crocus** (May–June) A crocus-like perennial, growing from a 2·5–5cm long, scaly brown corm, leafless at flowering time (Aug.–Oct.) and developing its fruit with the leaves (March/April). The leaves are 10–30cm long, oblong-lanceolate, glossy. The flower scape is short but elongated in fruit. The perianth is pale purple, the segments united below into a 5–20cm long paler tube; the lobes are 3–5cm long, oblong, subobtuse. The fruit is obovoid, 3–5·5cm long, many-seeded.

Habitat in damp soil in meadows, open woods and similar grassy localities. Distribution in Europe from Denmark and the Netherlands southwards. In England northwards as far as Durham and Cumberland; rare in Scotland. Active ingredients alkaloids (mainly colchicine). Effect arrests mitosis of cell-nucleus and prevents cell-division. Parts used the seeds, more rarely the fresh corm. Application **C**: in homoeopathy preparations from the fresh corm as well as the seeds are prescribed for arthritis, rheumatism, gout and abdominal colics. In allopathic medicine the drug is only successfully used for acute attacks of arthritis and gout. Note *in no circumstances should this dangerous plant be used in the home.*

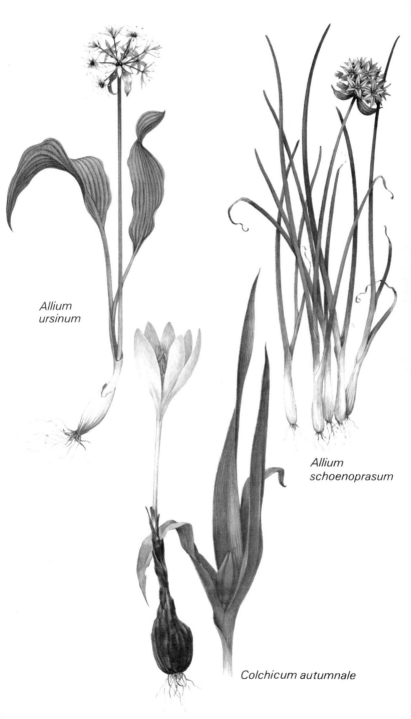

*Allium
ursinum*

*Allium
schoenoprasum*

Colchicum autumnale

☠ **_Veratrum album_** L. Liliaceae

Ⓜ **False Helleborine**   A robust perennial herb, growing with a stout vertical rhizome covered with remnants of old leaf sheaths. The stems are stout, simple, 50–175cm tall. The leaves are alternate, simple, 10–25cm long (becoming gradually shorter above), broadly ovate to elliptic, with many parallel veins, usually overlapping, narrowed into a sheathing base. The flowers are numerous, 1·3–2·7cm in diameter, arranged in a terminal branched panicle, shortly pedicelled, usually hermaphrodite. The 6 perianth-segments are free, up to 1·6cm long, elliptical to lanceolate, outside white, inside greenish-white or greenish or yellowish inside and outside. The stamens number 6. The fruit is a many-seeded pubescent capsule.

Habitat moist grassland. **Distribution** over most of Europe; absent from the British Isles. **Active ingredients** the alkaloids protoveratrine, germerine, germidine, germitrine and others, resin, fatty oil, a bitter principle. **Effect** anaesthetic, reduces blood pressure, irritates mucous membrane, violently emetic. **Parts used** the dried rhizome and roots; collect in the autumn, wash and dry in sun or artificial heat. **Application C:** the toxicity of this drug (2g taken internally are lethal) is such that it is *never used on its own* in medicine but its alkaloids are used by the pharmaceutical industry.

☠ **_Paris quadrifolia_** L. Trilliaceae

Herb Paris (May–Aug.)   A glabrous erect perennial herb with a creeping rhizome. The stem is 10–45cm tall. The leaves are typically arranged in a whorl of usually 4 (rarely more), 4–14cm long and 2·5–8cm broad, obovate from a heart-shaped base, almost sessile, with a network of veins between the main nerves. The flowers are regular, solitary and terminal, hermaphrodite. The sepals number 4 (rarely up to 6), up to 3·75cm long, lanceolate, acute, green. The petals are as many as the sepals, almost as long but much narrower, awl-shaped, greenish or yellowish-green. The stamens are as many as the perianth-segments; the filaments are rather short; the anthers are linear. The fruit is a capsule, fleshy and berry-like, globose, black, splits lengthways.

Habitat damp woodland or similar shady localities. **Distribution** scattered throughout the British Isles. **Active ingredients** include two saponins (paridine and paristyphnine). **Application C:** although this plant has been used in the past (in France) for homoeopathic preparations it is on account of its toxicity *not to be used for medicinal purposes!*

Ⓜ **_Iris germanica_** L. Iradaceae

Garden Iris (Sept.–Oct.) (not illustrated)   A robust perennial with a thick (up to 6cm in diameter) branching rhizome. The leaves are sword-shaped, 2–5·5cm broad, never exceeding the inflorescence, sheathing at the base. The flowers are hermaphrodite, regular, 8–11cm in diameter, fragrant, at the base enveloped by a spathe which is scarious above. The perianth-segments are in 2 series; the outer ones are ovate-oblong, deflexed, purple, with yellowish-white and purple-brown basal venation, bearded yellow, the inner of same size, bent inwards, pale purple. The styles have paddle-shaped, petal-like branches. The fruit is an ovoid capsule.

Habitat usually in waste places when found outside cultivation. **Distribution** native in the Mediterranean area but naturalized in many parts of the British Isles. Widely and extensively cultivated for ornament and for perfumery purposes. **Active ingredients** starch, mucilage, traces of essential oil, fatty oil, sugar, the glycoside iridin. **Effect** mildly expectorant, mildly diuretic, mildly purgative. **Parts used** the dried rhizome; dig up in second or third year, best after rain, peel and dry in sun. Only completely dried material yields scent. **Application M:** an infusion (1–2 teaspoons per cup water, allow to stand for 8–12 minutes) is taken 2–3 times a day as a diuretic and purgative but there are more effective remedies available. In the past the dried rhizome was given to teething babies for chewing but this practice is now discontinued for hygienic reasons. **Note** the plant in the illustration represents **_Iris pseudocorus_** L., the Yellow Flag, which is also occasionally used for medicinal purposes but the rhizome is poisonous and the plant should therefore not be used in the home. It differs from *I. germanica* by having longer outer perianth-segments and a tube which is as long as or usually shorter than the ovary.

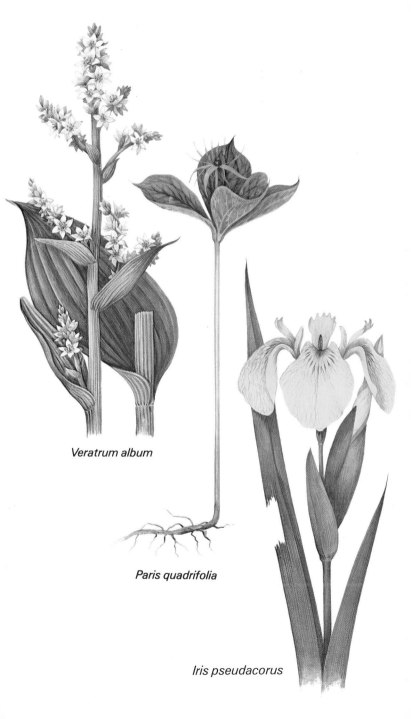

Veratrum album

Paris quadrifolia

Iris pseudacorus

☙ *Tamus communis* L. Dioscoreaceae

Ⓜ **Black Bryony** A climbing dioecious perennial herb with a large (sometimes over 20cm long) ovoid, blackish, subterranean stem tuber. The stems are twining anti-clockwise, slender, unbranched, over 3 or 4m long. The leaves are spirally arranged, 2·5–11cm long, broad-ovate from a heart-shaped base, glossy, curving main nerves with a network of lateral nerves, long petiolate. The flowers are small, yellow-green, arranged in axillary racemes; the female ones are sessile, the male pedicelled and slightly larger. The perianth is 6-lobed. The fruit is a berry, 1–1·3cm in diameter, red; seeds few, yellow, rugose.

Habitat hedgerows, scrub, edges of woods and copses, along fences, usually on calcareous soil. **Distribution** throughout S. and W. Europe northwards to Belgium and England. **Active ingredients** traces of an alkaloid, glycosides, a histamine-like substance, mucilage, potassium-oxalate. **Effect** irritant, diuretic; causes redness of the skin. **Parts used** the fresh tuber. **Application C:** the tuber is peeled and either sliced or made into a pulp. The slices (or the pulp) are applied or rubbed on to the skin of the parts affected by rheumatism, gout, arthritis, or myalgia. But since this treatment may cause painful blisters the drug cannot be seriously recommended for domestic use. **Note** the entire plant, but especially the berry, is *poisonous*.

Ⓜ *Orchis mascula* (L.) L. Orchidaceae

Blue Butcher, Early Purple Orchid A perennial herb with subglobular to ovoid tubers. The stem is 12–65cm tall, fairly robust. The leaves are 3–22cm long, narrowly or broadly oblanceolate-oblong, obtuse, usually with black-purplish markings. The orchid flower is purplish-crimson, arranged in a loose 4–16cm long spike; the bracts are about as long as the ovary. The spur is about as long as the ovary, cylindrical, curved upwards or straight, horizontal or ascending.

Distribution this plant as well as all other native orchids is strictly protected by law in Europe as well as in Britain. When used for medicinal purposes the plants are always imported from countries where they occur in abundance (Yugoslavia, Greece, Turkey etc.). **Active ingredients** abundant mucilage, starch, sugar, protein. **Effect** soothes irritation. **Application M:** the powderized drug is mainly used in pediatry for various forms of abdominal catarrhs and diarrhoea. It is either given orally or by way of the back passage. In the past this nutritious powder was also used for culinary purposes in the same way as arrow-root.

Ⓜ *Acorus calamus* L. Araceae

Sweet Flag (Sept.–Oct.) A stout aromatic aquatic perennial herb, growing from a long (1–2m), branching, creeping rhizome. The leaves are sword-shaped, numerous, crowded, 30–110cm long and 1–2cm wide, with a prominent midrib and undulate margins, fragrant when bruised. The flowers are all hermaphrodite, very small, with 6 free perianth-segments, yellowish, arranged in a solid 6–8·5cm long spike (spadix) which is laterally attached (at an angle of about 45°) to a flattened scape; the scape is reddish at the base, tapering above the inflorescence to an acute apex. The stamens number 6. The fruit does not develop in Britain and C. Europe.

Habitat at the edges of lakes, ponds, rivers, ditches, canals, always in shallow water. **Distribution** over most of Europe and the British Isles (naturalized since the 16th-17th centuries). **Active ingredients** essential oil with mainly asarone, bitter principle, mucilage, tannin, starch, sugar, choline, resin. **Effect** digestive, aperitive, mildly sedative; stimulates gland secretion. **Parts used** the dried rhizome; wash off mud, peel, cut lengthwise, dry thoroughly in shade or a warm room. **Application M:** in allopathic medicine this drug is contained (usually together with other aromatic bitter herbs) in brands of proprietary medicine prescribed for flatulence, dyspepsia, anorexia and gall bladder disorders. In homoeopathy a tincture is prepared for the same ailment. In the home an infusion (1½–2 teaspoons per cup water, allow to stand for 12–15 minutes) 2–3 times a day before meals can be taken for loss of appetite or sluggish digestion. It can also be used as a gargle for bleeding gums or added to the bathwater to overcome nervous exhaustion and fatigue.

Orchis mascula

Tamus communis

Acorus calamus

☠ *Arum maculatum* L. Araceae

Lords and Ladies, Cuckoo-pint (flowers: April–May; fruit: July–Aug.) An erect perennial herb 15–50cm tall, with a fleshy tuber. The leaves appear in spring long before the flowering shoots, long petiolate, 5–20cm long, triangular from a base with lobes pointing backwards, usually with blackish markings and a network of veins. The flowers are unisexual, very small, without perianth-segments, arranged in a solid spike (spadix) with the female ones below, followed by sterile and then male ones. The inflorescence is surrounded by a 12–27cm long, convolute, greenish-yellow, or (in the upper part) purplish spathe. The fruit is a *poisonous* berry, 3·5–5·5mm in diameter, scarlet, fleshy.

Habitat woods, copses, hedge banks and similar shady localities. **Distribution** throughout the region (rarer in parts of Scotland). **Application C:** in contrast to common belief, this plant is *poisonous* (especially the red berries) and should therefore never be used for medicinal (or culinary) purposes.

Ⓔ *Typha latifolia* L. Typhaceae

Great Reedmace, Cat's-tail A stout perennial herb with a branched, long rhizome. The stems are erect, simple, robust, up to 2·75m tall. The leaves exceed the inflorescence, linear from a sheathed base, 0·8–2cm wide, twisted. The flowers are unisexual, numerous and very small, crowded into a dense uninterrupted terminal spadix, with the male above the female, interspersed with numerous hairs and scales. The male flowers have up to 5 stamens. The fruit is dry, cylindrical, stalked.

Habitat in shallow water in ponds, lakes, ditches, slow-flowing streams and rivers. **Distribution** throughout the region. **Parts used** the rhizome (best collected from late autumn to early spring when they are rich in starch). The young shoots in early spring and the flowering shoots before the flowers mature. The pollen can be used like flour or arrow-root: the mature spadix is placed over a shallow container, slightly tapped and the pollen brushed off with a fine brush and then separated from other parts of the inflorescence by passing it through a fine sieve. **Application E:** young shoots are boiled for 3–8 minutes in salted water and then slightly sautéd in olive oil.

Ⓜ *Carex arenaria* L. Cyperaceae

Sand Sedge (March–April) A mat-forming and far-creeping perennial herb, growing with a much-branched rhizome, with shoots at about every fourth node. The stems are 8–60cm (up to 90cm) long, sharply triangular in cross-section. The leaves are ribbed, up to 60cm long, 1·5–4mm wide, expanded, tapering to a fine point, rigid; the leaf sheaths often become fibrous and remain on the horizontal rhizomes. The inflorescence is dense, up to 8cm long. The spikes are 0·9–1·5cm long; the lowermost are female, followed by mixed or female in the middle, the uppermost entirely male.

Habitat mainly on fixed dunes and on wind-blown sand. **Distribution** along the coasts of Europe and British Isles (rarely inland – the Brecks and Lincoln heaths). **Active ingredients** abundant silicic acid, tannin, saponin, glycoside, resin, starch, traces of essential oil. **Effect** diuretic, stimulating metabolism and sweating. **Parts used** the rhizome; brush clean, dry in the sun or shade. **Application M:** in the home an infusion (2 teaspoons per cup water, allow to stand for 12–15 minutes) 3–4 times a day is taken for bronchitis and catarrhs, abdominal and stomach disorders, liver complaints, arthritis, rheumatic pain and skin conditions (eczema, pruritus).

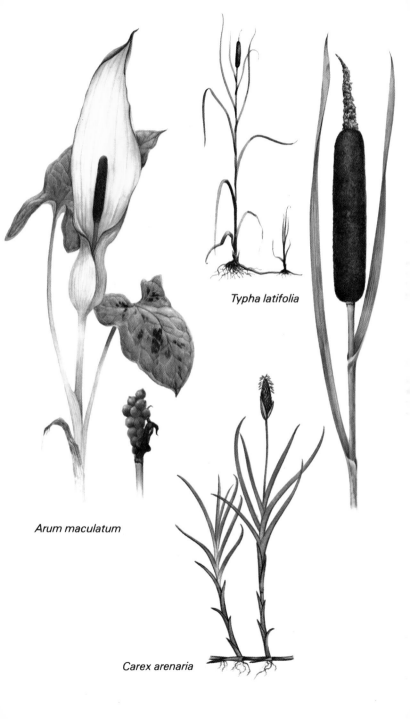

Typha latifolia

Arum maculatum

Carex arenaria

Ⓜ *Elymus (Agropyron) repens* (L.) Gould

Couch-grass, Quack-grass, Twich (March–April and Sept.–Oct.) A perennial grass with numerous branched, wide-creeping, sweet-tasting rhizomes. The leaves are linear, hardly more than 1·5cm wide, bright green or greyish-green, scattered hairs on the upper surface; the sheath smooth, glabrous or initially pubescent. The culm is 25–85cm (up to 105cm) tall, glabrous, spikelets 0·9–2.2cm long, 2 to 6 flowered, arranged in a 5–22cm long, stiff, erect terminal spike with a pubescent rachis. The glumes are almost equal, up to ¾ the length of the spikelet, lanceolate acute, with thin, translucent margins; the lower ones are 3-veined, the upper 5-veined. The lemma is lanceolate with the apex obtuse, acute or awned.

Habitat arable land, waste places, roadsides; weed in gardens and fields, difficult to eradicate. **Distribution** all over the region. **Active ingredients** triticin (a polysaccharide), mucilage, traces of essential oil, silicic acid, sugar, saponin, fatty oil. **Effect** diuretic, anti-irritant, antiseptic. **Parts used** the dried (in homoeopathy fresh) rhizome; dig up, wash, dry in the sun or shade or in a warm room (under 35°C). **Application M:** a decoction (1½–2 teaspoons per cup of cold water, heat and boil for about 2 minutes, allow to stand for 8–12 minutes) 2–3 times a day for a period of several weeks is taken for bronchial catarrhs, arthritis, rheumatism, cystitis and skin disorders. It is harmless and can be drunk as a herbal tea for purifying the blood or for metabolic disorders.

Ⓜ *Anthoxanthum odoratum* L. Gramineae

Sweet Vernal-grass (July–Sept.) Coumarin-scented, tufted perennial grass, 18–50cm tall. The leaves are relatively short, narrowly lanceolate, tapering to a fine point, scattered hairs; the ligule acute to almost truncate, 2·5–4mm long; sheath fairly tight, finely striate, smooth, glabrous or pubescent. Inflorescence a dense and compact panicle, oblong to narrowly ovate-oblong in outline. Spikelets with 2 lower sterile and 1 upper hermaphrodite florets, 6–10mm long. Glumes rather unequal, keeled, translucent; the lower ovate, 1-nerved; the upper ovate-lanceolate, 3-nerved, twice as long as the lower and longer than the spikelet, very shortly awned.

Habitat meadows, pastures, margins of woods, heaths, moors, etc. **Distribution** throughout the region. **Active ingredients** coumarin, silicic acid. **Effect** stimulates circulation, soothing (relieving pain), prevents spasms. **Parts used** whole mature inflorescence and fragments of whole plant, sorted out after hay-making. **Application M:** this remedy is only used externally for bathing or preparation of compresses for rheumatic pain, inflamed joints, myalgia, chilblains, metabolic disturbances, nervous and/or physical exhaustion, insomnia. The grass is either used on its own or in a mixture of other meadow and pasture grasses.

Anthoxanthum odoratum

Elymus repens

Phycophyta Algae (Seaweeds)

Algae are unicellular or multicellular water plants with variously coloured pigments. Their sexually reproductive organs are usually unicellular and in the lower groups the reproductive cells (spores, gametes) are flagellate; in the higher groups only the male gamete is equipped with flagellae.

Out of the vast number of algae (around 33,000) about a dozen species are of interest to us in the context of this book. They all belong to one of the classes with a high level of organization (e.g. possessing advanced type of tissue), namely the *Chlorophyta* (green algae), the *Phaeophyta* (brown algae) and the *Rhoclophyta* (red algae).

(E) ### *Enteromorpha intestinalis* (L.) Link Chlorophyta

A transparent, pale green plant. The thallus is hollow, inflated or rarely flattened, usually tubular and slightly constricted at intervals, crinkled, very rarely branched, 5–60cm (rarely up to 100cm) long, 1–3cm wide.

Habitat singly or in groups on rocks or in rock pools near the upper tide-line, sometimes free-floating; usually in water with reduced salinity (the plant can survive in fresh water for some time). **Distribution** North Sea, English Channel, Atlantic, Baltic; otherwise cosmopolitan. **Parts used** the whole plant, fresh or dried; best harvested in spring and early summer. **Application E:** mainly used for culinary purposes in the Far East and either eaten fresh in salads or dried and used in pulverized form for various dishes or as a condiment.

(E) ### *Ulva lactuca* L. Chlorophyta

Sea Lettuce A variable plant, light yellowish-green to dark green, sometimes iridescent. The thallus is leaf-like, 10–80cm long, thin, of irregular shape (heart-shaped, ovate, lanceolate or variously lobed), sometimes perforated, undulate, 2 layered in cross-section but not hollow; stipe solid, short, present or absent.

Habitat on rocks or timber-work, sometimes epiphytic on other algae, rarely free floating, sometimes washed up; sometimes in pools but usually between the tide-marks. **Distribution** North Sea, English Channel, Baltic, Atlantic. **Parts used** the whole plant, usually fresh; best harvested from early to late spring. **Application E:** eaten raw in salad (as in Scotland) or in sandwiches; it can also be added to soups. In the Far East the plant is also served with meat and fish dishes.

(E) ### *Chorda filum* (L.) Stackh. Phaeophyta

An olive-brown or caramel-coloured plant. The thallus is rounded in cross-section, hollow, 2–4·5m long, 2·75–4·5cm in diameter, flexible, whip-like, tapering at both ends, not branched, slimy, the central hollow divided into compartments and filled with air. The holdfast is disc-like, very small.

Habitat in shallow water (1–20m deep) on stones or rock, rarely epiphytic on other algae, also on sandy ground. **Distribution** North Sea, Atlantic, English Channel, Baltic. **Parts used** the fresh plant harvested in summer. Often difficult to gather. Either cut off with a sickle or by using a grapnel. **Application E:** best eaten fresh in salads or finely chopped in sandwiches.

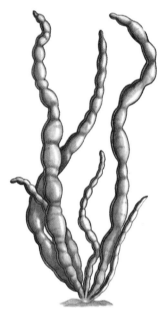

Enteromorpha intestinalis

Ulva lactuca

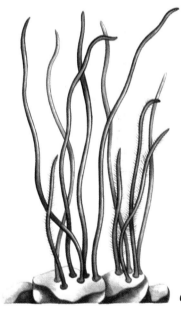

Chorda filum

Ⓔ **Alaria esculenta** (L.) Grev. Phaeophyta
Dabberlocks An olive-brown to dark brown plant. The thallus is 10–80cm (some-times over 200cm) long, 5–15cm wide, consisting of a short stipe rounded in cross-section and a long leaf-like blade. The blade has a flattened midrib throughout (this is the main distinguishing feature), undulate, thin, often lacerate to the mid-rib. The stipe has a number of reproductive finger-like protuberances containing unilocular sporangia.

Habitat on rocks in the shallow seabed and on the lowermost shore. **Distribution** North Sea, N. Atlantic. **Parts used** the blade excluding the midrib, the midrib alone (fresh) or midrib with stipes and sporophylls (fresh). **Application E:** the blade (when used on its own) is usually kept in water for at least 24 hours before either used fresh or dried. The midrib and/or stipe are eaten raw in salads or on sandwiches or (fresh or dried) in soups, stews etc.

Ⓔ **Laminaria saccharina** (L.) Lamour. Phaeophyta
Sugar Kelp, Poor Man's Weatherglass A chestnut-brown to olive-brown plant, consisting of a blade (phylloid), a stipe (cauloid) and a holdfast (rhizoid). The blade is leathery, 20–300cm long, 10–30cm wide, undivided, with strongly undulate margins and a crumpled centre part; different zones of growth are marked by constrictions. The stipe is 10–40cm long, 0·5–1cm in diameter, round in cross-section. The holdfast is branched, with the branches at different levels.

Habitat on rocks, stones and shells between the lowest tide mark and up to 20m of depth. **Distribution** North Sea, English Channel, Atlantic, W. Baltic. **Parts used** the blade (best of first year plants) or the stipe. Harvest in late spring or during summer, cut with a sickle or use a grapnel. **Application E:** the young stipes can be eaten raw either in salads or in sandwiches. The famous 'pain des algues' of Brittany and Normandy is based on a mixture of this plant with *Chondrus crispus*.

Ⓔ **Laminaria digitata** (Huds.) Lamour. Phaeophyta
Oarweed, Tangle A plant which is similar in structure to the above species, olive-brown to dark brown. The blade is 100–200cm long, 30–55cm wide, thick, leathery, digitately or palmately divided into strap-like segments. The stipe is 10–45cm long, 1–2cm in diameter, evenly rounded in cross-section, smooth, flexible, usually without epiphytes, slightly flattened towards the base, and above gradually widening into the blade. The holdfast is as above.

Habitat on rocks or large stones from the lowest tide-mark to 4–7m depth, often forming large stands and sometimes intermixed with the following species; often washed up. **Distribution** North Sea, Atlantic, English Channel, Baltic. **Parts used** the fresh or dried blade; best harvested in spring and early summer when its vitamin C content is highest. **Application E:** the plant is eaten in various soups, used for preparing a stock or turned into a condiment.

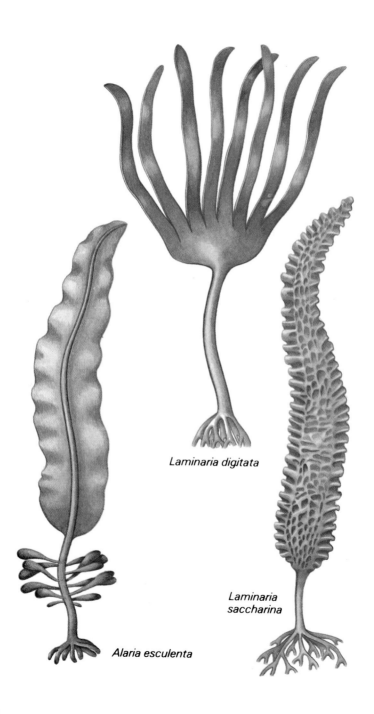

Laminaria digitata

Laminaria saccharina

Alaria esculenta

Ⓔ *Laminaria hyperborea* (Gunn.) Fosl. *(L. cloustoni)* Phaeophyta
This plant is similar in habit to the above species but is distinguished as follows: the blade is usually ovate from a slightly heart-shaped base; the stipe is much longer (30–120cm) and always tapers towards the blade; it has a rough surface and thus provides a hold for epiphytes or animals.

Habitat on rocks and large stones on the lowest shore beneath the tide-mark, usually just beneath of or overlapping with the preceding species, and forming large underwater 'forests'. Distribution , parts used and application E: as for the above species.

Ⓔ *Fucus vesiculosus* L. Phaeophyta
Bladder Wrack A conspicuous olive-brown to dark greenish-yellow plant. The thallus is 15–100cm long, 0·5–2·25cm broad, strap-shaped, dichotomously branched, flat, fairly thick and leathery, with a distinct midrib, with air-bladders (usually arranged in pairs) and with receptacles (olive-brown reproduction bodies) at the apex of lateral lobes; the margins are entire, not serrate.

Habitat on rocks, large stones and shells, forming a distinct zone on the middle shore. Distribution the Atlantic (European coasts as far as the Bay of Biscay), English Channel, North Sea and Baltic. Parts used usually the dried lateral branches of the thallus. Application E: fresh or dried parts are boiled or stewed with fish, meat or vegetable dishes: sew 1–2 tablespoons, or more according to taste and quantity, into a linen bag and suspend it (sachet-like) for the first 15–20 minutes of cooking. Dried (dry first in the sun and then in artificial heat, store in an airtight container) the plant makes an excellent and healthy herbal tea (infusion of 1½–2 teaspoons per cup water, allow to stand for 5 minutes). In the past this plant, which can easily be harvested in large quantities, was one of the main sources for industrial iodine-production.

Ⓜ *Chondrus crispus* Stackh. Rhodophyta
Ⓔ **Irish Moss, Carragheen** A red-purple to brown-red plant (may turn green in intense light). The thallus is 3–16cm tall, cartilaginous, several times dichotomously divided, flat; the segments are wedge-shaped, usually all in one plane; the stem is not channelled, thus differing from the otherwise similar *Gigartina stellata* which in older specimens displays pimples on the surface. The holdfast is disc-like.

Habitat on rock and stones on the lower shore, in shallow water near the shore and in rock pools. Distribution North Sea, English Channel, Atlantic, W. Baltic. Active ingredients mucilage (up to 80%), iodine, bromine, iron, various mineral salts, protein, sugar, vitamins A and B1. Effect mildly expectorant, skin softener, mildly laxative. Parts used the dried thallus; dry in sun (wet intermittently); store in airtight container. Application M: although contained in a few brands of proprietary medicine (usually with *Thymus, Primula, Althaea, Cetaria* and *Ephedra*) for bronchitis and coughs the drug is obsolete. In the home an infusion (1–1½ teaspoons per cup water, allow to stand for 8–10 minutes) 2–3 times daily is taken for the same complaints. E: the fresh or dried thallus is turned into a gel for blancmange, jellies or aspic-dishes. It is also eaten in soups.

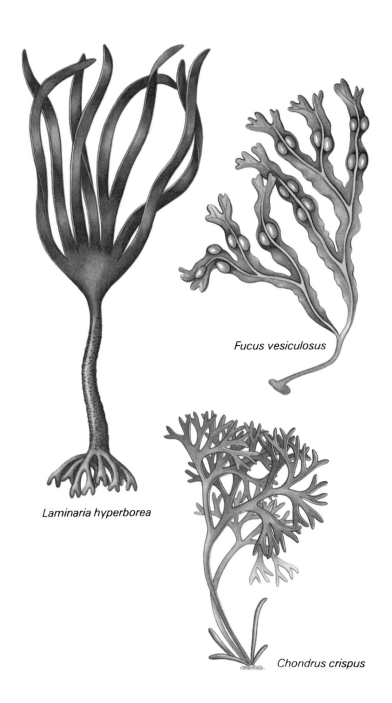

Fucus vesiculosus

Laminaria hyperborea

Chondrus crispus

Ⓔ **Porphyra umbilicalis** (L.) J.G. Agardh Rhodophyta

'Purple Laver' A flat plant, red-purple-green or reddish-brown. The thallus is flattened, leaf-like, membranous, gelatinous, 5–20cm in diameter, undulate to handkerchief-like folded, attached to the substratum at one point (umbicule-like).

Habitat on rocks or large stones, harbour walls, wharfs, sand-covered rocky surfaces, or pendulous on overhanging boulders. **Distribution** North Sea, Atlantic, part of the Mediterranean. **Parts used** the thallus, usually fresh. **Application E:** this plant is the base of the famous Welsh laver bread. Also in Wales and in other parts of S. England it is eaten raw. In Scotland and Ireland it is boiled with vinegar or lemon juice and served like mint sauce with meat dishes.

Ⓔ **Rhodimenia palmata** (L.) Grev. Rhodophyta

Dulse A very variable dark-red to brown-red stipeless plant. The thallus is flattened and leaf-like, 8–40cm tall, tough, leathery, digitately or more often irregularly divided, often with marginal leaf-like proliferations, the final lobes rounded.

Habitat on rocks, stones or epiphytically on larger algae (e.g. *Fucus serratus* and stipes of *Laminaria*) on middle and lower shores and in shallow water. **Distribution** North Sea, English Channel, Atlantic, W. Baltic. **Parts used** the entire thallus, fresh or dried. Harvest from late spring or early summer till Sept./Oct. **Application E:** the plant has a delicious flavour and is easily digestible; it is therefore best eaten raw in salads or sandwiches. One can also add it to soups, stews etc, or serve it as a vegetable with meat or fish. Hot Rhodimenia-lemonade is a satisfying evening drink in winter and a remedy for chills and colds. For drying the plant must be thoroughly rinsed in seawater and dried in sun and fresh air; in the process it will turn black temporarily.

Porhyra umbilicalis

Rhodimenia palmata

Lichens

Lichens are a large group of plants which form a physiological and morphological association (a so-called symbiosis) of a fungus (or a fungal hyphae) with an algae. Whereas most of the algae found in lichens exist also free in nature, the fungal partner can never be found on its own, and is generally a fungus which determines the shape of a lichen species. Lichens are very slow-growing. They can be found on rocks, bark, walls or on the soil. The basic body is termed the thallus; it is firmly attached to the substratum by hyphal strands (the so-called rhizinae). Reproduction of lichens is effected by vegetative propagation: small portions of the thallus (soralia) become detached and are then dispersed by wind or water. As a matter of fact almost every part of a thallus can regenerate into a new plant.

Ⓜ *Cetraria islandica* (L.) Ach.
Ⓔ **Iceland Moss** The thallus is strap-like, deeply divided, shrubby and forms entangled mats, 1–15cm high, only loosely attached to the substratum. The lobes are thin, either curled inwards almost into tubes or flat, shining chestnut-brown on the upper surface and lighter on the lower, often reddish towards the base; the margins somewhat incised and ciliate.

Habitat heaths and moors chiefly in mountain areas. **Distribution** throughout most of Europe. In the British Isles mainly in the Scottish Highlands. **Active ingredients** abundant mucilage, digestible carbohydrates, lichesterinic acid and sometimes protolichesterinic acid, traces of iodine, vitamin A. **Effect** mildly stimulates gland secretion, anti-irritant, aperitive, mildly antiseptic, tonic. **Parts used** the entire plant; collect during dry period; store in well-ventilated place. **Application M:** mainly contained in brands of proprietary medicine or herbal mixtures for bronchitis, asthma, lack of appetite or anorexia and gastric disorders. In homoeopathy a tincture is prescribed for the same ailments. In the home a decoction (2–3 teaspoons per cup of cold water, heat and boil for 1 minute, allow to stand for 8–12 minutes) 3–4 times a day is taken for the same conditions or for bathing slow-healing cuts. **E:** this plant is said to be edible when ground down to produce a flour which is mixed with ordinary flour for baking bread and cakes but the process of removing the bitter taste of this plant is far too time-consuming and tedious to be countenanced.

Ⓜ *Usnea barbata* (L.) Weber *(U. sensulato)*
Old Man's Beard A variable plant with a densely to loosely, much-branched bushy thallus, often blackened near the holdfast, trailing, erect or pendant, rounded in cross-section with a central core, covered with rough warts and small spines, rarely smooth, grey-green to yellowish-green, rarely brownish-red or greyish-red, up to 100cm long; secondary branches pointed, sometimes constricted where they join the main branches. **Note** modern taxonomic research has shown that several distinct species are now to be recognized, but for the purpose of this book all the species with a pendular habit can be treated under the old circumscription since they contain the same or similar active ingredients.

Habitat growing on trees, fences and sometimes rocks. Common in damp woods away from areas affected by air-pollution. **Distribution** throughout the region. **Active ingredients** salazinic and usnic acids. **Effect** antibiotic, aperitive. **Parts used** the whole plant; collect during a dry period and after drying store in a well-ventilated place. **Application M:** this drug is used in the home as a decoction (3–4 teaspoons per cup of cold water, heat and boil for 1–2 minutes, allow to stand for 10 minutes) 2–3 times a day for colds and influenza or – less certain – internal haemhorrhages. Usnic acid is a powerful antibiotic and to my knowledge utilized by the pharmaceutical industry in Scandinavia. In Portuguese folk medicine this plant is rubbed on to slow-healing burns, cuts and bruises.

ⓜ *Lobaria pulmonaria* (L.) Hoffm.

Lungwort A plant with flattened, leaf-like thallus, branched, usually attached at the end, about 3–17cm long, bright green or olive-green on the upper surface when wet, turning khaki or greyish-green when dry, usually light tan and covered by a darker tomentum forming a veined pattern on the lower surface; the lobes are much broader than in *Cetraria islandica*, usually with incised margins; the upper surface with rounded depressions often with ridges resembling coral.

Habitat usually on the bark of deciduous trees, more rarely on heather stems or on mossy rocks. Chiefly confined to old forests and medieval parkland. **Distribution** throughout the British Isles but now very rare in the eastern parts. **Active ingredients** stictic, constictic and norstitic acids, mucilage. **Effect** digestive, aperitive, mildly antibiotic, mildly astringent. **Parts used** as for the preceding species. **Application M:** in homoeopathy an essence, prepared from fresh material, is prescribed for bronchial and nasal catarrhs and for rheumatism. In the home a decoction (as for the above species) is taken for the same ailments (not for rheumatism) as well as for asthma, kidney and bladder complaints, lack of appetite, sluggish digestion. **Note** in the past this plant on account of its appearance was sold as a cure for tuberculosis, hence its name. The positive effect of the cure was probably due to its stimulating appetite combined with its mildly antibiotic effect.

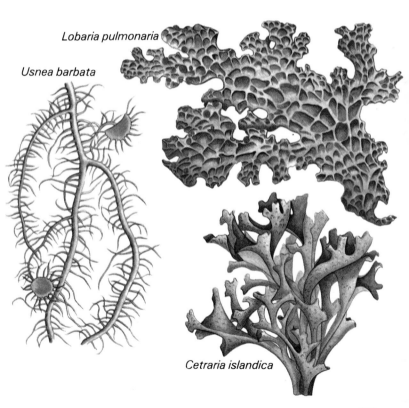

Lobaria pulmonaria

Usnea barbata

Cetraria islandica

What are mushrooms and toadstools?

Mushrooms and toadstools are popular names given to the fruiting bodies of many of the larger fungi. This group of plants differs from the others described in this guide in that they are devoid of chlorophyll and are not able to produce their own nourishment by the photosynthesis of water and carbon dioxide. In common with members of the animal kingdom their life depends on existing organic materials. They thrive either as saprophytes on dead organic matter or as parasites on living organisms.

The structure of a mushroom is often deceptive in that the fruiting body, which is usually considered to be the main part, is only a relatively small part of the entire plant and is responsible for producing and dispersing the spores. However, the most extensive area of the mushroom is beneath the surface and consists of a web-like structure known as mycelium made up of microscopic threads called hyphae. It is through the mycelium that the fungus extracts its nourishment. This part of the fungus persists throughout the year whilst the fruit-body is usually only short-lived. However, in some bracket fungi the fruit-body can remain for many years.

Scientists have described over 100 000 different fungi and many more are still awaiting discovery. They occupy every possible environment, the majority being microscopic and easily transported. Many types are serious plant pests and others can cause dangerous disorders in animals. Some, however, form a close symbiotic association with their host plant. In many cases these associations, which are termed mycorrhizae, are highly specific and may even be confined to one host species.

How to collect mushrooms

In general the same basic rule which has been given for the collecting of medicinal and culinary herbs applies for mushrooms but must here be especially emphasized: only collect and eat a species when you are absolutely sure about its identification. As a beginner do not rely entirely on books but ask a more knowledgeable person to join you when collecting or have them properly identified afterwards. The selection of species in this guide is confined to easily identifiable and distinctive mushrooms.

Place your harvest in baskets or perforated cardboard boxes; never use plastic bags, sealable glass or metal containers. Remember not to destroy the mycelium underground by digging or tearing your mushrooms out of the soil otherwise you may destroy the locality and deprive yourself and others of a further harvest at the same place. Just cut the stem above the ground or remove the mushroom with a slight twist; *always* check the base of the stem to make sure it is not a Destroying Angel or Death Cap.

Do not collect old specimens or mushrooms which are partly eaten by insects, snails or are infested with maggots. Leave mushrooms of which you are not certain in their place, never destroy any specimen even when

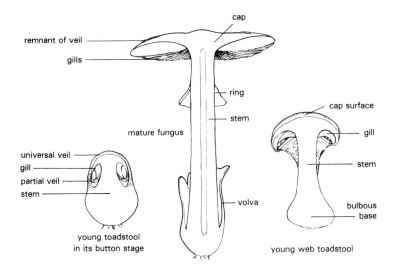

cap

remnant of veil

gills

ring

stem

mature fungus

cap surface

gill

stem

universal veil

gill

partial veil

stem

volva

bulbous base

young toadstool
in its button stage

young web toadstool

you have recognized it as poisonous; there is a purpose for every living organism in Nature.

The only way of identifying a mushroom and to find out whether it is edible or not is by visual means, i.e. by comparing your specimen with the samples given in this guide or any other books. Since some of the more important characteristics only appear in mature specimens avoid very young ones, especially when they are still covered by their veil (button-stage). There is no other test for establishing the edibility of a mushroom. Many a fatal accident has occurred to people who followed the old Folk tale that a silver spoon or coin or an onion turn brown or black when boiled together with a poisonous species. Moreover the fact that a mushroom is eaten by insects or that it has a pleasant and agreeable smell does not mean it can be consumed by man.

Preparing mushrooms for eating

Use only fresh specimens, and consume them as quickly as possible or store them in the fridge for not longer than two days. Indefinite storage can render even commonly edible and harmless mushrooms dangerous. It is therefore inadvisable to warm up mushroom dishes again even after they have been kept in an ordinary fridge (see also deep-freezing below!).

Avoid washing them if they are not too dirty. Adherent particles can be removed by gently tapping the cap, held vertically, with a wooden spoon or removed with a soft brush. The surface should first be wiped (best immediately after picking) with a dry cloth. Remove the skin of sticky specimens. If all fails rinse them quickly with cold water and place them on a dry cloth or kitchen towel for drying. If the stems are hard use them either separately or discard (they can also be dried and used as a powder where appropriate). Taking off the skin is rarely necessary and, contrary to often given advice, do not remove the gills because the spores contained therein provide a rich source of protein and often determine the taste of a mushroom; moreover when used in soups they often imbue a rich brown colour to the broth in boiling.

Whether one eats a species on its own or mixed with others is a matter of taste; some hints to this as well as to the suitability for certain cooking methods are given with each description.

The best method for stewing mushrooms is as follows: heat some butter or oil in a frying pan or casserole and stew finely cut onions in it until they become just transparent; add the mushrooms (cut into small pieces) and spices and stew gently for 15–20 minutes, add fresh cream or thicken according to taste with potato- or cornflour, only add salt shortly before serving. Larger mushrooms can be fried like 'schnitzel'.

The preservation of mushrooms

Recent experience has shown that deep-freezing mushrooms or mushrooms dishes can enhance their flavour. Fresh mushrooms must be blanched before treated for freezing like any other vegetable. Most popular and time-honoured is the method of drying (not advisable for species with viscid caps). Small species or sliced large ones are placed evenly on a paper or cloth-covered metal grill and kept in a warm well-ventilated place until bone-dry. Sliced mushrooms can also be stringed (make sure the pieces are separated) and suspended over a heat source or dried in the sun.

Dried mushrooms must be kept in sealed glass containers where they may last for years. Before using they should be soaked in cold water until soft (some species like *Cantherellus* will not soften up and should be used as powder; this species, incidentally, turns bitter when deep-frozen).

Other methods of preservation, including pickling, are to be found in most cookery books.

Mushroom poisoning

If every care is taken this should never happen. Nevertheless a few words of advice about what to do if suspected mushroom poisoning has occurred may not be out of place. The symptoms vary greatly but the first signs are usually severe abdominal pain accompanied by diarrhoea and vomiting; there can also be a sudden change of pulse, a dramatic lowering of blood pressure, nausea and in severe cases, hallucinations and finally death, caused by either liver or kidney damage or heart failure. It is especially alarming when these symptoms occur only 10–24 (or even over 40 hours) after mushrooms have been consumed as is usually the case with the two most dangerous mushrooms. The victim should at once be taken to hospital, and if possible one of the eaten specimens (even the vomit) should be shown to the doctor.

Poisoning caused by other mushrooms is usually less severe and often only upsetting. It may also be caused by edible species which have been kept for too long, or some people may just be allergic to some species of mushrooms as others are to shellfish or other food.

Some species are only poisonous in the raw state (e.g. *Russula* and *Lactarius*) but the toxic ingredients are rendered harmless by cooking. As a rule one should never eat raw mushrooms unless it is specifically stated in their description (but even then only fresh and healthy looking specimens should be consumed).

Some species are only poisonous when consumed with alcohol (see *Coprinus*); but it should be noted that the poisoning may still take place when alcohol is consumed up to *three or more days* after eating these mushrooms, which are therefore clearly only food for total abstainers.

☠ *Boletus satanas* Lent. Boletineae

Devil's Boletus This species is structurally and in appearance similar to *Boletus edulis*. It is, besides its size – the cap can be between 6–20cm (up to 30cm) in diameter – distinguished from all the other species of the genus as follows: the cap is rather fleshy, white or greyish-white (sometimes reddish at the edges); when old it is leather to ochre-coloured, velvety; the pores are narrow, distinctive blood-red (only yellowish when very young). The stem can be up to 10cm in diameter, yellowish to orange-coloured above, purplish below, all over with a usually raised red reticulation.

Habitat in open deciduous woods on calcareous soil; it prefers warm situations. Rare in the British Isles and almost confined to S. England. **Note** this is the only poisonous species of the genus *Boletus* but not easily mistaken for any of them. When consumed it has a violently emetic effect but is not necessarily deadly. In order to avoid accidents beginners should not eat any mushroom with red or reddish pores.

☠ *Amanita virosa* (Lam.) Quél. Agaricineae

Destroying Angel In most aspects similar to *A. phalloides*. The cap is at first egg-shaped, then conical to flat, 5–10cm in diameter, usually pure white but rarely slightly tinged ivory to fox-brown in the centre, sticky when moist, silkily glossy when dry; the remnants of the veil are sometimes present; the gills are pure white, with somewhat crenate edges. The stem is slender and usually a little curved, 6–10cm tall, shaggy (somewhat rough and floccose), pure white; the ring below the cap is white, the volva is large with irregular edges, often appressed and then sometimes not observed.

Habitat often in coniferous woods on mossy ground but also in mixed woods, hardly ever in grassland. Sometimes side by side with *A. phalloides* but much rarer; more common in N. Europe, not common in the British Isles. **Note** this species is as poisonous as *A. phalloides* and can likewise be confused – especially when young – with similar looking edible mushrooms which beginners should avoid (even experienced collectors have been poisoned by this species). It has a white and soft flesh, smells sweetish at first but develops later a rather off-putting (laboratory-like) scent.

☠ *Amanita pantherina* (DC) Kummer Agaricineae

The Panther The cap is 5–12cm in diameter, at first strongly convex, later cushion-shaped to almost flat, pale greyish-brown to dull brown, sometimes greyish-olive, covered with irregular white bark; the periphery of the mature specimen is striate; it is sticky to the touch when moist; the remnants of the veil fall off soon; the skin comes off easily. The gills are white, free from the stem, rather broad. The stem is 7–9cm tall, white, silky and shiny, smooth, squat to slender, at first solid, later often hollow. The ring around the middle is not flaring, often obliquely attached, in older specimens sometimes absent; the base is bulbous with a volva consisting of several (usually 2–3) concentric rings. The spores are white.

Habitat fairly common on the Continent, uncommon in the British Isles; in deciduous woods (mainly under beech trees) but also in mixed and coniferous woods. **Note** the consumption of this species leads to severe illness and can sometimes be fatal. It tastes quite like a radish and the flesh, which remains white, sometimes smells like raw potatoes. Because of the often absent ring it can be mistaken for the edible but not recommended *A. spissa* (= *A. excelsa*). The related Fly Agaric (*A. muscaria*) which is clearly recognizable by its red cap with whitish warts, is, contrary to common belief, also poisonous and must not be eaten in any circumstances.

Boletus satanas

Amanita virosa

Amanita pantherina

☠ ***Amanita phalloides*** (Vaill.) Quél. Agaricineae

Death Cap The cap is 4–12cm (rarely up to 15cm) in diameter, at first convex (the very young specimens are egg-shaped), later flattened, without warts or seeds, white to pale yellow or olive-green, with faint lines radiating from the centre to the margins, sticky when moist, milky when dry and with remnants of the veil rarely present (the skin can be peeled off easily). The gills are free from the stem, dense, broad, always white. The stem is 7–12cm tall, usually of even thickness throughout, but somewhat constricted below the cup, white or sometimes of the same coloration as the cup, frequently with horizontal bands, at first solid, later hollow from above downwards; the ring is attached below the cup, always well-developed, skirt-like, usually striped; the stem base is bulbous, usually deep in the soil, typically surrounded by a sack-like persistent volva. The spores are white, thin and translucent.

Habitat in wood and park-land (often under oak trees) but also in rich shady meadows, sometimes in gardens, often common, solitary or in groups. **Note** as the common name implies this species is one of the most poisonous mushrooms, and even the consumption of part of a single specimen will lead to fatal poisoning. Its flesh is white, soft and, unfortunately, of pleasant taste; early on it smells honey-like and sickly-sweet but later specimens develop an off-putting smell. The poisonous ingredients (amanitin and phalloidin) are only effective after between 1 and 3 days when they have entered the bloodstream and have caused irreversible damage to the liver. Most fatal mushroom poisonings in Europe are caused by this species. Since it can be easily mistaken for some edible species the beginner should avoid all of them.

Ⓔ ***Craterellus cornucopioides*** Pers. Cantharellaceae

Horn of Plenty, Black Trumpet (Aug./Sept.– Nov.) The cap is not well-defined, the entire fruit-body is funnel-shaped, 3–10cm in diameter, dark brown to almost black (paler when not moist), with thin undulate to almost lobed irregular margins, the skin is somewhat rough, the lower surface is without gills or ridges, fairly smooth but sometimes with shallow wrinkles, dirty ash-grey, bluish-violet to almost black when wet. The stem is short, of similar colour as the cap but paler, hollow throughout. The spores are whitish.

Habitat in deciduous and (more rarely) coniferous woods, in damp situations, usually amongst rotting leaves. It usually grows in large numbers, almost always in colonies and reappears in the same locality year after year. Very common in Europe and the British Isles. **Note** the flesh of this spicy mushroom is rather thin and hardens with age. It is best used mixed with others (stewed, fried, or in soups) or as an excellent condiment (dried and powdered) for sauces, soups and stews. Both colour and shape as well as the absence of gills makes it very difficult to confuse this species with any other mushroom. Somewhat similar, however, but with a more defined stem and distinct folds on the underside is the also edible, *Chantarellus cinereus*.

Ⓔ ***Lepista personata*** (Fr.) W.G. Smith **(*L. saevum*)** Agaricineae

Common Blewit, Blue-leg (Oct.– Dec.) The cap is 6–12cm in diameter, at first convex, later flattened, with involute margins, buff, yellowish-brown or greyish, smooth, not sticky. The gills are densely arranged, attached to slightly decurrent on the stem, white to pinkish-buff or flesh-coloured. The stem is rather stout, short, blue-lilac (contrasting conspicuously with the colour of the cup and gills). The spores are flesh-coloured.

Habitat usually in open grassland, hedgerows, parks and gardens, more rarely in openings in deciduous woods; in colonies, often forming rings, rarely solitary. Common throughout the region. **Note** a very popular mushroom for the table and especially welcome when found in early winter when most other species have disappeared. It is suitable for frying and stewing but not recommended for soups. One should never eat this species raw; since it does not agree with everyone it is advisable to start with small quantities. Similarly delicious and usable is the Wood Blewit (*L. nuda* [Bull. ex Fr.] W.G. Smith) which differs by having a lilac or violet to brown-violet cap and violet to brown-violet or lilac gills.

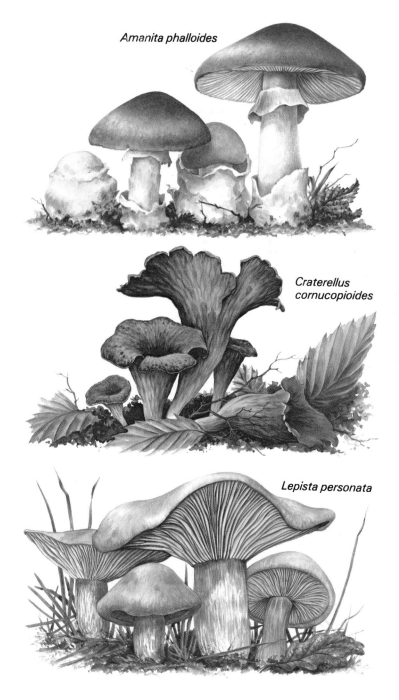

Amanita phalloides

Craterellus cornucopioides

Lepista personata

(E) **Marasmius oreades** (Bolt. ex Fr.) Fr. Agaricineae

Fairy-ring Champignon (May–Oct./Nov.) The cap of this small mushroom is 2–6cm in diameter, at first convex, later flattened but distinctly raised in the centre, often with the margin vertically grooved, pale red-brown, buff, ochre-tan or pinkish-buff. The gills are broad, thickish, of unequal length, somewhat distant, almost free from the stem, whitish. The stem is rather slender, 4–10cm long, of the same colour as the cap or whitish, smooth stiff and tough. The spores are whitish (yellowish in deposit).

Habitat forming extensive rings in lawns, meadows, fields and similar grassy localities. Very common in the region. **Note** although very small (the species makes good for this by occurring in large numbers) this is a most valuable and tasty mushroom for the table. The caps (stems must be discarded) are best fried or used for soups. It can also be dried and used as a powder for soups and sauces. This species is rather distinctive and not easily mistaken for others. Be careful not to pick the poisonous *Clitocybe rivulosa* which grows in similar habitats; the cap of this species has, however, not a pronounced raised centre and is white to pale pinkish brown; its gills are densely arranged and usually slightly decurrent on the usually twisted stem.

(E) **Lactarius deliciosus** (L. ex Fr.) S.F. Gray Russulineae

Saffron Milk Cap (July–Oct.) The cap is 3–10cm in diameter, fleshy, at first convex, later with a deep central depression to funnel-shaped, orange-red or brick-red, often turning slightly green, usually with concentric colour tones, somewhat sticky when moist, smooth; the skin is not easily peeled off. The gills are broad, orange- to saffron-yellow, of different length, brittle, densely arranged, somewhat decurrent on the stem, forked. The stem is 2·5–5cm tall, up to 2·25cm in diameter, orange-red to brick-red, finally usually tinged green, almost cylindrical, stout, at first solid, later often hollow, spores cream-coloured or whitish.

Habitat in coniferous woods, usually pine-woods and, on the Continent, near Juniper; also on moors. Frequent in Europe, in the British Isles confined to northern parts. **Note** this species contains a mild-tasting, saffron-yellow to orange-red or carrot-coloured milk which soon stains the white brittle flesh. The mushroom gives off an aromatic scent and has a piquant spicy taste. This most valuable species is highly esteemed on the Continent where it is usually fried or used for improving the taste of mixed mushroom dishes. On its own it is not recommended as a vegetable or for soups. In the British Isles its less tasty but commendable relative *L. deterrimus* is more widely common. The cap of this species always displays concentric colour-zones; the colour goes through a reddish stage before turning green. *Lactarius* species, many of which are not edible, are not easily confused with other mushrooms.

(E) **Russula vesca** Fr. Russulineae

Bare-edged Russula (June–Oct.) The cap is 5–10cm in diameter, at first convex, later flattened, often with a central depression, usually with a well-defined margin; on first appearance almost white, then buff, reddish-brown, olive-coloured or pinkish-brown or even blood-red, often with the skin partly peeled off. Gills rather firm, densely arranged, narrow, usually cream-coloured, usually forked towards the stem and attached to it and sometimes slightly decurrent, brittle. The stem is 3–10cm tall, cylindrical, white, stout. The spores are white.

Habitat deciduous woods (especially under oak and beech) but occasionally also in coniferous woods. Common in the region. **Note** the flesh of this species is firm, white but sometimes with rust-coloured spots. Its taste is mild and 'nutty'. Certainly a mushroom for stews and frying either on its own or mixed with others; the young specimens can be eaten raw. It can be easily recognized by its receding skin. However, as it is in some respects similar to the deadly poisonous *Amanita virosa*, the beginner should seek advice if in any doubt.

Marasmius oreades

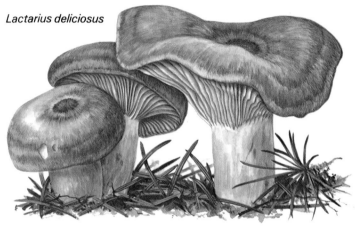

Lactarius deliciosus

Russula vesca

(E) *Camarophyllus pratensis* (Pers. ex Fr.) Karsten **(Hygrophorus pratensis)**
Agaricineae

Karsten, Buff Meadow Cap (Aug.–Dec.) The cap is 2–8cm in diameter, at first convex then flattened, either with a slight depression or centrally raised arch, buff or pale tawny (rarely orange-brown), mat and dry, with a well-defined edge. The gills are not densely arranged, thick, waxy, usually of the same colour as the cap, long decurrent on the stem, basally usually cross-connected by veins. The stem is stout 3–8cm tall, gradually widened into the cap, similar in colour to the cap but paler. The spores are white.

Habitat in open grassland, meadows, pastures, large openings in woods, banks, edge of woods. Throughout the region. **Note** the flesh of this tasty mushroom is best used on its own either fried or stewed. Because of its shape and its habitat (not in woods) it cannot easily be confused with any harmful species.

(E) *Clitocybe odora* (Bull. ex Fr.) Kummer Agaricineae

Anise Cap (Aug.–Oct./Nov.) The cap is 3–9cm in diameter; usually at first convex. The stem is flattened and often shallowly funnel-shaped at the end, with undulate margins, of irregular outline, green to bluish-green. The gills are also bluish-green but usually a little paler, slightly decurrent on the stem. The stem is relatively short, often slightly curved, swollen at the base, of similar coloration as the cap but paler. The spores are white.

Habitat in deciduous woods, rarely under conifers; usually growing amongst decaying leaves and often found alongside forest roads. Usually in groups. Frequent to common in Europe including the British Isles. **Note** the flesh of this mushroom is soft, whitish and tastes and smells of aniseed. It is not to everyones taste but is highly valued by many (especially in France). This mushroom is best used in small quantities for flavouring purposes or eaten mixed with other species. It may be confused with other species, e.g. *C. rivulosa* which is very poisonous, but can always be recognized by its pretty greenish coloration. Beginners should refrain from collecting it without advice.

(E) *Morchella esculenta* Per. ex St. Am. Pezizales

Common Morel (April–May/June) The head of the fruit body is 3–12cm long (the whole fruit body up to 16–20cm tall). Sponge- or honeycomb-like in appearance, yellow-brown to ochre-brown, rarely deeper brown or ash-grey (the edges turning black when old). The stem is white, whitish or cream-coloured, cylindrical, brittle, sometimes longitudinally grooved, usually hollow. The spores are colourless or lightest yellow.

Habitat hedgerows, fields, woods, parks, gardens, and various grassy localities, usually in rich calcareous soil. Scattered over Europe and the British Isles, but only locally common; often found on disturbed soil. **Note** this is one of the most valued mushrooms. Its flesh is waxy, white and brittle and smells and tastes aromatic-spicy. It can easily be dried and powdered and then be used for flavouring sauces and meat dishes. Fresh, it can be used either on its own or with others, and competes with the finest vegetables on the market. It is advisable to cut it into small pieces before cooking or drying. One must be careful not to mistake this species for the False Morel (*Gyromitra esculenta*). Even though it is named 'esculenta' (in Latin, edible) this species can be *deadly* poisonous. It occurs mainly in woods and can be recognized by its irregularly (brain-like) convoluted brown head.

Camarophyllus pratensis

Clitocybe odora

Morchella esculenta

(E) *Pleurotus ostreatus* (Jacq. ex. Fr.) Quel. Agaricineae
Oyster Mushroom (Oct. – Dec./April) The cap is asymmetric, shell-shaped, 7–13cm broad, flattish or variously arched, with involute margins, fleshy, intensive brown to buff, grey or bluish-black (when young). The gills at first white, later yellowish or cream-coloured, the stem densely arranged, forking towards the base and decurrent on the stem. The stem is usually very short, rarely completely absent, attached laterally, white, usually hairy at the base. The spores are purplish or lilac, produced in large quantities.

Habitat growing on dead or living trunks of deciduous trees (beech, poplars and others) in woods and parks. Fairly common in Europe and the British Isles. **Note** this mushroom, which grows usually in large and dense clusters, has a soft but somewhat fibrous flesh when young; smell and taste are pleasant. Only young specimens should be eaten (the flesh becomes tough when old). It is best used in mixed mushroom stews or fried on its own (sprinkled with flour or breadcrumbs and egg). For the regular consumer of wild mushroom this species is greatly valued at a time of the year when none of the others are available. On account of its shape, colour and habitat it cannot easily be confused with other species, at least not with any poisonous one (other similar looking species belong mainly to the genus *Polyporus*, all of which are harmless, some edible but not recommended).

(E) *Lycoperdon perlatum* Pers. Gasteromycetales
Common Puff-ball (July – Oct./Nov.) The fruit body is globose on a short stem to pear-shaped, rather large, 5–8cm tall and 4–7cm in diameter. It is white or greyish white at first, later becoming yellow and finally yellow-brown; the outer veil is densely covered by stout pointed warts (after these have fallen off the surface shows an irregular hexagonal pattern). The spores are olive-brown.

Habitat in woods, pastures, fields, on sandy soil. Common throughout the region. **Note** the flesh of this species is initially white, then becomes yellow, and develops into a mass of brown spores within the hardened and somewhat shrivelled skin. It can only be eaten when young and the flesh is still firm and white. This mushroom is especially suited for quick frying either in a batter or without. It may be confused with other Puff-balls, none of which are really poisonous but most are inedible. Very delicious, however, is the young flesh of the Grand Puff-ball (*Calvatia gigantea* (Pers.) Lloyd) which grows in similar localities and represents one of the largest fungi on earth. It has a pure white smooth skin and is usually between 20 and 60cm in diameter.

(E) *Leccinum versipelle* (Fr. Hök) Snell *(Boletus testaceao-scabrum)* Boletineae
Sponge Cap (July – Nov.) The cap is 7–15cm in diameter, at first convex (often almost semi-globular), later flattened, yellow-orange to orange-brown or tawny, often with some scales in the centre and a membranous fringe around the edges. The tubes are whitish or somewhat cream-coloured; the pores are very small, at first dark grey to almost black, later paler. The stem is stout, 7–15cm tall, up to 3cm in diameter; white or greyish-white to buff, densely covered with stout short rough blackish woolly scales. The spores are brown.

Habitat typically associated with birch trees. Fairly common in Europe including the British Isles, often growing in large numbers. In favourable conditions some specimens may develop a weight in excess of 1kg. **Note** the flesh of this species is firm and becomes soft with age, it is white at first, then pinkish to slate-blue (greenish-blue at the base of the stem); when boiled it turns blackish. A most delicious and rewarding species best used in mixed mushroom dishes or fried. It can also be dried but is not recommended for soups. This characteristic mushroom can only be confused with one or two other species of the same habitat which are all edible, e.g. *L. aurantiacum.*

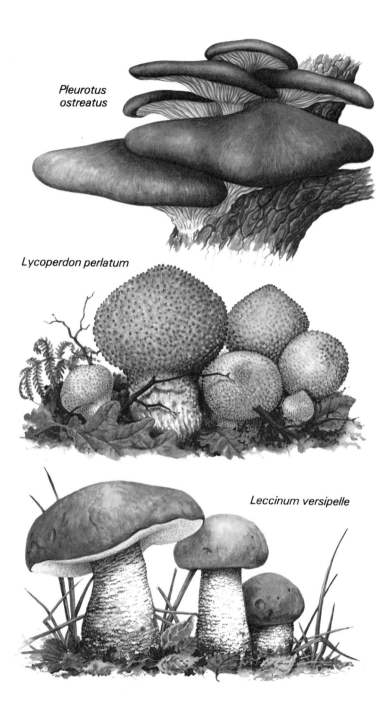

Pleurotus ostreatus

Lycoperdon perlatum

Leccinum versipelle

Ⓔ **_Boletus erythropus_** Fr. Boletineae

(Sept.–Nov.) The cap is 5–16cm in diameter, at first convex, later flattened, sometimes slightly tomentose but usually smooth, deep chestnut to olive-brown, paler around the edges. The tubes are yellow to greenish-yellow (blackish-blue when bruised); the pores are small, brownish-red (sometimes maroon) or orange and with yellow edges. The stem is robust, cylindrical but sometimes thickened at the base, up to 5·5cm in diameter, 4–15cm long, without a network of veins but usually with orange dots on a yellowish-brown or yellow background. The spores are olive-brown.

Habitat mostly in coniferous woods but also under deciduous trees, on acid soil. Fairly common throughout the region. Growing solitary or in groups. **Note** the flesh of this species is firm, vividly sulphur- or lemon-yellow and turns blue when cut, broken or bruised. It has a fine taste but does not agree with everyone; it should therefore initially only be eaten (best stewed) in small quantities. By the less experienced it may be confused with _B. satanas_ (especially young specimens) but this species is always white-capped, has whitish flesh, which, however, may turn light blue on cutting. If in doubt discard the specimen.

Ⓔ **_Boletus badius_** Fr. Boletineae

Bay-capped Bolete (Aug.–Nov.) The cap is convex, 3–15cm in diameter, rather fleshy, bay-brown to chestnut- or ochre-brown, at first somewhat tomentose, later glabrous, sticky when moist. The tubes are yellow or cream-coloured at first, later usually blue-green. The stem is usually cylindrical, stout and solid, straight 4–8cm (up to 12cm) long, up to 3cm in diameter, same colour as the cap but much paler, often with longitudinal ridges. The spores are olive-brown.

Habitat in woods both deciduous and coniferous. Common throughout the region. **Note** the pale flesh of this species becomes blue when cut or bruised. It is of similar quality as _B. edulis_ (below) and can be used likewise.

Ⓔ **_Boletus edulis_** Fr. Boletineae

Penny Bun, Ceps (Aug.–Oct./Nov.) The cap is 5–20cm in diameter, at first convex later less so, to almost flat, rather thick and fleshy, deep brown, chestnut brown, brownish-red, usually paler around the margins. The tubes are whitish to grey, and yellow; the pores are at first white, then cream-coloured and finally yellow. The stem is stout, narrowly bottle-shaped or cylindrical, thick, up to 7·5cm in diameter, 2·5–24cm long, white or sometimes tinged pale brown, usually with a whitish raised network of veins all over or towards the apex only. The spores are olive-brown.

Habitat in deciduous, mixed or coniferous woods. According to habitat this species occurs in a number of forms which are all edible. Common all over the region. **Note** the flesh of this most popular of all edible mushrooms is firm and usually white (reddish just beneath the skin) and remains that way longer than in many other species. Its uses are manifold; it can be fried, used in stews, as a vegetable on its own or mixed with others, and also in soups. This mushroom can easily be kept in the dried state (or powdered) and is widely sold as such on the Continent. Moreover, it is one of the four species which can safely be eaten raw (e.g. in salads). There is no danger of confusion with any poisonous species, and the only poisonous mushroom of this group (_B. satanas_) is sufficiently distinct to be easily recognized.

Boletus erythropus

Boletus badius

Boletus edulis

Ⓔ *Coprinus comatos* (Mull. ex Fr.) S.F. Gray **Agaricineae**
Lawyer's Wig, Shaggy Ink Cap (April–Dec.) The cap is at first ovate or elliptical-ovate, narrowly bell-shaped, 3–5cm in diameter, 5–15cm long, white to pale brown or yellow-brown, covered with soft woolly brown scales, frequently sticky at the apex. The margins are usually light brown becoming black with time and rolled downwards after splitting. The gills are relatively narrow, densely arranged, free from the stem, at first white, later turning from pink to black, and finally dissolving into a blackish ink-like substance. The stem is slender, tall, 8–20cm long, cylindrical or thinner towards the apex, smooth, white, usually hollow; the ring is narrow, thin, movable, the spores are black or purple-black.

Habitat meadows, pastures, parks and gardens, road-sides, refuse dumps, compost heaps, in greenhouses etc. Common throughout the region. Usually growing in individual groups, short-lived. **Note** the flesh of this species is very tender and white (discoloration sets in soon) and is regarded as a great delicacy when consumed young. It is not suitable for frying but can be used in soups; however, it is best served as a vegetable. It can be mistaken for its relative the Common Ink Cap (*Coprinus atramentarius*), the cap of which is grey or greyish-brown and hardly scaly; this species is edible as well but becomes *poisonous when consumed with alcoholic beverages.*

Ⓔ *Agaricus campestris* L. ex Fr. **Agaricineae**
Field Mushroom (July–Oct./Nov.) The cap at first is strongly convex, later less so to nearly flat, 4–12cm in diameter, white (rarely brownish or yellowish-brownish), often covered with some delicate, smooth, silky scales, often with remnants of the veil at the margins; the gills are at first pinkish or reddish or salmon-coloured, later deep brown to black-brown, densely arranged, free from the stem. The stem is 4–8cm tall, white, robust, smooth, solid or sometimes later partly hollow, clearly detachable from the cap; the ring is attached in the upper third, thin, not lasting. The spores are blackish-brown or dark purple-brown.

Habitat meadows, lawns, pastures and similar localities. Usually appearing in large numbers on warm days after rain. Common throughout the region. **Note** this is a popular and versatile wild mushroom which is sold in large quantities in markets all over Europe. Its flesh is soft, it gives off a pleasant aromatic scent and has a mild nutty taste. It can be used for stews, soups or fried like the mushroom of commerce (*Agaricus brunnescens = A. bisporus*). There must, however, be a word of caution: the Field Mushroom can be confused with the Death Cap and the Destroying Angel, especially when young. Always make sure of the dark brown gills and the absence of volva at the base. If the flesh turns red when bruised (sign of a further poisonous species) or if in doubt discard the specimens.

Ⓔ *Agaricus arvensis* Schaeff. ex Fr. **Agaricineae**
Horse Mushroom (July–Oct.) The cap is 5–17cm in diameter, at first almost globular, later convex to flattened, white, silky (turning yellow or brown when pressed), smooth; the gills are narrow, free from the stem, at first white, later reddish-grey and finally dark chocolate-brown to blackish-brown, densely arranged. The stem is 5–16cm tall, cylindrical but often slightly widened at the base, smooth, white (usually turning yellowish when bruised), easily removable from the cap, at first solid, later partly hollow; the ring is attached in the upper third, thicker than in the preceding species, reflexed or spreading, white when viewed from above, with brownish marking below, the spores are dark-brown or purple-brown.

Habitat fields, alongside paths, grassland, at the edges of coniferous woods, hedgerows, pastures, rarely in open woods. **Note** this species has a firm but soft white flesh, gives off a scent reminiscent of almonds or aniseed, and a most appealing taste (it can be eaten raw). It is used in the same way as the preceding species. For dangerous confusion with other species see note above.

Coprinus comatus

Agaricus campestris

Agaricus arvensis

Ⓔ ***Macrolepiota procera*** (Scop ex Fr.) Singer **Agaricineae**

Parasol Mushroom (July–Oct./Nov.) The cap of this large and conspicuous species is 8–25cm in diameter, at first globular (at this stage the whole plant looks like a drumstick), later slightly convex to flat, always with a raised nipple-like centre, pale brown, cream-brown to hazelnut-brown, covered with coarse flaking darker brown scales, fringed at the margins; the gills are densely arranged, broad, free from the stem, white to whitish-cream coloured. The stem is slender and straight, rather tall, 15–30cm high, cylindrical, bulb-like and swollen at the base, pale brown to cream-brown with irregular darker brown transverse bands throughout; the ring is attached well above the middle, usually thick and split, white from above, later becoming loose and movable along the stem. The spores are white.

Habitat in grassy openings in woods, along the edges of woods and fields, but also in hedgerows, pastures, meadows, parks and gardens (often found near ant-heaps). Common all over the British Isles. It grows usually in large groups and in great numbers, sometimes forming rings. Note the flesh of this mushroom is soft (fibrous and harder in the stem), white, smells like sperm and has a pleasant nutty taste. Very young specimens (before the cap flattens) are ideal for mixed mushroom dishes (served as a vegetable with meat); otherwise the cap is best used for frying, in batter of bread-crumbs, egg, spiced with ground pepper; the stem should be discarded. Older specimens can be dried and used as powder in sauces and soups. The related Shaggy Parasol (*M. rhacodes*) is smaller (up to 16cm in diameter), has a shaggy stem without brown transversal markings. It is similarly edible. Smaller, similar looking species are best avoided by the beginner.

Ⓔ ***Hydnum repandum*** (L. ex Fr.) Fr. **Cantharellaceae**

Wood Hedgehog (July/Aug.–Oct./Nov.) The cap is rather thick and fleshy, 3–12cm in diameter, at first convex, later unevenly flat, usually with irregular outline and with the margins involute, ochre-orange to yellow or tinged pinkish; the gills are absent but the lower surface is covered with short, densely arranged, pinkish to bread-coloured spine-like structures. The stem is rather thick and short, 3–8cm long, often attached to the cap, somewhat out of centre, whitish. The spores are white.

Habitat in deciduous, mixed and coniferous woods, usually in groups or forming rings. Common in the British Isles and over most of the rest of Europe. Note this species has a white (later turning brownish) brittle, pleasantly smelling flesh. Its taste is mild in young, somewhat acrid in older specimens (an occasionally observed bitter taste disappears after cooking). It is ideally suited for frying and stewing but not at all for soups. The reddish, but smaller species, *Hydnum rufescens* is also fairly common. It has a reddish cap and is usually found under conifers. This species is also edible; there is no danger of mistaking this mushroom (on account of the spines!) with any other.

Ⓔ ***Cantharellus cibarius*** Fr. **Cantharellaceae**

Chantarelle The cap is not well-defined, 2–10cm in diameter, at first convex, later flat and finally irregularly funnel-shaped, with involute and irregularly undulate margins, sometimes distinctly lobed, egg-yellow to orange-yellow, fleshy, smooth; the gills are represented by longitudinal, forked folds or ribs connected by small lateral veins. The stem is rather short, 5–8cm tall, the same colour as the cap but sometimes paler and occasionally reddish at the base, fleshy, solid. The spores are pale ochre or cream.

Habitat in deciduous woodland, under groups of birches, but also in coniferous woods, in mossy ground and under pines in moorland; often along roads, usually occurring in large groups, always dependent on the presence of trees. Note the Chantarelle is one of the most tasty and popular wild mushrooms, widely collected and traded in markets in Europe. The flesh is rather firm, smells of apricots and has a peppery taste; the skin of the cap cannot be peeled off. Although the taste of this mushroom is second-to-none it is not easily digestible and should therefore be thoroughly prepared, that is cut into small pieces and well stewed. It is an ideal vegetable prepared in a white sauce and served with meat (especially veal) dishes (do not fry,) but it is not suitable for drying.

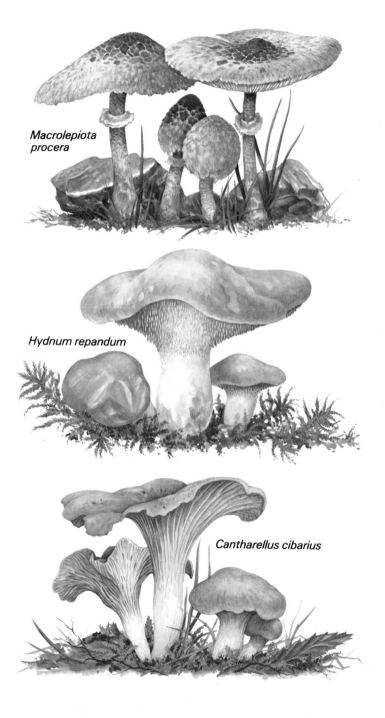

Macrolepiota procera

Hydnum repandum

Cantharellus cibarius

Plants for medicinal purposes which are either cultivated or not European but mentioned in this book. All of these are commercially available.

Ⓜ *Allium sativum* L. Liliaceae
Ⓔ **Garlic** Active ingredients alliin, allicin, essential oil, silicic acid, vitamins, A, B, and C, antibiotic substances. Effect stimulates secretion in gall bladder and stomach, inhibits fermentation, prevents spasms, reduces blood-pressure. Parts used the bulblets (cloves). Application **M:** this universal drug is contained in numerous brands of proprietary medicine for arterio-sclerosis, chronic infections of the intestines and the stomach, gall disorders, flatulence, heartburn, bronchial catarrhs, and lack of appetite. **E:** in the home it is best eaten fresh.

Ⓜ *Asparagus officinalis* L. Liliaceae
Asparagus An annual herb with a long creeping rhizome, erect, branched, 25–120cm (up to 150cm) tall stems, glabrous. The leaves are reduced to small, triangular-lanceolate, 3–5·5mm long scales (scarious, whitish, much smaller and arrowhead-shaped on the branches) with clusters of needle-shaped shoots in their axils. The flowers are solitary or in pairs, axillary, pedicellate, usually dioecious. The perianth is bell-shaped, with free segments, in female flowers 3·75–4·25mm long, yellowish green; in male flowers 5–6·2mm long, yellow. Fruit a globose, red berry, 7–8·5mm in diameter.

Habitat waste places, dunes, widely cultivated as a vegetable. Distribution over most of Europe; casual in the British Isles. Active ingredients asparigin, arginin, asparagose, saponin. Effect strongly diuretic. Parts used the rhizome. Application **M:** rarely in use as a drug on its own but contained in various brands of proprietary medicine (together with *Calendula, Solidago, Mentha piperita, Arctostaphylos, Phaseolus, Betula*, and others) prescribed for cystitis, pyelitis, and nephrolithiasis. The drug produces no harmful side effects.

Ⓜ *Cassia angustifolia* Vahl. Caesalpiniaceae
Senna Active ingredients essential oil, resin, mucilage, some tannin anthraquinone-glycosides. Effect mainly purgative. Parts used the dried leaves; the dried fruit-pods (milder in action) Application **M:** with *Franqula* and *Aloe ferox* this drug is one of the most important purgatives and is contained in many brands of proprietary medicine for constipation. In the home it should only be used under medical supervision and *should on no account be used during pregnancy*. Herbal mixtures containing the drug should only be used as infusions and never be boiled. In normal usage there are no harmful side effects.

Ⓜ *Cinnamomum zeylanicum* Bl. Lauraceae
Cinnamon Active ingredients essential oil (with cinnamaldehyde), tannin, mucilage, starch, cinnamic acid, terpenes, eugenol. Effect stimulating secretion of gastric juices. Parts used the dried bark. Application **M:** this drug, although contained in a few brands of proprietary medicine for anorexia, hyperacidity, is mainly used as a spice and for various purposes in the pharmaceutical, cosmetic, and liquor industry. In the home heated red wine spiced with cinnamon (not powderized) acts as an antidiarrhoeal and an aid to mentrual flow.

Ⓜ *Citrus aurantium* L. *subsp. aurantium* Rutaceae
Bitter orange Active ingredients essential oils, bitter principles, the glycoside hesperidin. Effect mildly sedative, mildly relieves spasms, stimulates appetite and gland secretion. Parts used the outer peel of the fruit, the flowers and the leaves. Application **M:** the drug is contained in various brands of proprietary medicine for stimulating appetite or with sedative ingredients, disorders of the stomach and bowels, nausea and insomnia. In the home the fresh or dried leaves and/or flowers are used as infusion (2 teaspoons per cup water, allow to stand for 5 minutes) 3–4 times a day for colics of the intestines, stomach disorders, or sluggish digestion.

Ⓜ *Elettaria cardamomum* Maton Zingiberaceae

Cardamom Active ingredients essential oil. Effect relieves flatulence. Parts used the fruit. Application **M:** the drug which has no harmful side effects is, besides being a well-known spice, contained in some proprietary brands of medicine for flatulence and disorders of the liver.

Ⓜ *Glycyrrhiza glabra* L. Papilionaceae

Licorice Active ingredients glycyrrhicin, glycyrrhici acid, resins, liquiritin, oestron, oestradiol, coumarin, sugar, traces of essential oil, and tannin. Effect expectorant, relieves spasms, mildly purgative (mildly similar to cortison). Parts used the peeled roots and the stolons; the juice. Application **M:** the drug is contained in many pharmaceutical preparations for coughs, arthritis, rheumatism and stomach ulcers, spastic stomach pains, gastritis. Licorice is widely used in sweets, in beer and in the liquor industry. Although the drug is harmless, excessive use leads to increased blood pressure.

Ⓜ *Juglans regia* L. Juglandaceae

Walnut Active ingredients tannin, essential oil, flavones, juglone, organic acids. Efect astringent, anti-inflammatory, purifying the blood. Parts used the leaves; rarely the outer layers of the fruit. Application **M:** the drug, of which no harmful side effects are known, is contained in some brands of proprietary medicine for rheumatic disorders, diarrhoea, dyspepsia and various skin ailments. In the home an infusion (1½ – 2 teaspoons per cup water, allow to stand for 8 minutes) is taken 2 – 3 times a day for the same complaints.

Ⓜ *Linum usitatissimum* L. Linaceae

Flax, Linseed Active ingredients mucilage, fatty oil, linoleic and linolenic acids, protein, the glycoside linamarin. Effect mildly purgative, analgesic, anti-inflammatory, emollient. Parts used mainly the seeds; in homoeopathy the fresh herb. Application **M:** this ancient remedy is contained in some medicinal preparations for gastritis, diarrhoea, dyspepsia and chronic constipation. In the home the freshly bruised (if kept in this state they turn bitter) seeds are taken, 2 teaspoons at a time, with water in the morning and the evening for the same disorders (the seeds swell considerably within the intestines and stimulate the peristalsis). Bruised seeds mixed in water are directly applied to slow-healing cuts, skin-disorders and burns.

Ⓜ *Phaseolus vulgaris* L. Papilionaceae

Bean Active ingredients salicic acid, glucokinin, some amino acids, hemicellulose, arginin, flavones. Effect mildly diuretic, slightly reducing the sugar content of the blood. Parts used the dried mature pods after the seeds have been removed. Application **M:** the drug is used as a diuretic in the treatment of diabetes. In homoeopathy an essence prepared from the entire fresh herb is prescribed for rheumatic conditions, arthritis and disorders of the urinary tract. In the home an infusion (1 teaspoon per cup water, allow to stand for 5 – 8 minutes) is taken 2 – 3 times a day as a diuretic.

Ⓜ *Pimpinella anisum* L. Umbelliferae

Anise Active ingredients essential oil (with anethole), fatty oil, cholin, sugar. Effect relieves flatulence, expectorant, very mildly narcotic, in many ways similar to *Foeniculum vulgare*. Parts used the mature fruits. Application **M:** the drug is contained in various brands of proprietary medicine for chest infections (coughs, bronchitis, etc.) as well as for the relief of flatulence; it is also used as a sedative for children and for stimulating lactation. In industry Anise is widely used for teas, toothpastes, other cosmetic preparations, for the production of liquors and for herbal tea-mixtures.

ⓜ *Piper cubeba* L. Piperaceae

Active ingredients essential oil, resin, cubebin, organic acids. **Effect** mildly diuretic, stimulates stomach functions. **Parts used** the fruit. **Application M:** the drug is contained in a few medicinal preparations for inflammation of the urinary tract but also for bronchial catarrhs. Its use as a condiment is now discontinued but the fruits are widely used in perfumery.

ⓜ *Rheum palmatum* L. Polygonaceae

Rhubarb **Active ingredients** mainly anthraquinone compounds, gallic acid, rheidine, sennidine, tannins, pectin, oxalic acid, resin, starch. **Effect** purgative, stimulates stomach functions, mildly astringent. **Parts used** the dried rhizome. **Application M:** the drug is contained in many proprietary brands of medicine for constipation, flatulence and disorders of liver and gall bladder. In normal doses the drug is harmless, but it should not be used by sufferers of arthritis, rheumatism, and breast-feeding mothers (some ingredients appear in the milk and have a purgative effect).

ⓜ *Zea mays* L. Gramineae

Sweet Corn **Active ingredients** saponin, essential oils, fatty oil, tannin, a trace of an alkaloid, resin, glycosidal bitter principle, a gum. **Effect** mainly diuretic, also reducing sugar content in the blood. **Parts used** the styles and stigmas before pollination occurs. **Application M:** in homoeopathy a tincture based on this drug is prescribed for cystitis, pyelitis, kidney and bladder stones, dropsy, arthritis, and rheumatism. In the home an infusion is occasionally used as a diuretic. The styles are best used fresh; after a time, especially when not dried properly, the diuretic effect ceases and the drug has the effect of a purgative.

ⓜ *Syzygium aromaticum* (L.) Merr. et L. M. Perry Myrtaceae

Cloves **Active ingredients** essential oil (mainly eugenol), tannin, mucilage, resin, fatty oil. **Effect** disinfectant, mildly anaesthetic, aperitive. **Parts used** the flowers before opening. **Application M:** the use as a spice in Europe is reported as far back as the 12th century. It is contained in a variety of brands of patent medicine for gastritis, flatulence, toothache (mouthwashes and toothpastes!), sluggish digestion and lack of appetite. The oil is rubbed on to the skin against insect-bites.

Appendix I

Notes on the most important active ingredients of medicinal plants.

Alkaloids

These are plant-produced organic nitrogenous chemical compounds which are physiologically active and have an effect on the central and, to a lesser extent, peripheral nervous systems. They represent a chemically heterogeneous group. They occur in usually closely related plant groups (e.g. within the Solanaceae, Apocynaceae, Rubiaceae, Papilionaceae) but can be completely absent in others (Labiatae, Rosaceae, Coniferae, etc.). Their functions within the plant are so far unexplained (some scientists claim that their bitter taste repels insects and other pests but there are known instances of alkaloid-containing plants which are devoured by insects). The number of known alkaloids to date (the first were isolated between 1803 and 1816) goes into the thousands and new ones are still being discovered. Some of them are powerful drugs (e.g. strychnine, caffeine, quinine, morphine, etc.) but they must only be used under strict medical supervision since they represent some of the most potent poisons of plant origin.

Bitter principle

Under this heading fall a number of totally unrelated chemical compounds which have in common a bitter taste and the ability to stimulate the production of digestive juices. They actually act on the gustatory nerves in the mouth which leads to a psychosomatic secretion of gastric juices. Moreover they affect secretion in the gall bladder and, further, peristalsis. Their main application is therefore as appetizers but also to promote digestion and metabolic functions.

Three types are commonly distinguished.

1 Amara tonica (pure bitter). Examples of plants are *Menyanthes, Gentiana, Centaurium.*
2 Amara aromatica. These are bitters which also contain essential oils. Examples of native wild plants are: *Angelica, Acorus, Artemisia.* They are used in the same way as pure bitters but have the additional benefit of acting as an antiseptic; moreover they are usually slightly diuretic.
3 Amara acria. These are drugs which are bitter and acrid. There is hardly a usable representative of this group amongst our native wild plants, but the best known are tropical plants such as pepper and ginger. Their usefulness in aiding digestion is common knowledge.

Essential oils

These substances, which are also known as volatile oils, are produced in special glandular cells or cell-groups, secretory ducts, surface glands or glandular hairs which are situated in various organs (leaf, flower or part of it, fruit, bud, stem or bark, root, seed, etc.). One usually finds that they only occur in one (e.g. rose petals, iris rhizome) or in a few morphologically related organs (e.g. flower and fruit). If they are contained throughout a plant they are often of different quality and of different chemical composition for each organ. This is known to the producer of perfume, for example; the bitter orange yields three different essential oils: the flower contains the expensive orange flower absolute (as well as the less costly neroli oil), the peel of the fruit yields the ordinary oil of orange, and the leaves and twigs what is known as 'petit grain'. This fact is of great importance for medicinal plants, and one should therefore always use only the part of the plant which is indicated in each individual description. The essential oil is usually contained within the plant cell in the form of globules.

Out of a number of about 250,000 known flowering plants only around 2,000 contain essential oil; these species belong to between 55 and 60 not necessarily related families. The most notable and important in respect to medicinal plants are the Labiatae, Rutaceae, Lauraceae, Myrtaceae, Umbelliferae, Compositae, some Coniferae and a few others.

The reasons for the formation of essential oils in plants are not yet explained by science. They are possibly waste-products or essential stages in certain life processes.

Essential oils have the following physical properties in common: they are volatile, soluble in alcohol and other organic solvents, are colourless when fresh and, unlike fixed or fatty oils, do not leave a permanent mark on paper. Chemically they form a rather heterogeneous group (so far the number of analyzed compounds exceeds 600). They generally constitute hydrocarbon mixtures or oxygenated derivatives of hydrocarbons. The most important groups are: terpenes or sesquiterpenes, alcohols and esters, aldehydes, ketones, phenols, ethers and peroxides.

Essential oils are in their effect bacteriostatic, anti-inflammatory, antispasmodic, sedative, carminative, appetizing, rubefacient and, sometimes, expectorant.

Often associated with essential oils are the so-called gums and resins. They are pf complicated chemical nature. They are solid in the cold state but soften and finally melt when heated. Like essential oils they are produced by special plant cells and secreted into cavities or contained in glandular ducts. In medicine they are mostly used as irritants.

Flavones and Flavonoids

The pharmacological action of these substances is not yet fully understood. Flavones and their derivatives the flavonoids are substances which occur either free within the organism or in glycoside compounds. Chemically they belong to the phenols. Some of the more important compounds are the coumarins and the anthocyanins; the latter substance is responsible for the blue and red colour of many flowers. The flavones proper and most of their derivatives are usually yellow (Latin *flavus* = yellow). Both the flavones and the anthocyanins are soluble in the cell sap; otherwise they are not easily soluble and are therefore difficult to isolate, and this is one of the reasons why they have not been sufficiently tested for their medicinal properties in animal experiments.

Flavones occur in abundance in some plant families such as the Compositae, Papilionaceae, Rutaceae and others.

The two best researched flavonoids are hesperidin and rutin. The latter is found in *Fagopyrum* and the former in citrus fruits; their main effect is to decrease the blood flow in the capillaries and they are therefore used for hypertension and certain coronary conditions. Some flavonoids have a diuretic effect. A plant which has been used widely in the past for ailments of the liver (*Silybum marianum*) on the Continent contains the flavonoids silybin and silymarin. The yellow colour of Liquorice is caused by several flavonoids; this ancient remedy has recently come into prominence again in the treatment of various conditions such as peptic ulcers, arthritis and various inflammatory disorders.

Glycosides

Together with alkaloids, glycosides not only form the basis of a large number of important and most effective drugs but also represent some of the most dangerous poisons found in nature. They occur widely in many not necessarily related families of flowering plants. When hydrolysed (split by the action of water, acids or enzymes) they separate into sugars (glycone) and the so-called aglycones. The latter are usually the pharmacologically active ones, whereas the sugars make them soluble in water. Their chemistry is too complex to be dealt with in detail here, and the same applies to their pharmacological effect. The following are medicinally the most important:
Cyanogenetic glycosides
One of the split-products of hydrolysis is hydrocyanic acid; the best known representative is amygdalin which occurs widely within the Rosaceae (*Prunus, Malus, Pyrus*), Papilionaceae (*Phaseolus, Cassia, Trifolium,* etc.), Caprifoliaceae (*Sambucus*), Linaceae (*Linum*) and a few others. Some are used as drugs (cough preparations, sedatives and purgatives).

Anthraquinone glycosides
On hydrolysis these produce anthraquinones which play a role in purgatives and are contained in plants such as *Cassia senna, Rhamnus catharticus, Frangula alnus, Rheum* and others.
Cardiac glycosides
These vary in chemical composition but have in common a specific action on the cardiac muscle. Several hundred are known to date. They are produced in several families of flowering plants, notably the Apocynaceae, Scrophulariaceae (*Digitalis*), Ranunculaceae (*Adonis, Helleborus* and others) and Asclepiadaceae. They count among the most poisonous groups of the plant kingdom.
Saponin glycosides (see Saponins); *Flavonoid glycosides* and *Coumarin glycosides* (see Flavones).

Many of the plants containing coumarin are of medicinal importance (*Asperula, Melilotus, Aesculus*, etc.) and frequently used as antispasmodics.

Mucilages

Mucilages are complex carbohydrates with a high molecular weight. They are not soluble in alcohol. They swell or dissolve in water and often form very viscous solutions or large slimy masses. Most are formed by the cell wall.

In *Plantago indica* the mucilage is contained in the testa (coat) of the seed; it has the highest swelling factor (the mucilage produced in 24 hours by 1g of plant material) known in native wild plants, namely between 12 and 13. Other species which yield sufficient mucilage to render them useful for medicinal purposes are *Althaea, Linum* and *Cetraria*.

The main pharmacological effect is anti-irritant: it forms a thin protective layer above the mucous membrane and thus prevents irritants from reaching infected surfaces. They are therefore applied for inflammation of the intestinal tract and infection of the chest and throat. Their ability to retain water allows them to loosen the bowel contents; they are therefore frequently used as mild but effective remedies for chronic constipation. The same property makes them ideal for external application for disorders of the skin.

Since mucilages are never absorbed by the body tissue their effect is always confined to the area of application.

Saponins

Saponins are glycosides with a high molecular weight. Their most important physical property is that they produce a frothing effect in aqueous solutions and have therefore a detergent action (the name is derived from the Latin *sapo* = soap). For this reason the rhizome of *Saponaria officinalis* has been used in Europe for centuries for cleansing purposes.

Saponins have haemolytic properties when allowed to enter the bloodstream; they must therefore be regarded as highly toxic. However, when taken orally they are relatively harmless and have the effect of a purgative or mild diuretic; they are also slightly expectorant and may be used in antitussives and for gargling preparations (e.g. *Salvia*). Since saponins aid intestinal resorption they are also given with other drugs. In no circumstances should herbs containing saponins be used for decoctions.

The so-called steroidal saponins which are contained in a number of plant families (e.g. Liliaceae, Amaryllidaceae, Dioscoreaceae and others) play an increasing role in modern medicine especially in conjunction with so-called cardiac glycosides (as in *Strophanthus* and *Digitalis*).

Silicic acid

This mineral compound is contained in the soil and taken up by a number of plants notably Gramineae, *Equisetum* and some members of the Boraginaceae (see *Lithospermum*), and deposited in the cell membranes (the ash of *Equisetum* contains $92-97\% \ SiO_2$ which remains in the form of a fine skeleton when a piece of the plant is completely oxidized on a plate of platinum). Remedies containing silicic acid are used where a lack of this substance in the body is apparent, mainly through faulty nutrition (it is important for the growths of hairs, finger and toenails and certain connective tissues). *Equisetum* may also be used for mouthwashes, gargling, and as an addition to the bathwater.

Medicinal plants contain also other mineral substances to a varying degree, but since they are supplied to the body in a well-balanced diet anyway they play only a minor role in the use of medicinal herbs.

Tannins

Tannins are substances which precipitate proteins. The term is applied to a variety of astringent compounds. Their ability to combine with protein has been utilized for centuries for turning animal hides into leather.

They are divided into hydrolysable tannins, condensed tannins, and pseudotannins which have a much smaller molecular weight (gallic acid belongs here) than the others. Tannins are common throughout the plant kingdom but among wild European plants are especially concentrated in oak bark, the rhizome of *Potentilla* and other species of the Rosaceae, in bilberries, willow bark etc. The role which they play within the plant is not known: they may represent waste material or secondary products of the metabolic cycle.

Tannins possess astringent properties and are therefore widely used against diarrhoea, dysentery, for slow-healing wounds, bleeding gums, throat infections etc. By precipitating protein in mucous membranes tannin deprives bacteria of nutrition, hence its antibiotic effect.

Prolonged use of tannin-containing drugs should be avoided since tannins are known to be carcinogenic (the relatively high tannin content in real tea is rendered harmless, however, when it is drunk with milk).

Vitamins

The importance of vitamins for sustaining life is common knowledge. The body cannot build them up metabolically so they must be supplied from outside. People who have a well-balanced diet will usually receive them in sufficient quantity and quality. There are only a few medicinal plants which contain sufficient amounts of any vitamin to make its application for this purpose worthwhile (exceptions are *Petroselinum*, *Hippophaë*, *Rosa canina* and some others). When using any wild plant as a source of vitamins, one has to bear in mind that its vitamin content is greatly reduced by long storage and the vitamins themselves are often destroyed by heat. The best way to take them is therefore as freshly pressed juice, but since this is only rarely practicable in the home, anyone who is suffering from a vitamin deficiency would be advised to obtain ready-made preparations from the chemist or health-food store.

Appendix II

Table of edible plants with their uses

Ba	baking additives
Be	used in beer brewing
D	for drinks other than tea, coffee or alcoholic ones
Fl	for the making of flour
Ja	for making jams and preserves
Je	jellies (for meat dishes)
Ju	for juices
L	for the preparation of liquors
M	meat, fish and poultry condiments
O	yielding oil
S	for salads and sandwiches (i.e. can be eaten raw)
Sps	for soups and sauces
Sy	for syrup making
V	for use as a vegetable
Vi	as a vinegar ingredient
W	for wine making

Achillea millefolium	**S, V**
Aegopodium	**S, Sps, V**
Alaria	**M, S, Sps**
Alliaria	**S**
Allium sativum	**S, Sps, V**
Allium schoenoprasum	**S, Sps**
Allium ursinum	**S, Sps, V**
Anchusa	**V**

Anethum	S, Sps	*Mentha aquatica*	L
Angelica archangelica	L, V, Sps	*Mentha x piperita*	L
Anthriscus	S	*Mentha pulegium*	Sps, M
Apium	Sps	*Meum*	Sps, V, M
Arctium	V	*Myrrhis*	S, V, Ja
Armoracia	S		
Asperula	L	*Oenothera*	V
Atriplex hastata	V, Sps	*Onopordum*	V
Atriplex hortensis	V	*Origanum*	Sps, M
Atriplex patula	V, Sps		
		Pastinaca	Sps, V
Balsamita major	Ba	*Petroselinum*	S
Barbarea vulgaris	V, S	*Plantago lanceolata*	V
Bellis	S, Sps	*Plantago major*	V
Berberis	Ju, Ja	*Polygonum bistorta*	V
Betula pendula	W	*Porphyra*	V, M
Betula pubescens	W	*Prunus spinosa*	L, Je
Borago	V, Vi, S	*Portulaca*	S, Sps, V
		Pteridium	V
Campanula	S	*Pulmonaria*	S, Sps, V, M
Cardamine	S		
Carum	Ba, V, S, Sps	*Quercus robur*	**Coffee**
Castania	M		
Cetraria	Fl	*Ranunculus*	S, V
Chamaenerion	S, V	*Raphanus*	V
Chenopodium album	Sps, V	*Rhodimenia*	S, Sps, M, D
Chenopodium bonus-henricus	S, Sps, V	*Ribes nigrum*	Ja
Chondrus	Sps, Je	*Ribes rubrum*	Ja, Je, W
Chorda	S	*Rorippa*	S, Sps, V
Chrysanthemum	S, W	*Rosmarinus*	M
Cichorium	S, V	*Rubus fruticosus*	Sy, Ja
Cirsium arvense	S, V	*Rubus idaeus*	Sy, Ja
Cirsium vulgare	S, V	*Rumex acetosa*	S, Sps, V
Cochlearia	S, Sps	*Rumex acetosella*	S, Sps, V
Cornus	Ja, W, D, Sps		
Corylus	O	*Salicornia*	Sps, V
Crambe	V	*Salsola kali*	S, Sps, V
Crataegus	Ja	*Salvia*	**Spice**
Cydonia	Ja, Je	*Sambucus*	Sps, Ju, Ba
		Sanguisorba minor	S, Sps, V, W
Echium	V	*Sanguisorba officinalis*	S, Sps, V
Enteromorpha	S	*Satureja montana*	M
		Sedum reflexum	S, Sps, V
Fagopyrum	Fl	*Sempervivum*	S
Fagus	O	*Silene*	S, Sps, V
Foeniculum vulgare	S, V, L	*Sinapis*	V
Fragaria	Ja, Sy, W	*Sisymbrium*	S, Sps
Fucus	M, V	*Sonchus arvensis*	S, Sps, V, M
		Sonchus oleraceus	S, Sps, V, M
Galinsoga	V, Sps, M, Ju	*Stellaria*	Sps, V
Glechoma	V, Sps, W		
		Taraxacum	S, V, W
Heracleum	V, Sps	*Thlaspi*	S, Sps
Hippophaë	L, Ju, Ja	*Thymus*	**Spice**
Humulus	S, Sps, V, Be	*Tragopogon*	S, Sps, V, M
		Trifolium pratense	S, Sps, V
Juniperus	**Spice**	*Trifolium repens*	S, Sps, V
		Triglochin	S, V, M
Laminaria digitata	Sps, M	*Tussilago*	S, Sps, V
Laminaria hyperborea	Sps, M	*Typha*	V, Fl
Laminaria saccharina	S		
Lamium	S, Sps, V	*Ulva*	S, Sps, M
Lapsana	S, Sps, V, M		
Lepidium campestre	S	*Vaccinium myrtillus*	Sps, W, Ja, Ba
Lepidium densiflorum	S	*Vaccinium vitis-idaea*	Sps, W, Ja, Ba
Levisticum	S, M, L	*Valerianella*	S
		Veronica beccabunga	S, V
Melissa	S, Sps, W	*Viola odorata*	S, Sy, Vi, Ja, Ba

Appendix III

Recipes for edible plants

Soups

Herb soup à la Alexander von Humbold

The following herbs are gathered for Alexander von Humbold's favourite soup: quantities of watercress, chervil, ground ivy, daisy, greater saxifrage, burnet, portulac, sorrel, yarrow, *Sedum reflexum* and *Asperula odorata*. They are finely chopped and simmered in a mild tasting stock. Serve this soup with croutons.

Porphyra soup

Heat 1 tablespoon cooking oil in a pan and sauté 1 small sliced onion and ½ cup sliced celery for 5 minutes over a moderate heat. Stir in 5mm freshly minced ginger, 1 tablespoon soy sauce, 3 cups beef stock, 1 cup water, 2 cups fresh *Porphyra* fronds and bring to the boil, then simmer for 5 minutes.

Alaria soup

Take 4–5 cups fresh seaweed cut into small pieces (1–2cm across) and sauté them in 4–5 tablespoons olive oil (alternatively butter or any cooking oil or lard) until a bright green colour develops (you may add a small onion at this stage and cook until golden-brown). Place it in a cooking pot, add 1½ litres of water and boil for about 1½ hours. Add 3–5 carrots and 1 large onion (both chopped), salt to taste and freshly ground pepper and boil for another 30–45 minutes. Add 1 cup of beef or chicken stock, and grate 1 medium potato into it; boil for 5–8 minutes, season and serve.

Soup with *Chondrus crispus*

Use about 1–1½ kilos of best stewing beef (or 1 boiling fowl), 1–1½ kilos of beef bones, 2–3 litres of water, 2 medium sized onions, 2 sticks of celery, 4–6 carrots, 1–2 cloves of garlic, 3–5 tablespoons tomato purée, 1 cup chondrus, 1 or 2 bay leaves, freshly ground black pepper, salt, a pinch of thyme, a pinch of sage, a pinch of parsley and a little red pepper. Simmer until meat is tender; before serving add 1 glass dry white wine or dry sherry.

Caraway soup

Chop carrots, celery, parsley roots and a little white cabbage. A soup plate of the above vegetables is enough for 2 litres of liquid. Melt 70g butter and fry the vegetables until golden. Stir in 3–4 tablespoons flour and cook for 1 minute. Meanwhile 2 litres of water have been brought to the boil with 1 tablespoon caraway. Add the vegetables, stir well and simmer for 15 minutes. The soup may be put through the blender if desired.

Soup recipe for spring herbs

The herbs in question are ground ivy, milfoil, greater burnet, saxifrage, dandelion and stinging nettles. They should be used before flowering. Wash 2–3 handfuls of the mixed herbs as obtainable and simmer in meat or bone stock. Remove and chop finely. Thicken the stock with flour, blend the herbs and return to the stock. Cream or yolk of egg may be added to the soup at the end of the cooking process. Serve with croutons. Equal quantities of sorrel and spinach may be used instead of the spring herbs.

Polish sorrel soup

Simmer 4 cups sorrel leaves in ½ cup water for about 20 minutes in a covered pan. Drain and make a purée. Add 2 tablespoons butter and season with salt and pepper. Scald 4 cups of fresh milk then add the purée. Cook gently for 2–3 minutes, stirring constantly. Remove from heat and add 1 small carton sour cream. Quarter 4 boiled eggs and serve in the soup.

Purslane soup

Boil ¼ cup water, lower heat and add 2 cups purslane leaves, then simmer for 3–5 minutes. Drain and chop. Melt 2 tablespoons butter in a heavy pan, add purslane, ¼ cup white wine or cider, juice of 1 lemon and 1 tablespoon Worcester sauce. Season and heat thoroughly.

Goosegrass soup

Cut up a 1 kilo shoulder of lamb (or take a similar quantity of neck or leg) and place in a pan with 4 cups water and 1 teaspoon salt. Boil, lower heat and simmer for 1 hour. (Alternatively, pressure-cook the meat). Strain, removing bones and fat. Melt 2 tablespoons butter in a frying pan and add 2 cups of washed goosegrass sprigs. Fry lightly for a few minutes. Add 1 tablespoon rolled oats to the soup, stirring well, then the goosegrass. Simmer for 1 hour.

Nettle Bouillon

Boil 1 cup nettle leaves for 1 minute in 1½ cups water. Drain and rinse in cold water. Add to 2 cups beef stock, simmer for a couple of minutes and serve with croutons.

Sorrel soup

Gather a small basketful of young sorrel and clean it. Take 2 heads of lettuce, wash and chop. Blanch both vegetables in salted water. Drain and simmer gently in good meat stock to which 140g butter and an onion have been added. Melt a further 140g butter in a large pan, add 2 tablespoons flour and cook until the flour is golden. Add 2–10 litres of good meat stock and simmer for 1 hour, skimming as necessary.

Chestnut soup

Peel 1 kilo of chestnuts, immerse in boiling water so that the second skin loosens, and remove this also. Rinse and cut away any bad parts. Put into a saucepan with 140g butter, a piece of lean raw bacon, an onion stuck with one or two cloves, salt, 1 teaspoon sugar and ¼ litre beef stock. Cook until tender, remove the onion and bacon and pass the soup through a sieve. Thin with a good beef stock and pass through a sieve again. Season to taste and serve with croutons. Alternatively add finely chopped capon meat to the finished soup, pass through a sieve yet again then add two tablespoons cooked rice.

Orache soup
Melt 1 tablespoon butter in a pan and fry 1 small chopped onion until golden-brown. Add 4 cups chopped orache leaves, cover and cook until soft. Pass through a sieve and return to the pan. Add beef or chicken stock, seasonings, and reheat.

Lamb's quarters leaf soup
Wash 4 cups of lamb's quarters leaves and place in a pan with a small chopped onion, a chopped celery stalk, 2 cups water, and salt. Bring to boil, then simmer for 15–20 minutes. Pass through a sieve. Melt 3 tablespoons butter in a saucepan, blend in 3 tablespoons flour and cook for a minute. Slowly add a large carton of single cream and stir into mixture until thick and smooth. Add lamb's quarters, salt and pepper to taste, and blend well.

Watercress soup
Liquidize watercress. Heat 450ml of milk, adding salt and pepper to taste. Add watercress and simmer briefly. Add ½ carton sour cream before serving. Blend until smooth, reheat and serve with croutons. Chicken stock may be used instead of milk.

Mallow soup
4 cups washed mallow leaves with the stems removed are chopped or puréed in a blender. Simmer in chicken or beef stock for 10 minutes. Sauté 1–2 cloves of chopped garlic in oil and add cayenne pepper and salt. Add this mixture to the soup. Simmer for 2–3 minutes.

Shepherd's purse soup
Bring chicken or beef stock to the boil, add 1 teaspoon of chopped ginger, 1 teaspoon of soy sauce, 1 teaspoon sunflower or olive oil, salt and pepper. Add the shepherd's purse leaves and simmer for 10 minutes. The soup may be thickened with a little arrowroot or potato flour or grated raw potato 5 minutes before it is ready. Serve hot.

Nettle soup with tomatoes
Chop 2–3 onions and fry in butter until golden in a heavy pan. Add a bowl of nettle tops and cook, stirring constantly until the nettles are tender. Add ¾ litre meat stock and simmer for 20 minutes. Pass through the blender and season with salt and pepper. Skin 1 kilo tomatoes, then cut them in half and remove the seeds. Slice them and add to the soup. Add 1 glass of white wine. Chop a sprig of parsley finely and stir into the soup. Boil up briefly. Add a little cream before serving.

Nettle soup
Chop 2–3 onions and fry in butter in a heavy pan until golden. Add a bowl of nettle tops, cook gently for a short time, then add 4 diced raw potatoes. Top up with ¾ litre of meat stock. Cook for 20 minutes. Whisk or blend. Thin the soup with 1–2 cups of milk and season with grated nutmeg and salt.

Caucasian sorrel soup
Make a rich brown stock from a piece of beef, 2–3 peppercorns and water. Lightly fry a carrot, an onion, and the sorrel, all finely chopped, for a minute or so in butter. Add the stock and simmer the soup until well done. Slice the beef and serve separately or in strips in the soup. Put a spoonful of sour cream or yoghurt into each soup bowl before serving. Eat with rye bread.

Green potato soup
Fry finely chopped onion in plenty of butter, add chopped sorrel, dandelion or ground elder leaves and diced raw potato. Cover, shake the pot, then fill up with stock. Cook for 30 minutes over medium heat. Season with salt, pepper and thyme, and serve with fried sausage. Single cream should be available on the table to add to the soup as desired.

Italian herb soup
Wash well 450g raw spinach and chop finely. Fry lightly in 2 tablespoons butter and leave to cool. Add ¼ teaspoon nutmeg, 1 whisked egg and 1 tablespoon Parmesan cheese. Top up with boiling stock and cook for a few minutes, stirring constantly. Serve with croutons.

Hamburg eel soup
Skin 450g eel, bone and cut into finger-sized strips. Simmer in a little mild vinegar water or white wine with 1 bayleaf, 1 onion, 3–4 peppercorns and salt. Meanwhile peel, core, and quarter 3–4 cooking pears and simmer in a light white wine with water, sugar and a stick of cinnamon. In another pan boil a selection of soup vegetables, adding according to taste a cup of green peas or 4 chopped asparagus shoots. Add to this a bunch of chopped herbs (parsley, marjoram, basil, chervil, sage, celery leaves and thyme). Warm up any meat stock of low fat content. Remove excess fat from the eel liquid and add the stock and 1 glass of white wine. Thicken with butter in which flour has been cooked until golden brown and add all the other ingredients.

Mushroom soup with champagne
Take 100g lean boiled ham, 100g lean veal, 100g smoked bacon, 1 small onion, 1 handful of fresh parsley, 1 sprig of thyme, 1 clove of garlic, and chop or mince all of them and lightly fry in their own fat. Pour over ½ bottle of champagne and simmer for 20 minutes. Add truffles or previously soaked Polish dried mushrooms. Add the rest of the champagne, 1 clove, 1 bayleaf, and a little nutmeg. Simmer for a few minutes longer.

Sow-thistle soup

Wash and shred the leaves. Melt 3 tablespoons of butter, add the leaves and 1 clove of crushed garlic. Stir, cover and simmer for 15 minutes. Pass the mixture through a sieve. Return to pan. Add sour cream or lemon juice, salt, pepper and 450ml of milk. Reheat. Garnish with hard-boiled eggs and/or croutons.

Snacks, starters and main dishes

Stuffed mushroom starter

Take 8 large flat mushrooms, wash thoroughly. Remove the stalks by slightly twisting them. Place mushrooms upside down in a shallow fireproof dish which has been well brushed with olive oil. Chop 3 medium sized onions finely. Chop the mushroom stems and 4 cloves of garlic finely. Put into a bowl with the onions. Add 4 heaped tablespoons breadcrumbs. Mix and season with freshly ground pepper, paprika, oregano and salt. Add 5–6 tablespoons olive oil and mix again. Place 1–2 tablespoons of the mixture on to each mushroom and bake in a moderate oven for about 20 minutes. For a slight variation grate Parmesan cheese on top of the mushrooms before cooking.

Comfrey cocktail starter

Simmer and then blend the following: a basinful of comfrey leaves, ¼ cup grated carrot, 1 chopped leek, 1 tablespoon chopped mint, 1 tablespoon chopped tarragon leaves, juice and rind of a lemon, ½ cup of water, salt and pepper. Mix purée with 2 small or 1 large tin(s) tomato juice. Serve on the rocks, with a slice of lemon.

Watercress snack

Mix chopped watercress, 2 chopped hard-boiled eggs, mayonnaise and a drop of milk if the mixture is too solid, and use as a sandwich filling. Garlic may be squeezed in if desired.

Buckwheat grain pottage

Mix 1 cup buckwheat with an egg and ½ teaspoon salt. Cook in oil in a heavy pan stirring constantly. Add 2 cups of beef, chicken or vegetable stock, cover and allow to steam for about ½ hour. Serve hot with gravy.

Nettle breakfast

Boil 1 cup young nettle leaves in 1½ cups water for 2–3 minutes and keep. Melt 1 tablespoon butter in a pan, add nettle leaves and a small carton of sour cream. Cook, stirring, for 2 minutes. Remove from heat and serve with eggs and bacon.

Flambéd snails with fresh herbs

Cook the snails, 1 dozen per person, in the usual way in their own juice. Take out the snails and reduce the juice by half. Pass through a sieve and keep warm. Fry the snails briefly and lightly in butter in an iron pan. Place the pan on a spirit-burner and season the snails with salt and pepper and sprinkle with the juice of half a lemon. Chop a selection of herbs (*Anthriscus*, parsley, *sanguisorba*, a small amount of basil, water mint or peppermint and watercress) and mix with the snails. Pour over several glasses of Slivovitsch or Hambeergeist or similar and ignite. Serve the snails with rice and green salad.

Boletus in scallop shells

Wash a plateful of young *Boletus edulis*, blanch them, and cut into thickish slices. Sprinkle with salt and flour. Melt 65g butter in a pan, add the mushrooms and partly cook them over a low heat. Scald 3–4 tablespoons cream with one small onion, pour over the mushrooms and simmer until cooked. They must not dry out. Place in scallop shells or shell-shaped dishes, sprinkle with breadcrumbs and pour over a little melted butter. Bake for 10 minutes in the oven before serving. Most kinds of edible mushrooms may be served in this way.

Eggs stuffed with sorrel

Take four hard-boiled eggs and cut in half. Remove the yolks, mash and mix with 2 tablespoons finely chopped sorrel leaves and 2 slices chopped fried bacon. Add approximately 2 tablespoons sour cream, mayonnaise or a mixture of 1½ tablespoons olive oil and ½ tablespoon lemon juice. Season and fill the egg halves with this mixture.

Chicken with purslane

Cook 4 cups purslane leaves in water for 3–5 minutes. Drain, chop and keep. Brown 6–8 chicken pieces in olive oil for 20 minutes. Add the purslane, 1 clove minced garlic, a small tin of tomato purée and cover. Cook gently for approximately 45 minutes. Add ½ cup white wine or cider and juice of half a lemon. Cook for a few minutes more. Serve hot.

Purslane casserole

Sauté 2 cups of purslane leaves in 1 tablespoon butter. Boil ½ cup rice, 225g smoked turkey slices and the purslane. Melt 2 tablespoons butter in another saucepan, add 2 tablespoons flour, stock, and salt to taste. Whisk until smooth. Pour into the casserole and bake for 45 minutes. Serve sprinkled with Parmesan cheese.

Baked eggs with purslane

Simmer 2 cups purslane leaves in water for 3–5 minutes. Drain and keep. Melt 1½ tablespoons butter in a frying pan and sauté the purslane with ½ chopped onion. Place in a fireproof dish and crack 6 eggs over the purslane. Sprinkle with a mixture of breadcrumbs (¼ cup) and grated cheese (½ cup). Pour a little beer over each of the eggs. Bake for approx. 20–25 minutes until eggs are set. Serve hot.

Fried eggs with purslane

Simmer 2 cups purslane leaves in water for 3–5 minutes. Drain and keep. Melt 1½ tablespoons butter in a frying pan and add purslane, 2 teaspoons white wine vinegar and salt and pepper to taste. Fry gently for 5 minutes. Fry 4 eggs in butter in a second pan and pour the purslane mixture over them. Serve immediately.

Nipplewort omelette for one
Whisk one egg with 2 tablespoons yoghurt. Add nipplewort leaves, two rashers of chopped, cooked bacon, 1½ tablespoons chopped onion, salt and pepper. Stir then fry the omelette mixture in butter or olive oil.

Sow-thistle stew
Wash the leaves and chop. Brown one chopped onion in butter. Add leaves, cover and cook for a few minutes until tender. Season. Add 225g chopped continental sausage (garlic sausage, cabanos, Spanish chourizo or similar. If Frankfurters are used, garlic must be added separately). Place in casserole and cook in the oven for 20 minutes. Caraway seed may be added as an extra flavouring prior to cooking in the oven if desired.

Watercress toasts
With a fork blend chopped watercress, a little tuna, 1 chopped hard-boiled egg, 6 chopped anchovies, 1 teaspoon Worcester sauce, 1 tablespoon mayonnaise. Toast or fry bread and cut into small pieces, spreading with mixture. Tinned salmon or sardines may be used instead of tuna and a dressing of olive oil, lemon juice and paprika instead of mayonnaise.

Mallow macaroni cheese
Remove the mallow leaf stems, wash the leaves in water and simmer for 3 minutes. Drain and keep. Heat ¼ cup milk or single cream. Make a smooth sauce then add 1 cup grated cheese. Stir sauce until cheese melts in. Add mallow and seasonings. Serve with macaroni, rice, or potatoes.

Elderberry pancakes
Make a pancake mixture in the usual way. Fry one side lightly, then take a whole inflorescence of elderberry (do not wash it beforehand but make sure it is free from insects) and place it on the pancake like an upside-down umbrella; it should sink into the still soft mixture. Snip off the stalk, turn the pancake and complete the frying.

Chicory toast starter
4 slices German pumpernickel bread
1 tin sardines and their oil
12 chicory leaves, blanched
Juice of ½ lemon
¼ teaspoon Worcester Sauce
Grated Parmesan cheese
Salt and pepper
Make fingers of Pumpernickel toast. Place chicory leaf on each piece of bread, then half a sardine on top. Blend sardine oil, lemon juice, Worcester sauce, and seasonings. Pour over the toast fingers. Sprinkle with Parmesan before serving. Makes 12.

Sliced beef with burdock roots
2 burdock roots
1 tablespoon vinegar
⅓ cup chicken or beef stock
⅓ cup soy sauce
1 tablespoon demerara sugar
½ cup miria (sweet Japanese liqueur) or sweet sherry
½ cup sake or sweet white wine
500g thinly sliced beef steak
4 eggs
Scrape roots and slice very thinly. Soak for 15 minutes in water and vinegar. Rinse and drain. Combine stock, soy sauce, sugar, and miria. Place burdock in a pan, pour over half the quantity of sake. Cook for 20 minutes. Add beef, pour remaining sake over the meat. Cook for 10 minutes. When beef is nearly done, add remaining sauce and cook. Do not stir. Bring the mixture to the boil, pour the beaten eggs on top. Remove from heat when the egg begins to solidify (4 servings).

Thistle stew
1kg stewing steak
2 tablespoons wholewheat flour
¼ cup vegetable oil
1 clove garlic, crushed
1 chopped onion
1 cup beef stock
1 cup tomato purée
¼ cup chopped parsley
½ teaspoon thyme
1 bay leaf
12 peppercorns ⎫
3 cloves ⎬ In a cloth bag
½ cup dry white wine
1 cup young thistle leaves, de-thorned
1 cup peeled and chopped thistle roots
½ cup diced carrots
1 stalk chopped celery.
Flour the beef and brown in the oil. Reduce heat and add garlic, onion, stock, purée, herbs, spices and wine. Simmer for 1½ hours. Add thistles, carrots and celery and cook until tender. 4–6 servings.

Laminaria chips
Cut *Laminaria*-fronds into strips (5cm × 1–2 cm) or squares and dry in the sun. Deep-fry (like potato chips) in best cooking oil. Dry on a kitchen towel or linen cloth. Serve sprinkled with salt or sugar. *Porphyra umbilicalis* can be used in the same way.

Evening-primrose steak sauce
Peel 6 good evening-primrose roots and boil until tender in salted water. Changing the water a couple of times will remove sharp taste. Place the sliced roots with ½ cup sliced mushrooms into the frying pan with 2 tablespoons butter. Fry for a few seconds then add a glass of white wine. Cook until half the quantity of liquid remains and season. Serve with steak.

Curried evening-primrose roots

Peel 12 good roots and boil, changing water twice, until tender. Drain and slice. Fry gently in 3 tablespoons butter, 2 tablespoons curry powder and salt to taste for about 15 minutes. Enhances any meat dish.

Laver (Lava/Larva) bread

Keep in fridge and use as soon as possible. Do not taste until cooked (in case of pollution!).

1. Wash very thoroughly to remove any sand, and feel it over carefully in case sand is sticking to any holdfasts.

2. Put in a pan with enough water to cover it and simmer for *at least* 1½–2 hours; the water should boil away until you are left with a mushy substance of fairly firm consistency and no longer seaweed-like in texture (taste at intervals to find out).

3. When cold (which could conveniently be the next day), make into little cakes the shape and size of a fish-cake, coat with oatmeal and fry.

4. Best eaten with bacon, and with salt and pepper.

WITH KIND PERMISSION OF A. CHATER.

Dandelion in sour cream

Bring young leaves to the boil then simmer for 10 minutes. Drain. (Repeating this process over the same length of time will reduce bitterness). Chill and serve in sour cream. Garnish with fried bacon or ham. Yoghurt may be used instead of sour cream and lemon juice added to taste.

Sautéd goat's-beard roots

Wash and peel the roots, dip in milk, then in seasoned breadcrumbs. Sauté in butter until golden brown. Serve.

Wild lettuce greens

Add wild lettuce leaves to boiling water, reduce heat and simmer briefly. Drain. This first cooking will remove bitterness. Simmer again in boiled water or chicken or beef stock for a couple of minutes, drain and serve tossed in a melted butter and lemon juice mixture.

Purée of sorrel

Wash a basketful of green sorrel several times, drain and cook gently in butter until no liquid remains. Shake 2 tablespoons flour over it, add good meat stock and cook, stirring all the time until the mixture thickens. Place in a casserole and pour over a spoon of glaze (reduced bone stock) and leave to cool. Reheat stirring all the time and bind with a liaison of 5 eggs and a nut of butter. Purée sorrel makes a good omelette filling.

Hops as a vegetable

Use only the early shoots which emerge, asparagus-like, from the roots in spring. Clean carefully and blanch in salted boiling water. Drain and place on a cloth to dry. Melt butter with chopped parsley and onion, add a teaspoonful of sugar, salt and nutmeg. Add the hops and cook gently. Before serving add a few spoons of white sauce, a little glaze (reduced bone stock), toss gently and serve.

Hedge mustard chinese style

Heat oil in a frying pan or Wok and brown 1 cup chopped pork with 2 chopped onions. Add 2 cups chopped mustard leaves, sliced celery and mushrooms. Cook for a few minutes. Add 1 cup chicken or beef stock, ½ cup rice, salt and pepper. Cover and simmer for 25–30 minutes. Serve immediately. Cooked chicken or turkey may be used instead of pork.

Mallow with bacon

Simmer 2 cups of mallow leaves in water for 3 minutes. Drain and mix in a salad bowl with 1 teaspoon lemon juice, 2 cups chopped crispy bacon. Serve with good brown bread, spread with honey if desired.

Basic salsify recipe

Mix 1 tablespoon flour with water, add a drop of vinegar and more water. Peel and chop the salsify into inch-long pieces and immerse in the water to avoid discolouring. Melt some butter in a pan, dry the salsify in a cloth and place in the pan. Add a little salt, sugar and meat stock. Simmer until tender. Drain the vegetables, retaining the liquid, and keep warm.

Fried salsify

Peel and cut the salsify into inch-long pieces. Cook until tender in meat stock to which a little butter, sugar and lemon juice has been added. Remove the vegetable, dry in a cloth. Dip in beaten egg and breadcrumbs. Fry until golden brown.

Fried comfrey

Make a batter of 1 cup of flour, ¾ tablespoon baking powder, salt and pepper, ½ cup milk and 2 beaten eggs. Wash the comfrey leaves, leaving them on their stems, dry, dip in the batter and deep fry in oil for 2 minutes.

Comfrey vegetable

Wash and shred leaves. Bring to the boil in water, reduce heat and simmer for a few minutes. Drain. Add 1 tablespoon lemon juice, 1 tablespoon butter or yoghurt, or sour cream, salt and pepper. Place in serving dish. Sprinkle with nutmeg.

Fried burdock roots

8 burdock roots
1 tablespoon vegetable oil
¼ cup soy sauce
2 tablespoons sugar
2 tablespoons shredded dried shrimp or Japanese fish-soup powder
black pepper

Pare roots and slice thinly. Soak in water for 15–20 minutes, then drain, Sauté roots for 5 minutes. Add remaining ingredients and cook until liquid evaporates then season with the black pepper. 6–8 servings.

Burdock Japanese style (Gobo)
4 large burdock roots
½ teaspoon + 2 tablespoons vinegar
1½ tablespoons soy sauce
½ tablespoon sugar
1 tablespoon sesame seeds
Pare roots and slice thinly. Soak in water for a few minutes and drain. Add water to cover, 1 teaspoon vinegar, bring to the boil, then simmer for 10 minutes. Drain. Put all ingredients, except the seeds, into a saucepan and cook for 15 minutes. Sprinkle with seeds and serve. 4–6 servings.

Braised thistle roots
12 thistle roots
2 tablespoons butter
½ teaspoon salt
¼ cup beef or chicken stock
parsley.
Pare the roots and cut in half. Place in a fireproof dish, brush with melted butter, add salt and stock. Bake at 190°F. for about 45 minutes. Sprinkle with parsley and serve.

Stuffed coltsfoot leaves
Chop one aubergine finely and fry lightly in olive oil with 1 chopped onion, the juice of half a lemon, 1½ teaspoons oregano, 1 teaspoon dill and a clove of garlic, crushed. Season with salt and pepper and top up with 300ml water. Simmer for about 1 hour until the liquid is absorbed. Mix with 450g cooked rice. Adjust the seasoning. Place a spoon of the mixture into each of the washed coltsfoot leaves and wrap up.
Take 450g peeled, chopped tomatoes and season with basil, salt and pepper. Put the stuffed leaves into a fireproof dish which has been brushed with olive oil and cook with the tomatoes. Bake for ½ hour in a medium oven.

Nettle fritters
Blanch a bowlful of nettles in boiling water then rinse in cold water to retain the green colour. Drain and dry with kitchen towels. Chop and mix in a bowl with 1 egg. Season with salt and pepper and grated nutmeg. Form into small fritters and dab in flour. Fry in butter turning frequently. Serve with most meat dishes.

Comfrey shoots with capers
Boil a bowlful of comfrey sprigs in salt water for a few minutes, if possible in a pan with basket liner. Remove and drain. Make a dressing of the following ingredients: 2 hard-boiled egg yolks, 1 raw egg yolk, 2 or 3 tablespoons of olive oil, juice of ½ lemon, 1 tablespoon hot mustard, 1 tablespoon anchovy paste, pepper to taste. Add wild capers (3 tablespoons), 1 pickled cucumber and 1 tablespoon tarragon leaves (both finely chopped). Pour over the comfrey shoots and serve.

Salads

Advice for wild salads
Prepare dressing and add salad-leaves just before serving. To preserve its crispiness, best toss only at table at the last moment (this does not apply to potato or salads containing root-vegetables).
   The bitter or acrid taste of some wild leaf-vegetables can be alleviated as follows:
1   Pour water away after boiling (perhaps repeat this twice).
2   Use water in which leaves were boiled (always use just enough water as is necessary) for a white sauce served with the vegetable (finely chopped onions, milk or cream).
3   Boil 1–2 cloves of garlic with the leaves and remove them before serving.
4   Mask bitter taste with garlic, nutmegs, thyme, or other herbs.
5   Use milk (completely or partly) instead of water.

Sanguisorba leaf salad
Take a bowlful of sanguisorba leaves and chop small. Mix with a finely chopped onion. Make a dressing of 1 tablespoon olive oil, several tablespoons of tarragon vinegar, 2 hard-boiled egg yolks, 1 tablespoon hot mustard, 1 tablespoon tomato purée, 1 tablespoon red wine, salt and pepper. Mix with the sanguisorba and leave for 1 hour. A good accompaniment for pork fillet.

Daisy salad with cheese
Dig out enough daisy plants to fill a bowl, wash carefully and pluck the leaves. Make a dressing of 2 tablespoons olive oil, salt and black pepper, and toss the daisy leaves in it. Garnish with 2 chopped hard-boiled eggs, 100g ham and 100g Emmenthal cheese cut into short fine strips. Chill for 1 hour before serving.

Seaweed salad I
Take 2 cups of fresh *Alliaria* (cut into small pieces after removal of midrib) and 3–4 cups of any wild salad-plant (alternatively fresh young spinach or endives). Place in a salad-bowl and toss in dressing: olive or sunflower oil, crushed garlic, lemon juice, wine vinegar, salt, freshly ground pepper and a pinch of powdered dill.

Seaweed salad II
Use the dressing indicated above or alternatively prepare a dressing with soured cream or natural yoghurt, lemon juice or wine vinegar and pepper. Toss small pieces of both fresh *Ulva* and *Entoromorpha* (quantity according to need) and serve immediately.

Dandelion salad
Serve the leaves in a dressing of equal quantities of lemon juice and sunflower or olive oil. Season with salt, pepper and crushed garlic. Chill and serve. Young spinach or nettle leaves may be mixed with the dandelion leaves as a variation.

Wild lettuce salad

Toss washed lettuce in yoghurt. Sprinkle with grated Parmesan cheese, salt and pepper. A small clove of garlic, crushed, may be added to the dressing and cottage cheese may be used instead of Parmesan.

Nipplewort salad

Shred the nipplewort and mix with an equal quantity grated carrot, 2 tablespoons of raisins, 1 tablespoon lemon juice, 3 tablespoons mayonnaise (slimmers may omit this and add olive oil instead), ½ teaspoon fresh thyme, 1 teaspoon mint leaves, and salt to taste. Chopped apple may be added also, if desired, as a substitute for raisins.

Salsify salad

Peel, cut and cook the salsify in salted water to which a drop of vinegar has been added. Drain. Make a dressing of the sieved yolks of 6 hard-boiled eggs, salt, a pinch of sugar, pepper, oil, vinegar and a tablespoon of chopped blanched parsley. Toss the vegetable in the dressing and serve.

Chickweed salad

Serve washed chickweed sprigs in a vinaigrette dressing. They may be mixed with young dandelion or spinach leaves.

Cress salad

Mix watercress, chopped spring onions, two chopped tomatoes and 4 slices crispy chopped bacon. Make a vinaigrette and add. Sprinkle croutons on before serving. Garlic may be added, and a pinch of dill if desired.

Shepherd's purse salad I

Mix equal quantities of chopped shepherd's purse leaves and diced cucumber with double the amount of cottage cheese. Garnish with paprika and chopped parsley. Garlic and crushed caraway seeds provide a variation of seasoning.

Shepherd's purse salad II

Mix 2 cups young shepherd's purse leaves with 1 tablespoon parsley and 1 diced apple or half the quantity of raisins or pineapple. Make a dressing of lemon juice, sour cream, 1 teaspoon sugar, salt and pepper.

Veronica beccabunga salad

Veronica grows in springs, ditches and streams and is equally available in winter. Cut off the shoot ends with secateurs. Wash and cut the *Veronica* and mix with finely chopped onion. Make a sauce of 1 teaspoon hot mustard, 2 tablespoons wine vinegar, 2 tablespoons olive oil, salt and pepper. Toss the salad in this dressing. Garnish with slices of hard-boiled egg. Leave for 1 hour before eating.

Dandelion salad with tomatoes

Wash the dandelion leaves and cut into fine strips. Take a few rye-bread slices, toast lightly and rub with garlic. Fry 100g chopped streaky bacon lightly and keep warm. Cut the bread into cubes and fry a little in the bacon fat, taking care not to burn it. Make a dressing of olive oil, wine vinegar, salt and pepper and toss the dandelion leaves in it. Garnish with the bacon and bread pieces. Serve at once.

Ranunculus ficaria with *Allium ursinum* in burgundy dressing

Wash and cut the *Ranunculus* into medium sized pieces. Make a dressing of tarragon vinegar, olive oil, 1 teaspoon hot mustard, salt and pepper, the yolks of 2 hard boiled eggs and 1 glass of burgundy. Add finely chopped onion. Toss the salad in this dressing. The remaining egg-whites should be chopped and added along with the chopped *Allium* leaves. Leave the salad to stand for a while before serving.

Asparagus salad

Cut the tender parts of the asparagus into 1cm long pieces. Blanch in salted boiling water. Cool and allow to drain. Make a dressing of oil, vinegar, pepper and salt, blanched parsley, shallots, tarragon and burnet, all finely chopped. Mix the dressing with the asparagus. Small pieces of cauliflower may be used to garnish.

Sauces and spreads

Home-made fresh herbal salt

10 parts of fresh parsley
10 parts of fresh chives
2 parts of fresh dill
1 part of fresh thyme
¼ part of fresh bay-leaves
Change mixture according to taste
Chop all herbs finely, put a thin layer at the bottom of a glass jar, sprinkle a layer of salt on to it, followed by successive layers of herbs and salt (final layer must be salt), seal jar and keep in fridge.

Pennycress spread

¼ cup pennycress, chopped, 1 cup soft margarine, ¼ cup sour cream, paprika and salt to season are mixed together and spread on salami, ham, or cheese sandwiches. Store in the refrigerator.

Hedge mustard spread

1 cup of hedge mustard leaves, chopped, are added to 6 chopped hard-boiled eggs, 3 tablespoons mayonnaise, 2 tablespoons chopped olives, 1 chopped spring onion, 2 tablespoons butter, or half the quantity of olive oil, a few capers, salt, pepper and a dash of paprika. Use as a spread on bread or toast.

Herbal butter

Wild herbs such as *Portulaca*, *Rumex* and *Mentha* are finely chopped, seasoned with salt, pepper or paprika and then worked with a fork into soft butter which can then be used in sandwiches or served with steaks, fish or vegetables, cottage-cheese, potatoes, etc. To add flavour a small amount of garlic and/or finely chopped onions can be added. Alternatively the herbs can be worked into cottage cheese, Gervais or Philadelphia (butter or a little olive oil optional).

Laminaria stock (best species L. digitata)
Put 1 frond (cut into small pieces) into 3–4 cups water, bring to the boil and reduce heat immediately. Use as stock for soups or gravy. The remaining frond can be added to stews, fish dishes, casseroles, etc.

Seaweed powder as a condiment
Sun-dry Enteromorpha until completely brittle, alternatively dry in a warm well-ventilated room in medium heat (not over 35°C.); powder it with mortar and pestle. Store in an air-tight glass container. Use for savoury or sweet dishes. The same use can be made of Laminaria species, which, however, should always be dried in the oven. For savoury dishes only.

Sorrel sauce for a fish dish
Take ½ cup chopped sorrel leaves and cook gently in 2 tablespoons butter. Stir in 1 cup of scalded single cream. Serve with cooked fish.

Herb sauce for boiled beef
Take a selection of spring herbs such as sorrel, greater burnet, saxifrage, scurvy-grass, lady's smock, ground ivy, parsley and chives. Wash and chop finely. Crush the yolk of 1 hard-boiled egg with salt, vinegar and 2–3 spoons salad oil. Add the herbs. Dilute the mixture with white wine or water to the desired consistency and serve with the meat.

Rosehip sauce for venison, wild boar, mutton, turkey
Melt 100g butter in saucepan, stir in 1½ tablespoons of flour until golden-yellow, add mixture of rosehip purée and stock and allow to simmer until the correct creamy consistency is achieved. Season with pinch of sugar, pinch of ground cloves and a little rind of fresh lemon.

Peppergrass condiment
This is simply a mixture of ¼ cup chopped peppergrass shoots, 1 cup mayonnaise and a tablespoon each of capers, chopped olives, and chopped sweet pickles with salt and pepper to taste. Serve with fish and meat dishes.

Storksbill and tomato sauce
Simmer storksbill leaves in water for 5 minutes. Drain and keep. Sauté 1 clove of garlic, chopped, until slightly brown, add leaves, small tin of tomato purée, salt, pepper and oregano to taste. Mix well and reheat. Serve with pasta or rice.

Horseradish sauce
1 glass red port spiced with a pinch of salt, pepper, and freshly ground nutmeg is reduced by boiling to two-thirds its volume; add twice the same quantity of red-currant, heat again but do not boil, add freshly grated horseradish

(½–¾ cup full or more according to taste). Serve (hot or cold) with poultry, veal or fish.

Mint sauce
Chop 1 cup of fresh mint leaves, add 1–1½ tablespoons of sugar. Pour some boiling water on to it and add wine vinegar according to taste. Serve with fish and meat (lamb, mutton).

Horseradish-orange sauce
Grate or peel 5–7 large oranges on same amount of sugar, mix all the orange juice, the peel and sugar and 1½ glass dry white wine, heat but do not boil (enamel or earthenware pot!). Stir in ½–¾ cup of grated horseradish. Serve (hot or cold) with game, poultry or fish.

Sauce with Cardamine pratensis
Take 1 cupful of finely chopped stems with young inflorescences. Prepare sauce-base with milk, butter and onions, stir in herbs and add 2–3 cups of beef or chicken stock. Season with salt and pepper. Serve with fish (the water in which fish was boiled or stewed can be used instead of stock), veal or poultry.

Daisy sauce
Soak 1 cup of finely chopped daisies in 2 cups of milk. Heat 2–3 tablespoons of flour and ¼ cup of finely chopped onions in 3–5 tablespoons of butter in a saucepan till light brown; add milk and daisies to saucepan, stir until right consistency is achieved. Flavour with lime juice, chives or a little parsley.

Wild capers
Wild substitutes for the commercially sold capers are obtained from the following plants:
1 Daisy: the closed buds.
2 Ranunculus ficaria: the closed buds, and the bulbils which are found in the leaf-axils of the plant.
3 Allium ursinum: the small green bulbils which are formed in the middle of June after the flowering period. They are pleasantly sharp and have a slightly garlic taste. They are among the best of the wild capers. The bulbils may be preserved on the stalk and taken off when needed.
4 Sambucus nigra: the young, not over-ripe, berries. They have, however, very small stones.
5 Sarothamnus scoparius: the closed buds and the very small pods after part-boiling them in salted water.

Sweets, syrups, preserves, jellies and jams

Syrup of barberries
The berries should be picked when the first ripe ones fall. Mash them and boil up with a little water. Press well. For every 560g juice take 1kg 680g sugar, boil to the thread (until it is sticky) in a little water. Add the strained juice, boil up, skimming off any impurities. When cold pour into bottles and keep. This juice forms the basis of a good lemonade.

Rosehip jam

Take ripe rosehips and remove the seeds. Place in a bowl and leave to stand for several days, stirring frequently until they are quite soft. Pass through a sieve and for the quantity of fruit add an equal quantity of sugar. Boil up several times. Store in jars.

Syrup of violets

Pick the flower heads making sure that no green parts are used. Put into a suitable container and pour boiling water over them. Seal the container and leave overnight. Next day press the mixture through a cloth. Add 280g caster sugar per ³/₁₀ litre of the liquid. Put into an earthenware fireproof casserole, add the juice of one lemon. Heat gently until the sugar melts then increase heat. Remove any scum, allow to cool and transfer to small previously warmed bottles. Seal and keep to use as required.

Rose petal jam

Pull the petals from about 30 roses of which at least half the quantity should be red ones. Cleanse of greenfly etc. Place in a jam pan with 900g sugar and 1·2 litres water. Simmer, stirring frequently, for about 25 minutes. Add 1 teaspoon of citric acid. Simmer a further 10–20 minutes. Pour into jars and seal as usual.

Rose petal vinegar

Fill a bottle with rose petals (the choice of which will govern the colour of the resultant liquid) and top up with white vinegar. Shake the bottle daily. Use after 2 months.

Preserved quinces

Mash the yellow quinces and top and tail them. Cook the quinces until partly soft and drain, keeping the water. Plunge them into cold water and peel them. Cut and remove the cores. Return the quinces to the water in which they have already been partly cooked and continue to cook until tender. Drain, keeping the water yet again. Pour on to a cloth to absorb excess water. Take an equal quantity of sugar, add a little of the quince water, boil up and add the quinces, cooking them for about ½ hour. Avoid cooking them too long or they will be unattractive and hard. Place the quinces in jars, reduce the juice to a syrupy consistency and pour over. Seal and store.

Buckwheat pancakes

Mix together 1½ cups buckwheat flour, ½ cup white flour, and ½ teaspoon salt. Mix 1 egg, 3¼ cups buttermilk, 2 teaspoons molasses and 2 tablespoons vegetable oil. Add to the dry ingredients. Fry the pancakes and serve with maple syrup or your favourite sauce. The buttermilk may be substituted by 40ml yoghurt and 100ml milk.

Nettle cream

Boil 2 cups nettle leaves in 1½ cups salted water for 2–3 minutes. Drain, chop and keep. Melt 3 tablespoons butter in a pan, stir in 1 tablespoon flour, ½ cup cream and cook until nicely thickened. Add a pinch of sugar, salt, pepper and nutmeg to taste and serve with almonds sprinkled on top.

Mint fruit cup

Combine the following ingredients: 2 tablespoons peppermint leaves, one large orange, peeled and sliced, a dozen stoned cherries, or grapes or strawberries, cubes of ½ canteloupe melon (optional), a small can of pineapple chunks, 1 fresh peach, sliced, 1 pear sliced, 1 banana, sliced, 1 tablespoon lemon juice, 2 tablespoons fruit sugar, 2 tablespoons sherry. Serve chilled.

Salsify with sweet cream

Bring to boil 1½ cups of water, 2 teaspoons flour, 1 teaspoon lemon juice, and a pinch of salt. Add the peeled salsify and cook for 5 minutes. Drain and place in a dish. Mix 2 tablespoons whipping cream and 1 teaspoon brown sugar. Pour over and sprinkle with nutmeg.

Burdock stalks in syrup

6 burdock stalks
2 tablespoons salt
½ cup vinegar
2½ cups water
2 cups sugar

Peel stalks and chop into pieces. Cover with water and salt and leave to stand for 8 hours. Drain. Simmer in vinegar and water for a few minutes. Drain. Boil sugar and water for 10 minutes, pour over burdock. Leave overnight. Remove burdock and reboil syrup. Pour over burdock and leave overnight again. Simmer the whole confection until the stalks are soft. Store and use as desired.

Blackberry jelly

Pick ripe berries but include a few unripe ones to give extra pectin. Leave in open container and any grubs should come to the surface and can easily be removed. Rinse in a sieve.

Place in a jam pan with water to about quarter the height of the fruit. Boil over a low heat for 5–10 minutes, then turn off the heat and leave for some time to draw off the juice.

Strain the berries through a fine sieve or jellybag. Do not press the fruit: only the clear juice is wanted. Wash jam jars and lids in as hot water as possible. Place downwards on a clean teatowel. To make the jelly, take an equal weight of juice and sugar and cook small quantities in a large pan. Dissolve the sugar in the juice before the mixture reaches boiling point. Stir constantly with a wooden spoon. Boil rapidly for 3–4 minutes, reduce the heat, stop stirring and let the mixture simmer for 3–5 minutes. Take off the scum. Fill jars as full as possible with the hot jelly, clean the rim with a sterile cloth and close the screw tops immediately.

Preserving sugar will give a solid jelly, 50–50 preserving sugar and granulated give a firm jelly but for a soft jelly use all granulated.

Quince jelly

Take ripe quinces and rub off the woolly parts. Cut each into four pieces and remove the core or the jelly will not set. Pour enough cold water over the quinces to cover them, plus 3 cm. Simmer until the quinces are quite soft but do not disintegrate. Pour into a sieve and collect the liquid. Leave for 3–4 hours then pour off into a measure, leaving the sediment behind. To the measure of liquid take an equal amount of sugar. Boil the sugar up in a small amount of water then add the quince juice and boil for 25–30 minutes. When the jelly starts to make large bubbles test for thickness and take care that the jelly does not boil over. Stir frequently. The jelly is ready when it hangs in a long drop from the spoon. If this point is missed the jelly will become brown and remain liquid. Store in jars.

Holler pancakes

Pick about a dozen holler flowers (mid-May to the end of June). Make a batter of 100g flour, 3 eggs, salt, 1 glass of stout, and the flower heads. Fry the pancakes as usual. Flambé the pancakes with Slivovitch, Himbeergeist or similar.

Drinks

Rose wine

Cover 4 pints of rose petals with 8 pints boiling water. Leave to stand for 4 days, stirring occasionally. Strain through a cloth. Stir in the juice of 2 lemons, the juice of 1 orange, 1·5kg sugar and 15g yeast. Keep at 65–75°F and leave to ferment. When the bubbling stops stir the wine.

Dandelion wine

Place 4–5 quarts dandelion heads in an earthenware container. Pour boiling water over them and leave for 24 hours. Strain, add 1·5kg sugar, 2 sliced dried oranges and 2 sliced lemons. Boil for 10 minutes, strain and cool. Add a cup of raisins and 5g dried yeast. Leave for 2–3 weeks. Do not cork tightly before the process of fermentation is over. Store in cool dark place for at least 6 months. The wine should be clear when ready for drinking.

Daisy wine

5–6 litres daisy heads
6 litres boiling water
1·5kg sugar
500g raisins
500g wheat kernels
rind and juice of 2 lemons
rind and juice of 2 oranges
8g dried yeast

Place flowers in vat and pour over boiling water. Leave for 24 hours. Remove flower heads and add sugar, raisins, wheat, rind and juice of lemons and oranges. Dissolve yeast in 1 cup of warm water with 1 teaspoon sugar. After 10 minutes add to the liquid. Cover with cloth and leave for three weeks, stirring daily. Bottle and cork, but not too tightly. Do not use screw tops or breakage may occur. Store in a cool dark place. It should be drinkable after 6 months.

Chicory coffee

Wash and roast a few chicory roots (120°C), they must be brown and quite dry. Grind and store. Use 1½ teaspoons per cup of water, blended with normal coffee to taste.

Teas

There are a great variety of herbal teas many of which are commercially available today. As well as making pleasant, wholesome and refreshing beverages, many are reputed to have specific therapeutic or cosmetic values – a number of these have been mentioned under the individual entry for each herb or in the table on p.272. This section contains a few recipes for some of the more delicious tea preparations and substitutes which can be drunk at the end of a meal or at any time through the day.

Always remember that the flavours of these teas are very delicate. To avoid deterioration each herb should be packed apart in airtight containers. It is always best not to steep the leaves for too long: if a stronger infusion is required use more herb. Quantities are given for fresh herbs, but if dried herbs must be used one teaspoon per cup and one for the pot is generally sufficient.

Peppermint tea with orange peel

1½–2 teaspoons mint per cup water
1 teaspoon dried orange peel.

Let stand for 8–10 minutes. Add slice of fresh lemon or orange when serving.

Spicy mint tea

2 teaspoons mint
2 pinches cinnamon (ground) or ¼ teaspoon lemon rind
1 clove or 1–2 pinches all spice.

Allow to stand for 8–10 minutes (not longer).

Mint raspberry tea

1–3 teaspoons mint leaves
2 teaspoons wild raspberry leaves
3–5 crushed fresh raspberries.

Rose petal tea

3 cups white sugar
¾ cup water
3–4 cups fresh rose petals
1–2 tablespoons lemon juice.

Put all ingredients into earthenware or enamel pan, heat to the boil, stir all the time, until petals are completely dissolved. Cool, put into glasses or jars and refrigerate.

Comfrey and peppermint tea

Leaves or root may be used. Use 4 leaves or 4 finger-sized roots per pot. Slice and place into pot with 12 peppermint leaves. Pour over boiling water, leave for half an hour, reheat and serve with honey and lemon as desired.

Herbal mixtures which can be used as a substitute for China tea. These can be used daily over any period. The preparation takes the form of an infusion with quantities according to taste (usually 1–1½ teaspoons per cup water; allow to stand for 5 minutes).

Rubus fruticosus   (leaves)   2 parts
Rubus idaeus   (leaves)   2 pts
Mentha × piperita   (herb)   2 pts
Salvia   (leaves)   2 pts
Real tea or Mate   (leaves)   1 pt

Rubus fruticosus   (leaves)   5 pts
Rubus idaeus   (leaves)   3 pts
Fragaria   (leaves)   2 pts
Tilia   (flowers)   1 pt
Mentha × piperita   (herb)   1 pt

Tussilago   (leaves)   1 pt
Fragaria   (leaves)   2 pts
Rubus fruticosus   (leaves)   2 pts

Vaccinium vitis-idaea   (leaves)   5 pts
Rubus fruticosus   (leaves)   7 pts
Rubus idaeus   (leaves)   7 pts
Mentha × piperita   1 pt

Rubus idaeus   (leaves)   3 pts
Fragaria   (leaves)   3 pts
Asperula   (herb)   1 pt
Viola odorata   (flowers)   2 pts
Viola odorata   (young leaves)   1 pt
Primula   (flowers)   1 pt
Prunus spinosa   (flower buds)   3–4 pts
Fragaria   (leaves)   2 pts
Fragaria   (flowers)   1 pt
Rubus idaeus   (leaves and flowers)   2 pts
Rubus fruticosus   (leaves)   2 pts
Salvia   (leaves)   1 pt
Foeniculum   (leaves)   ½–1 pt

Apple peel   1 pt
Pear peel   1 pt
Rose petals   1 pt

Appendix IV

List of common ailments and plant species recommended as herbal remedies (the plants listed are only those which can be used in the home; plants used for homeopathic or allopathic preparations are excluded).

Abscess (Boils) Arctium; Geranium robertianum; Malva neglecta; Malva sylvestris; Ribes nigrum.

Anaemia Centaurium erythraea; Malus sylvestris; Nepeta; Rubia; Urtica dioica; Urtica urens.

Appetite Achillea moschata; Anethum; Angelica archangelica; Artemisia absinthium; Carum; Centaureum erythraea; Cetraria islandica; Cnicus benedictus; Foeniculum; Gentiana; Hyssopus; Inula helenium; Levisticum; Lobaria pulmonaria; Marribium; Menyanthes; Peucedanum; Rubia tinctorum; Ruta; Teucrium chamaedrys.

Arteriosclerosis Allium sativum; Allium ursinum.

Arthritis Acorus; Aesculus; Agropyrum; Anthriscus cerefolium; Bellis; Betonica officinalis; Betula pendula; Betula pubescens; Carex; Centaureum erythraea; Cnicus; Cochlearea; Equisetum; Filipendula; Fragaria; Fraxinus; Genista; Hedera (recommended for gout); Helichrysum; Ilex; Lithospermum; Malus; Mentha pulegium; Ononis; Physalis; Pinus; Polygala; Polygonum aviculare; Populus; Prunus padus; Ruta; Salix; Stellaria; Ulmus; Vaccinium vitis-idaea; Veronica officinalis.

Asthma Cetraria; Drosera; Lobaria; Pinus; Succisa.

Bladder (Bladder stones, cystitis, urinary tract; see also **Kidney**) Aegopodium; Agrimonia eupatoria; Agropyrum repens; Antennaria dioica; Arctostaphylos; Betula pendula; Betula pubescens; Calluna; Capsella; Chimaphila; Dictamnus; Eryngium; Filipendula; Fraxinus excelsior; Galium aparine; Galium verum; Geranium; Helichrysum arenarium; Herniaria; Hieracium pilosella; Juniperus; Lamium album; Levisticum; Lithospermum officinale; Lobaria pulmonaria; Lycopodium clavatum; Ononis; Parietaria; Physalis alkekengi; Polygala; Potentilla anserina; Prunus spinosa; Rorippa nasturtium-aquaticum; Rosa; Rubia tinctorum; Salix alba; Salix purpurea; Satureja montana; Solidago virgaurea; Urtica dioica; Urtica urens.

Blood pressure Allium sativum; Allium ursinum; Crataegus monogyna; Crataegus oxyacanthoides; Rosmarinus.

Boils see **Abscess**

Bowel (Including abdomen, intestine, enteritis, colic) *Allium sativum; Althaea; Anethum; Balsamita; Betonica; Calendula; Carex; Carum; Chamaemelum; Chamomilla; Cydonia; Eryngium; Euphrasia; Fumaria; Geum rivale; Geum urbanum; Glechoma; Hypericum; Inula; Malva neglecta; Malva sylvestris; Melilotus; Melissa; Mentha pulegium; Mercurialis; Nepeta; Origanum; Phyllitis; Potentilla erecta; Ribes nigrum; Sanguisorba; Silybum; Tussilago; Viola tricolor.*

Bronchitis *Adiantum; Aesculus; Alliaria; Althaea; Carex; Cetraria; Chondrus; Drosella; Foeniculum; Galeopsis; Hepatica; Hyssopus; Ilex; Inula; Levisticum; Malva neglecta; Malva sylvestris; Phyllitis; Pimpinella major; Pimpinella saxifraga; Plantago lanceolata; Plantago major; Populus; Primula; Pulmonaria; Sambucus nigra; Saponaria; Satureja montana; Succisa pratensis; Teucrium chamaedrys; Thymus; Tussilago; Verbascum; Viola odorata.*

Bruises *Anthyllis; Calendula; Dryopteris; Geranium; Hepatica; Hypericum; Knautia; Melilotus; Oxalis acetosella; Petasites; Rumex; Ruta; Tanacetum.*

Burns *Aegopodium; Althaea; Cydonia; Hedera; Knautia; Lamium; Malva neglecta; Malva sylvestris; Parietaria; Potentilla; Rumex; Ruta; Salix; Sedum acre; Sempervivum.*

Catarrh *Agropyrum; Angelica sylvestris; Anchusa; Arctium; Bellis; Carex; Chamaemelum; Chamomilla; Glechoma; Herniaria; Lamium; Lobaria; Malva; Papaver; Peucedanum officinale; Peucedanum ostruthium; Pinus; Polypodium; Prunus spinosa; Rorippa; Viola odorata.*

Chest (see also **Lungs, Catarrh, Bronchitis**) *Achillea millefolium; Agropyrum; Anchusa; Angelica sylvestris; Borago; Glechoma; Herniaria; Lobaria; Origanum; Papaver; Peucedanum officinale; Peucedanum ostruthium; Rorippa; Rosmarinus; Sanicula.*

Chilblains *Anthoxanthum; Equisetum.*

Circulation (see also **Blood pressure, Varicose veins**) *Crataegus; Equisetum; Rosmarinus.*

Cold, common *Arctium; Berberis; Calluna; Eupatorium; Hippophaë; Ilex; Nepeta; Pinguicula; Prunus padus; Rosa; Salix; Sambucus nigra; Tilia; Usnea.*

Colic see **Bowel, Gall, Kidney.**

Constipation *Anthyllis; Berberis; Centaurea; Cydonia; Fraxinus; Fumaria; Impatiens; Linaria; Linum; Plantago indica; Polypodium; Rhamnus catharticus; Rosa; Rumex alpinus; Sambucus nigra; Saponaria; Sorbus aria; Sorbus aucuparia; Vaccinium myrtillus; Veronica beccabunga.*

Coughs *Adiantum; Anchusa; Angelica sylvestris; Calluna; Castanea; Chondrus; Cydonia; Drosera; Equisetum; Eryngium; Foeniculum; Galeopsis; Hedera; Papaver; Petasites; Peucedanum officinale; Pimpinella; Pinguicula; Plantago lanceolata; Plantago major; Primula; Prunus padus; Pulmonaria; Ribes nigrum; Sambucus nigra; Sanicula; Saponaria; Sisymbrium; Succisa; Teucrium chamaedrys; Tussilago; Verbascum; Viola odorata.*

Diabetes *Vaccinium vitis-idaea.*

Diarrhoea *Alchemilla; Althaea; Antennaria; Artemisia vulgaris; Bellis; Betonica; Calluna; Conyza; Corylus; Cydonia; Daucus; Gentiana; Geranium; Geum rivale; Geum urbanum; Lavandula; Lysimachia nummularia; Malus; Parnassia; Phyllitis; Plantago lanceolata; Plantago major; Polygonum aviculare; Polygonum bistorta; Potentilla anserina; Potentilla erecta; Prunus spinosa; Ribes nigrum; Rubus fruticosus; Rubus idaeus; Sanguisorba; Succisa; Tilia; Ulmus; Vaccinium myrtillus; Vaccinium vitis-idaea.*

Digestion (see also **Indigestion, Stomach complaints, Appetite**) *Anethum; Angelica archangelica; Angelica sylvestris; Carum; Centaureum erythraea; Cnicus; Lobaria; Mentha aquatica; Mentha x piperita; Menyanthes; Nigella.*

Dropsy *Anagallis; Anthriscus cerefolium; Calendula; Cardamine pratensis; Centaurea cyanus; Chimaphila; Cochlearia; Conyza; Daucus; Eryngium; Eupatorium; Filipendula; Fraxinus; Fumaria; Galium aparine; Galium verum; Genista; Geranium; Hyssopus; Levisticum; Linaria; Ononis; Petroselinum; Polygonum; Ribes nigrum; Stellaria; Viola tricolor.*

Enteritis *Agrimonia; Conyza; Cydonia; Hieracium; Satureja montana; Vaccinium myrtillus.*

Enuresis (bedwetting) *Viola tricolor.*

Exhaustion (Physical and nervous, including nervous tension) *Achillea moschata; Anthoxanthum odoratum; Asperula; Atriplex hortensis; Berberis; Calluna; Cochlearia; Daucus; Hippophaë; Melilotus; Rosa; Rosmarinus; Urtica; Verbena.*

Eye Disorders *Centaurea cyanus; Euphrasia; Foeniculum; Hieracium; Quercus.*

Flatulence *Acorus; Anethum; Angelica archangelica; Artemisia vulgaris; Betonica; Carum; Chamaemelum; Chamomilla; Foeniculum; Hyssopus; Lavandula; Leonurus; Levisticum; Melilotus; Nepeta; Petroselinum; Peucedanum ostruthium; Plantago indica; Sanicula.*

Gall (Gall stones, gall bladder, colic) *Agrimonia; Ajuga; Anagallis; Antennaria; Aquilegia; Arctium; Armoracia; Balsamita; Berberis; Chelidonium; Cichorium; Cnicus; Eupatorium; Fragaria; Fumaria; Helichrysum; Hepatica; Inula; Marribium; Mentha aquatica; Mentha x piperita; Menyanthes; Petasites; Polypodium; Rosa; Rosmarinus; Saponaria; Taraxacum; Verbena.*

Headache (see also **Migraine**) *Achillea moschata; Erodium; Filipendula; Lavandula; Melissa; Primula; Prunus padus; Salix; Valeriana.*

Heart complaints *Humulus; Lavandula; Valeriana.*

Heartburn see **Indigestion.**

Haemorrhoids *Achillea millefolium; Aegopodium podagraria; Aesculus; Chamaemelum nobile; Chamomilla; Cichorium; Fumaria; Geum rivale; Geum urbanum; Impatiens; Linaria; Polygonum hydropiper; Populus; Potentilla anserina; Potentilla reptans; Quercus; Ranunculus; Ulmus.*

Indigestion *Achillea millefolium; Artemisia absinthium; Chelidonium; Cnicus* (recommended for heartburn); *Levisticum; Melissa; Mentha aquatica; Mentha x piperita; Peucedanum.*

Influenza *Arctium; Eupatorium; Filipendula; Hieracium pilosella; Ilex; Tilia; Usnea.*

Insomnia *Anethum; Anthoxanthum; Asperula; Humulus; Leonurus; Melilotus; Melissa; Valeriana; Verbena.*

Kidney (Kidney stones, colic, pyelitis) *Achillea moschata; Agrimonia; Apium; Arctostaphylos; Bellis; Berberis; Betula; Calluna; Capsella; Dictamnus; Eryngium; Filipendula; Galium aparine; Galium verum; Geranium; Herniaria; Hieracium; Juniperus; Lamium album; Lobaria pulmonaria; Lycopodium clavatum; Ononis; Parietaria; Physalis; Polygala; Polygonum aviculare; Potentilla anserina; Prunus spinosa; Rorippa; Rosa; Rubia; Sambucus nigra; Solidago; Sorbus aria; Sorbus aucuparia; Verbena officinalis.*

Lactation *Foeniculum vulgare; Galega.*

Liver complaints *Achillea moschata; Agrimonia; Anagallis; Aquilegia; Armoracia; Bellis; Berberis; Carex; Cnicus; Eupatorium; Fragaria; Geum rivale; Geum urbanum; Hepatica; Linum; Menyanthes; Nymphaea; Phyllitis; Plantago lanceolata; Plantago major; Rosmarinus; Silybum.*

Lungs (see also **Chest, Bronchitis**) *Achillea millefolium; Equisetum; Phyllitis; Polygonum aviculare; Thymus.*

Mastitis *Scrophularia; Sempervivum.*

Menopause *Alchemilla; Aquilegia; Leonurus.*

Menstrual disorders *Achillea millefolium; Achillea moschata; Adiantum; Aesculus; Alchemilla; Artemisia vulgaris; Berberis; Calystegia; Capsella; Convolvulus; Conyza; Dictamnus; Eryngium; Hypericum; Lamium; Leonurus; Malus; Nepeta; Nigella; Petroselinum; Peucedanum officinale; Polygonum hydropiper; Polypodium; Potentilla anserina; Potentilla reptans; Quercus; Rubia; Ruta; Sorbus aria; Sorbus aucuparia.*

Migraine (see also **Headache, Nausea**) *Dictamnus; Fumaria; Hypericum.*

Mouth complaints see **Oral disorders.**

Nasal complaints (see also **Catarrh**) *Capsella; Lobaria; Papaver; Pinus.*

Nausea *Mentha aquatica; Mentha x piperita.*

Nervous disorders *Hypericum; Leonurus; Melissa; Parnassia; Salvia; Valeriana.*

Oral disorders *Alliaria; Althaea; Borago; Calendula; Centaurea cyanus; Chamaemelum; Chamomilla; Cochlearia; Cydonia; Dryas; Geum rivale; Geum urbanum; Glechoma; Origanum; Pimpinella major; Pimpinella saxifraga; Polygonum bistorta; Potentilla erecta; Potentilla reptans; Prunella vulgaris; Quercus; Ribes nigrum; Sanicula; Succisa; Tilia; Ulmus; Vaccinium myrtillus; Viola odorata.*

Piles see **Haemorrhoids.**

Rheumatism (including neuralgia) *Acorus; Aegopodium; Aesculus; Agropyrum; Alnus; Angelica archangelica; Anthoxanthum; Arctium; Bellis; Betula; Borago; Calluna; Carex; Equisetum; Filipendula; Fraxinus; Genista; Hedera; Helichrysum; Ilex; Juniperus; Linum catharticum; Lysimachia; Ononis; Physalis; Pinus; Polygala; Polygonum aviculare; Populus; Prunus padus; Ribes nigrum; Rorippa; Rosmarinus; Ruta; Salix; Sorbus aria; Sorbus aucuparia; Stellaria; Taraxacum; Ulmus; Urtica; Vaccinium vitis-idaea; Viola tricolor.*

Skin complaints *Aesculus; Agropyrum repens; Alliaria; Anagallis; Anthriscus; Anthyllis; Aquilegia; Arctium; Aristolochia; Carex; Calendula; Cardamine; Chamaemelum; Chamomilla; Cochlearia; Cynoglossum; Eryngium; Fumaria; Galium aparine; Galium verum; Genista; Impatiens; Marribium; Melilotus; Menyanthes trifoliata; Ononis; Parietaria; Prunus padus; Quercus; Rorippa; Rumex acetosa; Saponaria; Scrophularia; Sempervivum; Solidago virgaurea; Stellaria; Succisa; Ulmus; Veronica; Viola tricolor.*

Spasms *Calendula; Cardamine; Potentilla reptans.*

Spleen *Eupatorium; Nymphaea; Phyllitis; Rubia.*

Spring cure *Anthriscus; Anthyllis; Atriplex; Betula; Cochlearia; Filipendula; Knautia; Plantago lanceolata; Plantago major; Rhamnus catharticus; Rorippa; Rosa; Sisymbrium; Sorbus aria; Sorbus aucuparia; Urtica.*

Stings *Aegopodium.*

Stomach complaints (Dyspepsia, gastritis; see also **Enteritis**) *Achillea millefolium; Ajuga; Artemisia absinthium; Artemisia vulgaris. Balsamita; Calendula; Carex; Cetraria islandica; Chelidonium; Cichorium; Cnicus; Dictamnus; Dryas; Fragaria vesca; Galium aparine; Galium verum; Gentiana; Geum rivale; Geum urbanum; Glechoma; Helichrysum; Humulus; Hypericum; Inula; Leonurus; Melissa; Mentha pulegium; Menyanthes; Mercurialis; Origanum; Polygala; Prunus spinosa; Ribes nigrum; Rubus fruticosus; Solanum; Taraxacum; Teucrium chamaedrys; Thymus; Tussilago; Veronica officinalis.*

Throat complaints (including tracheitis, pharyngitis etc.) *Achillea millefolium; Althaea; Calendula; Chamaemelum; Chamomilla; Cydonia; Dryas; Galeopsis; Geum rivale; Geum urbanum; Glechoma; Malva neglecta; Malva sylvestris; Origanum; Pimpinella major; Pimpinella saxifraga; Polygonum bistorta; Potentilla reptans; Prunella; Quercus; Salvia; Sanicula; Scutellaria; Succisa; Thymus; Tilia; Tussilago; Vaccinium myrtillus; Verbascum; Viola odorata.*

Ulcers *Chamaemelum; Chamomilla; Cynoglossum; Salix.*

Varicose veins (see also **Blood pressure, Circulation**) *Melilotus; Ruta; Tanacetum.*

Worms, intestinal *Antennaria; Calendula; Daucus; Polypodium.*

Wounds (see also **Stings, Burns, Bruises**) *Achillea millefolium; Aegopodium; Alchemilla; Alliaria; Althaea; Anthriscus; Arctium; Aristolochia clematitis; Betonica; Calendula; Capsella; Cetraria; Chamaemelum; Chamomilla; Chimaphila; Cnicus; Cochlearia; Cynoglossum; Equisetum; Fraxinus; Galium aparine; Galium verum; Geranium; Geum rivale; Geum urbanum; Glechoma; Hedera; Hepatica; Hieracium; Hypericum; Impatiens; Knautia; Lamium; Lysimachia; Malva neglecta; Malva sylvestris; Marribium; Melilotus; Parietaria; Petasites; Potentilla anserina; Potentilla erecta; Potentilla reptans; Ribes nigrum; Rumex acetosa; Ruta; Salix; Sanicula; Sedum acre; Sempervivum; Solidago; Stellaria; Tussilago; Ulmus.*

Plants used in preparations for gargling (for disorders of the throat) *Calendula; Chamaemelum; Chamomilla; Cydonia; Dryas; Equisetum; Foeniculum; Glechoma; Origanum; Pimpinella major; Pimpinella saxifraga; Prunella; Quercus petraea; Quercus robur; Ribes nigrum; Salvia; Sanicula; Succisa; Tilia cordata; Tilia platyphyllos; Ulmus; Vaccinium myrtillus; Viola odorata.*

Plants used as mouthwashes (for ulcers, gingivitis, inflammation of the gums, etc.)
Alchemilla; Centaurea cyanus; Chamaemelum; Chamomilla; Cochlearia; Cydonia; Equisetum; Foeniculum vulgare; Geum rivale; Geum urbanum; Pimpinella major; Pimpinella saxifraga; Polygonum bistorta; Potentilla erecta; Potentilla reptans; Prunella; Quercus petraea; Quercus robur; Salvia; Sanicula; Tilia cordata; Tilia platyphyllos; Ulmus; Vaccinium myrtillus; Viola odorata.

Mixtures and single species for herbal baths for nervous conditions and exhaustion.

Application 300–600g (according to amount of bathwater) are sewn into a linen bag and suspended in the bathwater. Alternatively an infusion (150–300g of the herb or mixture) is added to the bathwater which should not be hotter than 40°C. Usually the bath should last 15–30 minutes.

Rosmarinus (herb) 2 parts
Mentha × piperita (herb) 2 pts
Satureja montana (herb) 2 pts
Lavandula (flowers) 2 pts
Thymus (herb) 2 pts

Acorus (rhizome) 1 pt
Chamomilla (flowers) 1 pt
Lavandula (flowers) 1 pt
Satureja montana (herb) 1 pt
Mentha × piperita (herb) 1 pt

Mentha × piperita (herb) 1 pt
Rosmarinus (herb) 1 pt
Thymus (herb) 1 pt
Lavandula (flowers) 1 pt
Acorus (rhizome) 1 pt

A decoction can be made from the following species and added to the bathwater (bring the mixture to the boil, allow to simmer for 15 minutes and let stand for a further 12–15 minutes).
Juniperus (fruits) 1 pt
Chamomilla (flowers) 1 pt
Melissa (herb) 1 pt
Valeriana (rhizome) 1 pt
Melilotus (herb) 1 pt
Origanum (herb) 1 pt
This mixture also has a spasmolytic effect.

Sambucus nigra (flowers) 1 pt
Mentha × piperita (herb) 1 pt
Juniperus (fruit) 1 pt

Mixture for a steam-bath for disorders of the ear (othorrhea and otitis)
Malva (leaves) 1 pt
Chamomilla (flowers) 1 pt
Equisetum (herb) 1 pt
Melilotus (herb) 1 pt
Application use 8–10 teaspoons per litre of water; bring to the boil, cover head with towel and expose ear to steam (reheating if necessary) for 10–15 minutes.

Selected list of suppliers of medicinal herbs and plant-based preparations.

Heath and Heather, Beaver House, Byfleet, Surrey.

Salus-Hause, D-8206 Bruckmuehl/Obb. German Federal Republic. Offering perhaps the largest and most extensive selection of herbs and herb-mixtures anywhere; most available through several outlets in the United Kingdom.

Culpeper, 21 Bruton Street, Berkeley Square, London W1X 7DA. A fair selection, catalogue available. This firm has various outlets all over the United Kingdom.

Haelen Centre, 39 Park Road, London N8.

D. Napier and Sons, 17 Bristo Place, and 1 Teviot Place, Edinburgh, Scotland.

Kräuter Kühne, D-1000, Berlin 31, Karlsruher Strasse 7A-8. Very large selection (over 300 species). Catalogue. Mail order.

Schoenenberger, W. Pflanzensaftwerk G.m.b.H. and Co., D–7031 Magstadt bei Stuttgart. Specializes in pressed juices of medicinal plants; large selection, catalogue available.

Bibliography

Campbell, A.C. and Nicholls, J. 1976. *The Hamlyn Guide to the Seashore and Shallow Seas of Britain and Europe.* Hamlyn, London.

Clapham, A.R., Tutin, T.G. and Warburg, E.F. 1962. *Flora of the British Isles* (2nd ed.) Cambridge University Press, London.

Clarke, J.H. 1925. *Dictionary of Materia Medica.* London.

Culpeper, N. 1835. *The Complete Herbal.* Th. Kelly, London.

Fitter, R., Fitter, A. and Blamey, M. 1974. *The Wild Flowers of Britain and Northern Europe.* Collins, London.

Flück, H. 1973. *Herbes Medicinales.* Delachaux et Niestlé, Neuchatel, Switzerland.

Ministry of Agriculture, Fisheries and Food. 1960. *Culinary and Medicinal Herbs.* Bulletin No. 76, London.

Page, M. and Stearn, W.T. 1979. *Culinary Herbs.* The Royal Horticultural Society, London.

Rayner, R. 1979. *Hamlyn Nature Guides: Mushrooms and Toadstools.* Hamlyn, London.

Rottenhöfer, J. 1858. *Anweisung in der Feinen Kochkunst.* Munich.

Stobart, T. 1970. *Herbs, Spices and Flavourings.* David and Charles, Newton Abbot.

Tutin, T.G., Heywood, V.H. et al. (ed.). *Flora Europaea I–IV. 1964–1980.* Cambridge University Press, London.

Uphof, J.C.T. 1968. *Dictionary of Economic Plants* (2nd ed.) Steechort-Hafner, New York.

Usher, G. 1974. *Dictionary of Plants used by Man.* Constable, London.

Glossary of botanical terms

achene a dry fruit, single-seeded and not splitting
acuminate with a slightly drawn out point
acute sharply pointed
alternate staggered singly round the stem
annual a plant completing its life-cycle within one year
anther flower organ containing the pollen grains
auriculate with (usually small) ear-like lobes at the base
axil upper angle between a stem and leaf or bract
biennial a plant completing its life-cycle within two years (usually not flowering in the first)
biternate divided into three parts, each part itself divided in the same way
bract leaf-like organ supporting a flower
bulbil a small bulb or bulb-like organ growing in an axil
calyx the sepals of a flower considered as a whole
carpel functional unit of the female organ of a flower; may be joined, resulting in a partitioned ovary, or separate
casual an introduced plant that occurs irregularly in places even where it is not cultivated
ciliate margin surrounded by regularly projecting hairs
claw narrowed basal part of some petals
compound leaf or inflorescence with a branched main axis
corolla the petals of a flower considered as a whole
crenate margin with shallow rounded teeth
culm stem of a plant, especially the hollow jointed stem of some grasses
deciduous falling off, usually of plants losing their leaves in autumn
decurrent with the base continued down the stem as a wing
dehiscence process of opening of a dry fruit to shed its seed
dichotomous branching mode of branching by constant dividing into two
digitate dividing and spreading like the fingers of a hand
dioecious with separate male and female flowers borne on different plants
distichous arranged in opposite rows
drupe fleshy fruit with seed(s) surrounded by a stony layer
epiphyte a plant which grows on another but is not parasitic on it
filament part of the stamen; the stalk supporting the anther
flagellate producing runners or runner-like branches (e.g. strawberry)
floccose bearing woolly tufts or soft long hairs
glabrous without hairs
glaucous covered with a bluish or whitish layer
herb a vascular and non-woody plant
hermaphrodite flowers possessing both functional male and female parts
holdfast sucker-like attachment organ
hypha one of the thread-like elements in the mycelium of fungi
indehiscent not opening to release seeds
indumentum the hairy covering of any part of a plant
inflorescence flower cluster including the stem which bears flowers and bracts
internode the space between two nodes of a stem
keeled having a raised ridge or sharp folded edge, resembling the keel of a boat
laciniate divided deeply into narrow segments
lanceolate lance-shaped in outline
latex a white or yellow sap
lemma bract in a grass spikelet just below the pistil and stamens
ligule narrow projection from the top of a leaf sheath in grasses
linear narrow and more or less parallel-sided
lobed a leaf that is divided but not into leaflets
monoecious with separate male and female flowers both on the same plant
node point on a stem from which a leaf arises
ob- prefix meaning 'inverted' (e.g. obovate: ovate but widest above the middle)
obtuse blunt
ovate egg-shaped; widest below the middle, rounded at each end

palmate leaf with more than three leaflets arising from the same point

panicle branched inflorescence with each branch developing like a raceme

pedate palmately divided with the lateral lobes cleft or divided

pedicel stalk of a flower

peduncle stalk of an inflorescence

perennial a plant living for more than two years, flowering each year

perianth sepals and petals as a whole

petal flower segment, usually brightly coloured

petiole stalk of a leaf

pinnate compound leaf with many leaflets arranged either side of a central stalk (rachis)

pinnatifid pinnate but with the cuts reaching not quite to the midrib

pinnatisect pinnatifid but with some cuts reaching the midrib or very nearly so

pruinose covered with a white or greyish bloom

pubescent covered with short soft hairs

raceme inflorescence which adds new stalked flowers to the tip, the oldest flowers being at the base

rachis stem-like axis bearing leaflets or flowers

ray stalk of a partial umbel

rhizome underground stem, usually perennial

samara indehiscent dry fruit with a wing formed from part of the wall

scarious thin, dry and membranous

sepal part of the outer circle of a perianth, usually green

sessile stalkless

sorus cluster of sporangia (in ferns)

spathe bract-like or petal-like sheath enclosing an inflorescence

sporangium a case or sac containing spores

sporophyll a leaf-like structure which bears sporangia

stamen male productive organ of a flower

standard a large upper petal

stellate-hairy with star-like groups of hairs

sub- prefix meaning 'almost'

syncarp an aggregate fruit

ternate compound leaf divided into three parts

thallus simple plant body not differentiated into leaves, stem and root

tomentum a dense covering of short soft (felt-like) hairs

trefoil digitate leaf of three leaflets

truncate with a squarish transverse tip

umbel inflorescence with all the pedicels or peduncles arising from the same point

whorl arrangement with more than two organs arising from points at the same level around a stem

Leaf shapes

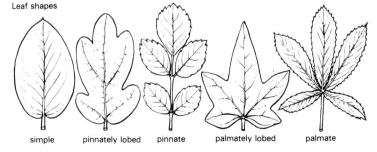

simple   pinnately lobed   pinnate   palmately lobed   palmate

Glossary of medical terms

abscess accumulation of pus due to disintegrating tissue

acne inflammation of the skin, forming pimples or pustules

allopathy method of treating disease by the use of agents producing effects different from those of the disease treated (*see also* homoeopathy)

amenorrhoea absence or stoppage of menstruation

analgesic relieving pain

anaemia depletion of red cells in the blood

anaesthesia loss of feeling, of (pain) sensation

anaesthetic producing anaesthesia

anorexia loss of appetite (anorexia nervosa: loss of appetite for emotional reasons)

antidiarrhoeal suppressing or counteracting diarrhoea

antiseptic preventing the development of bacteria and other micro-organisms

arteriosclerosis thickening of the artery walls reducing their elasticity, especially in older people

astringent causing contraction, thus diminishing discharges

boil a painful local thickening (nodule) in the skin caused by inflammation of the tissue through staphylococci penetrating hair follicles

colic sharp, convulsive abdominal pains

compress a pad made from folded linen applied with moderate pressure, either hot or cold, dry or wet, to the affected part of the body

convulsive pertaining to convulsion – involuntary contractions of the voluntary muscles

cystitis inflammation of the urinary bladder

digestant stimulating digestion

diuretic increasing of urine secretion

dropsy excessive build-up of fluid in cell tissues or cavities in the body

dysmenorrhoea menstruation accompanied by pain

dyspepsia indigestion: impairment of the ability to digest

eczema inflammation of the skin accompanied by weeping, oozing, scaling, itching, redness and blisters

emetic causing vomiting

emollient softening or soothing the skin or irritated internal surfaces

enteritis inflammation of the intestinal tract

expectorant an agent stimulating the formation of phlegm, mainly used in the treatment of coughs and similar throat and chest conditions

gastritis inflammation of the stomach

gingivitis inflammation of the gum

glossitis inflammation of the tongue

haematoma swelling or bruise filled with clotted blood

haemorrhage bleeding, usually internal

herpetic pertaining to herpes (inflammatory skin disease accompanied by blisters or vesicles)

homoeopathy method of treating disease by administering small quantities of drugs producing in a healthy person symptoms similar to those of the disease (*see also* allopathy)

mastitis inflammation of the breast

neuralgia pain spreading along one or several nerves

opiate sleep inducing drug; a drug containing opium

papule pimple

peristalsis wave-like muscular contractions which force food down the alimentary canal

pharyngitis inflammation of the throat

pleurisy inflammation of the pleura (the membranes which line the inner walls of the chest)

purgative a drug or agent causing the evacuation of the bowels

pustule pimple containing pus

pyelitis inflammation of the renal pelvis

revulsive causing revulsion (the drawing of blood from one part to another)

seborrhoea sicca a dry, scaly dermatitis

sedative reducing excitement and irritability

suppuration the formation of pus

tenosynovitis inflammation of a tendon sheath

tone muscle tension, muscle vigour

tonic an agent restoring or producing normal tone

tracheitis inflammation of the windpipe

vasoconstrictor agent used to contract the arteries causing an increase in blood pressure

vasodilator agent causing a widening of blood vessels so lowering blood pressure

vasotonic increasing tension of the vessels

veterinary pertaining to the medical treatment of animals

Index

Page numbers in bold type refer to illustrations